14

Reader's Digest

BOOKS

Selected and condensed
by the editors of The Reader's Digest

READER'S DIGEST ASSOCIATION
Pleasantville, N. Y.

The condensations reprinted in this book
are used by permission of and special arrangement with
the publishers holding the respective copyrights

Copyright 1948 by The Reader's Digest Association,
Incorporated

FIRST EDITION

PRINTED IN THE UNITED STATES OF AMERICA

Table of Contents

Foreword

THIS VOLUME was inspired by Reader's Digest subscribers, and they had much to do with the selection of its contents. Ever since the first book condensation appeared in the Digest more than fourteen years ago, these monthly supplements have been among the most popular features of the magazine. Readers frequently suggest that the cream of them be collected in a permanent library volume. In 1941 such a volume was published, and quickly became a runaway best-seller. Since then we have received frequent requests for back copies of book supplements, which could not be supplied because the magazines were practically out of stock. In addition, many readers have suggested that we publish a new collection.

So here, in one volume, we present the 14 most popular book condensations published in the Digest since the last collection appeared. These 14 titles are the ones most often requested by readers themselves—the titles Digest subscribers have "voted" most popular.

If you like this book, you can attribute your enjoyment to the Digest fans who urged its publication. Perhaps you yourself are one of them. The editors feel that the readers have chosen well.

THE EDITORS

Pleasantville, N. Y.

HOME COUNTRY

A condensation from the book by

ERNIE PYLE

ON April 18, 1945, Ernie Pyle met an untimely death by Japanese machine-gun fire on the island of Ie, near Okinawa. He was then by all odds the most popular and best-known correspondent of World War II. But many readers who treasured his war dispatches were unaware of the fact that, in a less spectacular setting, Ernie had been doing the same sort of homely, endearingly human reporting for years. The posthumously published book, *Home Country*, collects the finest of these early columns, which Ernie himself believed to contain the best writing he ever did.

HOME COUNTRY

FIVE YEARS AGO my boss in Washington got tired of my pestering him about the travel idea, so he said, "Oh, all right, try it as an experiment. We'll see how it turns out."

Since then, in five years of constant wandering, my wife and I have been at least three times into every state in the Union. We have been to every country in the Western Hemisphere, except two. We have stayed in more than 800 hotels, have crossed the continent exactly 20 times, flown on 66 airplanes, ridden on 29 boats, walked 200 miles, and put out approximately $2500 in tips. We have worn out two cars, five sets of tires, three typewriters, and pretty soon I'll have to have a new pair of shoes.

All this to make a living by writing a piece a day for the Scripps-Howard newspapers and some others. In five years those columns have stretched out to the horrifying equivalent of 20 full-length books.

People often ask me how we have stood all this travel. Well, there is almost no way for a constant traveler to fill his fountain pen, but the life has some compensations. You don't have to make your own beds. You don't have to buy coal. You can make new friends and go before they find out how dull you are. And you don't have to get up at four in the morning and milk the cows.

I DON'T KNOW whether you know that long, sad wind that blows so steadily across the thousands of miles of midwest flatlands in the summertime. If you don't, it will be hard for you to understand the feeling I have about it. Even if you do know it, you may not understand.

To me the summer wind in the Midwest is one of the most melancholy things in all life. It comes from so far and blows so gently and yet so relentlessly; it rustles the leaves and the branches of the maple trees in a sort of symphony of sadness, and it doesn't pass on and leave them still. It just keeps coming, like the infinite flow of Old Man River. You could—and you do—wear out your lifetime on the dusty plains with that wind of futility blowing in your face. And when you are worn out and gone, the wind—still saying nothing, still so gentle and sad and timeless—is still blowing across the prairies, and will blow in the faces of the little men who follow you, forever. One time in 1935, when I was driving across Iowa, I became conscious of the wind and instantly I was back in character as an Indiana farm boy again. Like dreams came the memories the wind brought. I lay again on the ground under the shade trees at noontime, with my half hour for rest before going back to the fields, and the wind and the sun and the hot country silence made me sleepy, and yet I couldn't sleep for the wind in the trees. The wind was like the afternoon ahead that would never end, and the days and the summers and even the lifetimes that would flow on forever, tiredly, patiently.

Maybe it's a bad job, my trying to make you see something that only I can ever feel. It is just one of those small impressions that form in a child's mind, and grow and stay with him through a lifetime, even shaping a part of his character and manner of thinking, and he can never explain it.

THERE's another impression that has come up with me out of childhood: I have a horror of snakes that verges on the irrational. I'm not afraid of being killed by a snake. It isn't that kind of fear. It's a horrible, unnatural mania for getting away, and it is induced equally by a six-inch garden snake and a six-foot rattler.'

Whenever I go home on a visit my mother never fails to tell about the time when I was a little fellow, maybe four or five. My father was plowing at the far end of our farm, and I was walking along behind the plow, barefooted, in the fresh soft furrow. He had just started the field, and was plowing near a weedy fence row. Wild roses were growing there.

I asked my father for his pocketknife so I could cut some of the roses to take back to the house. He gave it to me and went on plowing. I sat down in the grass and started cutting off the roses.

Then it happened in a flash. A blue racer came looping through the grass at me. I screamed, threw away the knife and ran as fast as I could. Then I remembered it was my father's knife. I crept back over the plowed ground till I found it. He had heard me scream and had stopped. I gave him the knife and started back to the house.

I approached the house from the west side, where there was an old garden all grown up in high weeds. I stopped on the far side and shouted for my mother. When she came out to see what I wanted, I asked her to come and get me. She said I should come on through by myself. I couldn't have done that if it had killed me not to. She ordered me to come through, and I began to cry. She told me that if I didn't stop crying and didn't come through, she would whip me. I couldn't stop, and I couldn't come through. So she came and got me. And she whipped me—one of the two times, I believe, that she ever whipped me.

That evening when my father came in from the fields, she told him about the crazy boy who wouldn't walk through the weeds and had to be whipped. And then my father told her about the roses and the knife and the snake. It was the roses, I think, that hurt her so. My mother cried for a long time that night after she went to bed.

It has been more than 30 years since that happened, but to this day when I go home my mother sooner or later will say, "Do you remember the time I whipped you because you wouldn't walk through the weeds?" And then she will tell me the story, just as I have told it here, and along toward the end she always manages to get the hem of her apron up around her eyes, just in case she should need it, which she always does.

My mother would rather drive a team of horses in the field than cook a dinner. But in her lifetime she has done very little of the first and too much of the latter. My mother is living proof that happiness is within yourself; for a whole lifetime she has done nothing but work too hard, and yet I'm sure she has been happy. She loves the farm there outside Dana, Indiana. She wouldn't think of moving to town, as the other "retired" farmers do. She would rather stay home now and milk the cows than to go to the state fair. She is the best chicken raiser and cake baker in the neighborhood. She loves to raise chickens and hates to bake cakes.

My mother probably knows as little about world affairs as any woman in our neighborhood. Yet she is the broadest-minded and most liberal of the lot. I don't remember her ever telling me I couldn't do something. She always told me what she thought was right, and what was wrong, and then it was up to me.

My mother has quite a temper. I remember once when the liniment man came, and said we hadn't paid him for a bottle of liniment. My mother said we had. The man said we hadn't. So my mother went and got the money, opened the screen door, and threw it in his face. He never came back.

She always tells people just what she thinks. A good many of our neighbors have felt the whip of her tongue, and they pout over it a while, but whenever they're in trouble they always thaw out and come asking for help. And of course they get it.

My mother doesn't realize it, but her life has been the life of a real prairie pioneer. You could use her in a book, or paint her picture, as one of the sturdy stock of the ages who have always done the carrying-on when the going was tough.

In recent years we had heard a lot about the "good neighbor" policy among nations. But to me, and I suspect to most of us, "good neighbor" had become a mere academic term; city dwellers had almost forgotten what a good neighbor is. But the country people still knew.

My mother had a stroke and became paralyzed on a Thursday night. By Friday morning the whole countryside knew about it. Help began to roll in instantly. The strongest men in the neighborhood came to help lift my mother in her bed. The women came to help with the housework.

Bertha and Iva Jordan came twice for half a day each to do the washing. Oll Potter's mother sent a whole basketful of fresh sausage, and a peck of apples. When I was a little boy, the Potters were the poorest people in all our neighborhood. They were just up from the Kentucky hills, and they never smiled. Dan Potter worked for farmers by the day. But the Potters toiled and saved their money, and all their boys grew up to be workers. Now they lived in a nice house and had a fleet of cattle trucks, and the whole country admired them for the way they'd raised themselves by the bootstraps.

Mrs. Frank Davis, the new neighbor just up the road, brought over freshly butchered pork ribs. My Aunt Mary said it was good of her, she not knowing us very well. Mrs. Davis said that once when she was sick over in Parke County people were mighty good to her; and when she told them she didn't know how she could ever repay them, they told her she didn't need to repay them personally, just so she did things for other folks when they needed it. And that's what she was doing.

On Sunday there were 38 people at our house. We couldn't get them all in the front room, and at one time the kitchen and dining room were so full that half of them had to stand up. Anna Kerns was one of the 38, and when she left she didn't say, "Now, if there's anything at all I can do . . ." She said, "Mary, I'll be here at 7:30 in the morning to do the washing for you." And she was too, and stayed all day.

For 40 years my mother was the one who went to all these people when they needed help. They hadn't forgotten, and now they were coming to her in droves. Indiana farmers know what a "good neighbor" policy is. It's born in them.

THE JOB of being a roving reporter teaches you one thing: he who laughs too long and loud at other people is liable to get sand in his mouth. The more you travel around and see all sorts of people the less inclined you are to stand up on a dais and look down at anybody, and laugh at him. Because he may be looking up, laughing at you.

Take Frank Murphy, for instance. A few years ago, when I was a smart guy and knew everything, I could have written a mighty clever piece about Frank. But now I can't figure out whether it's Frank who was crazy, or me, or maybe both of us.

Frank Murphy was an old man. Seventy-six, he said. He was tall and thin and not very clean, and he had a bushy gray beard, and gray eyes that stared out through horn-rimmed spectacles. Frank had come from the "old country," from an island off the coast of Ireland. He thought he had a son, but hadn't heard of him in 50 years, since his wife died. He didn't have anybody in this world at all.

He was a squatter. He lived just behind the Memphis city dump, right on the bank of the Mississippi. His home, every-thing he had—in fact, his whole livelihood—came out of the city dump. He had picked old auto hoods out of the dump, pounded them flat, and built himself a house. It wasn't one of these wobbly shantytown shacks, either; it was straight and solid. The doors closed snugly, the windows were tight; no rain or wind could get in. It had four small, fairly clean rooms, so full of home-made furniture and sundry trinkets you could hardly move around.

Murphy came pretty close to being self-sufficient. He had nobody to help him, and he made his own way. He got old tin pans and kettles out of the city dump and repaired them; he found steer horns and polished them up and mounted them; he filed down pieces of steel into butcher knives. All these things he peddled to housewives. "If they're too poor to buy them, I just give them away," he said. When he had enough for a few days' groceries, he didn't peddle any more, for he had many other things to do. He had a lot of painting and inventing to do, for instance.

His house painting was what captivated him. His house was daubed all over—not solid, or striped, or patterned in any regular way, but just daubed, like a speckled chicken. And every color of the rainbow. I asked why he painted it that way. He said so strangers would think he was crazy and wouldn't come near. But it worked out just the other way; people came nosing around just to look at it. He did his painting at night, so he couldn't see what he was doing. Then the next morning he would jump up and run out to see what it looked like. "And every time," he said, "I think it looks pretty." I thought so too.

"Do you want to see my house change color?" he asked. We said we sure did. So he ran back into the house, and after a while the panel alongside the front door started sliding back and forth, and sure enough, it was changing color. You see, there were slats in front of the panel, and right behind the slats he had painted the panel a different color. He said he was going to put a little windmill on the roof, and hook it up to the panel through some Rube Goldberg arrangement, so that the wind would keep the panel going back and forth all the time—and wouldn't strangers think it was funny?

He had a picture of Joan Crawford hanging on his porch, and in the house a self-portrait that he had painted looking in the mirror. Up by the window were a couple of slingshots. He said that when people got to nosing around he let 'em have it, and they jumped and never knew where the rock came from.

There were a lot of laughs in Frank's place, but I didn't laugh any. After all, why not paint in the dark? It looked a lot better than some daytime painting I've seen in art galleries. And how many of us could make something, or paint something, and then when we sneaked in next morning to see how it looked, always have it look pretty to us? And what's wrong with making your house "change color"? I'll bet you can't make your house change color.

I wonder—yes, I wonder very much—if when I am 76 years old I will be able to build a house with my own hands, and paint pictures that look pretty to me, and have time pass pleasantly, and have to depend on no man in this world either for company or for the necessities of life? If I should find myself so blessed, I'll consider myself a hell of a long way from being crazy.

Rudy Hale and his wife lived alone back of their little store 50 miles east of Yuma, and there was no one else for miles. Three steps from their door and you were ankle deep in bare sand. The Hales caught live rattlesnakes for a living. To me that would be ten thousand times worse than death. But they enjoyed it.

The Arizona sands are filthy with rattlers. Rudy and his wife worked the desert for snakes as a farmer works his land for crops. Rattlers built them a place to live, rattlers kept them in food and clothing, rattlers provided the start for their little gas and grocery business. They loved rattlers.

They started out by advertising in a San Diego paper. Before they knew it they were swamped with orders. They sold snakes to zoos all over the country, to private collectors, to medical centers for serum, to state reptile farms, to the Mayo brothers. "They say there aren't any snakes in Ireland," said Mrs. Hale. "But I know there are, because we've shipped snakes to Ireland."

They didn't even use forked sticks to catch snakes—just picked them up with bare hands and put them in a box slung over the shoulder. They usually hunted snakes for an hour after daylight and an hour before dark. In eight years they had caught approximately 20,000 rattlers. Rudy had caught as many as 50 sidewinders in one hour's hunting. They had the desert cleaned almost bare of snakes for 20 miles around.

There are 12 kinds of rattlers in that part of Arizona. The sidewinder is the most deadly, and the Hales specialized in sidewinders. They used to get 50 cents apiece for them. "I just wish I could get 50 cents again," Rudy said. "They're down to 20 cents now." The most he ever got for a snake was $7; that was a rare Black Mountain rattler.

Hale had caught rattlers as big around as his leg. He had caught them so big that they'd overpower him and pull his arms together, and he'd have to throw them away from him and then pick them up and try again. "I'm careful not to hurt a snake," he said. "Any snake I ship is a good healthy snake."

Both Hale and his wife would let rattlers crawl all over

them. She even carried them around in her pockets. Neither of them had ever been bitten. There's no danger if you watch your business, Hale said. You musn't be thinking about anything else when you're picking up a sidewinder. He said the hand was quicker than a snake's strike, and if you missed him the first grab you could jerk back in time. Lots of times when they saw a rattler coiled they would just ease up and slide a hand through the sand under it, and lift it up, still coiled.

Rudy had only one sidewinder on hand the day I was there. It was in a roofless concrete tank behind the house. He took me out for a look after dark and turned on a dim little electric light. He took a stick with a nail in it and got the sidewinder hooked over the nail, and had it lifted almost to the top of the tank. Just then his little red dog stuck its cold nose up my pants leg. I let out a yell and landed somewhere way over the other side of Gila Bend, and never did go back.

THE PRAIRIES are all right. The mountains are all right. The forests and the deserts and the clear clean air of the heights, they're all right. But what a bewitching thing is a city of the sea. It was good to be in Seattle—to hear the foghorns on the Sound, and the deep bellow of the departing steamers; to feel the creeping fog all around you, the fog that softens things and makes a velvet trance out of nighttime. And it was good to hear the tall and slyly outlandish tales that float up and down Puget Sound. . .

Once upon a time there was a tugboat on Puget Sound, dragging behind it a long tow of logs. There was no special hurry, so the tugboat was hardly moving at all. Furthermore, it was using its leisure time to run some oil tests on its new Diesel engines. The engineer had several five-gallon cans of different brands of oil. He would let the engine run until it exhausted one can, then cut in a different brand, start the engine, and plow ahead again.

All this left the captain bored, and with nothing at all to do. Furthermore, his feet hurt. He stood sadly on the deck, watching the shore which hardly moved at all, and now and then taking a look at the water around him. It looked so cool. Finally he took off his shoes and socks, sat down on the low rail and hung his feet over the side. Lordy, it felt good!

The water kept on feeling good, and the old captain was enjoying it immensely, until a seal popped up and swam past (or do they have seals in Puget Sound?). Anyway, the captain thought it was a dog. He leaned far out for a better look and fell overboard. By the time he had come up and had rid himself of that portion of Puget Sound which he had imbibed, his favorite tugboat had drawn away from him. But all was not lost, for the tow of logs was still coming along. So the old man drifted back and h'isted himself up.

A bunch of logs on the end of a towline is no place for a dignified shipmaster to be, so our captain kept running up and down, yelling to the engineer on the tugboat. But the engineer couldn't hear him for the engine noise, and wouldn't have heard him anyway, for he was asleep.

At this interval we must leave the captain a moment and switch to the shore. Somewhere along the Sound lived one of those delightful people whose sole profession is watching the boats go by. He stood on the shore, pulled up his telescope, leveled it first on the tug, and then on the tow, and finally on the captain. Aha! thought the watcher. Poor Captain Blank has gone off his nut. So he phoned the tug company's office that the captain had gone crazy, that he was back on the tow of logs, barefoot, running up and down and screaming like a wild man.

Now we shift back to the tugboat. One of those five-gallon cans of oil ran out. The engine stopped. The engineer woke up and went about his business of cutting in a new can and getting the engines started again. This gave the captain his chance. He jumped into the water, half swam and half pulled himself along the towline up to the tug, climbed aboard, sneaked into his cabin without anybody's seeing him, changed his clothes and was out on deck by the time they got going.

That evening they pulled into Port Angeles. The company officials were all down at the dock. So were an ambulance and the sheriff and a couple of policemen, just in case the old man should be really violent.

The captain stepped out on deck and greeted them. The company president began to fade slightly beneath his skin. "Why, Captain, I understood you were . . . ah . . . sick."

"Fit as a fiddle," boomed the captain. "Never been sick a day in my life."

I don't know how the company president explained to the sheriff. Anyway, he never said another word to the captain about the matter.

W<small>E</small> <small>DROVE UP</small> in front of the big Sun Valley Lodge in Idaho, where the rich people stay, and I got out of the car all wind-burned and bare-headed like a sportsman, and sauntered in through the lobby, and asked the man what he was gettin' these days for a room with twin beds and bath. The man looked up at the rate card, as if he didn't already know, and came back with the calm information that the least he was gettin' was $26 a day. Well, I didn't make a single one of the smart retorts I thought of half an hour later. I simply said, "I guess that's a little more than I want to pay," and marched sadly out of the lobby, just a hatless tourist covered with dust. Then we drove down into Ketchum, a mile from the lodge, and found a place where we could live very scrumptiously a whole week for just a little more than one day at the lodge.

Ketchum lies in a mile-wide valley nearly 6000 feet above sea level. The mountains, which look like an unbroken circle around the valley, are mostly bare, except for a foot-high growth of bluish-brown sage-brush. From a distance you can't even see this, and the slopes look clean and smooth. That's the reason the Union Pacific Railroad picked this spot to build up a skiing resort—on account of the smooth slopes.

There were two small hotels in Ketchum, and a group of nice cabins built around a hot-water pool. The business section consisted of one block: two grocery stores, three restaurants, one drugstore, and 12 combination saloons and gambling halls. These were called "clubs." Gambling was not legal in Idaho, and neither was liquor by the drink, but nobody in Ketchum paid any attention. Everything was wide open.

One night, sitting in one of the Ketchum "clubs" watching a twenty-one game, I noticed a nice-looking young fellow in overalls with only one arm. I sat speechless as he laid a cigarette paper on a crease in his pants, filled it with tobacco, and twirled as neat a cigarette as you ever saw.

For nearly 20 years I had rolled my own cigarettes. I did this because (1) I liked them better than ready-mades, and (2) people, especially in the East, admired this strange ability, and the distinction made me somewhat more of a drawing-room attraction than I would have been otherwise. My friends all knew that I could roll a cigarette in the dark, or in the wind, or behind my back, or riding a horse, or with my eyes shut. But that wasn't enough. What I really wanted to do was roll 'em with one hand. I'd rather roll a cigarette with one hand than be President. In the West I was always watching for a cowboy who might teach me to roll 'em with one hand. But I'd never seen a cowboy rolling a cigarette with one hand. Most of them couldn't even do it with two hands.

I walked over to the young man and said, "I saw you rolling that cigarette. I've always wanted to roll them with one hand, and I thought maybe you could teach me."

"Well," he said, "I don't know whether I can teach you, but I'll show you how to do it."

He pulled out his tobacco sack and demonstrated.

It seems he had lost his arm trying to stop a team of runaway horses. Ever since he had been having a hard time getting anybody to give him a job.

"Sometimes I get so blue and disgusted I feel like gettin' me a gun and just go shootin' up and down the street," he said.

Later I went back to the hotel and sat over a wastebasket and practiced rolling cigarettes with one hand. I had to keep my right hand in my pocket, so it wouldn't always be jumping up to help my left hand. And as I sat there it came to me that rolling a cigarette with one hand was a very trivial thing in the awful pilgrimage we were all making across the hard years to the goal of final sleep—just a little whim that didn't have to be humored at all. And yet I sat there and tried and tried and tried, till I got so mad and disgusted I felt like gettin' me a gun and shootin' at the floor or something.

THE HUNDRED OR SO people who were in the Hofbrau at Mohawk Lake, New Jersey, one Saturday about midnight would be surprised to know the ending of this story.

On Saturday nights the Hofbrau was a very gay place. Everybody came—young and old, families and everything— and sat around at tables and ate and talked. A little fellow in a white suit played the piano and sang in an old-fashioned tenor, and people were friendly and had a great time.

Things were going along like this one Saturday night when a couple came in, bareheaded and in summer clothes. They sat on a bench, both on the same side of the table, and ordered something to eat. They talked and listened to the music but otherwise paid little attention to what was going on about them, or to the people who were making a generalized gabbing sound, or to the ones dancing in the aisles because there wasn't any real dance floor. Each seemed very much interested in what the other was saying, and since each one during his say had quite a long say and was animated about it, an impression got about the place.

The impression was probably born first in the piano player's mind, for he went over and asked what they would like him to play. So he started playing and singing, and they went over and stood behind him and listened, and helped him sing a little now and then when they could remember the words. The crowd thought it was great too and gave a big hand when it was over.

Then the piano player asked them if they weren't just married, and they said yes, just two days ago. The piano player must have spread the word, for three or four people went over and gave the girl a lot of earnest advice on how to live happily, how to handle a husband, what not to do, and so on.

Then the couple, left alone, got started talking again, and they must have been in a deep discussion about something, because they were facing each other now and were talking with their hands too, and being explosive about it, and another impression got about—that they were having a quarrel, their first, maybe.

But they were unaware that anyone was noticing, so they were startled indeed when all of a sudden the piano playing stopped, and there was a great silence, and from somewhere out of it came a loud voice saying, "Aw, kiss and make up."

And that was followed by a louder and closer shout, sort of like an order, which said, "Go ahead and kiss her!"

The man and the girl looked around, and every person in the place was looking at them, waiting. So the man, being no doubt a gentleman, leaned over and kissed her—a great big one—and the wildest applause and shouting and hand-clapping you ever heard broke out all over the place. And then, one by one, everyone in the Hofbrau filed past and shook hands with them, and congratulated them on their marriage, and wished them long happiness and many good things. It wasn't a joke, either, for they were radiant about it, and serious too. The couple smiled and thanked them all. And as the last ones were filing by, the place was closing for the night, so the newlyweds left too, and got in their car with people still good-wishing them off into the night.

They drove away practically busting, because there was certainly a joke on somebody. Both of them had been married many years, and very happily too, but not to each other. So they drove on home and told their respective husband and wife about it, and everybody thought it was funny.

The man, for one—and probably the girl too—was quite happy about it, for all the people had been so genuine and enthusiastic. And then it was a little flattering too. Especially to the man.

I know this story is true, for I was there and saw it—I was the "bridegroom."

THE LAST BATTLE of the Civil War was fought in Mobile Bay, in 1905—some 40 years after you thought the war was over. The story of this battle was told me by a friend, who said it was true.

Steven Quayle, we shall call him, was a Mississippian of gentle birth and scholarly parts. He went North in search of adventure and fortune. He worked in many northern cities. and being frequently appalled at the climate and the bleakness of manners, he longed at times for gentler scenes. At length he adopted a definite routine. He would work diligently for six months, and then for the next half year, with his savings, he would travel on the magic carpet of strong liquor. He would move physically too, and always, of course, southward. It was during one of these periods that he found himself in Mobile. That particular night he had slept in a park. At dawn he wandered to the water front. He was penniless, and lank for lack of food. He sat down on a bench to watch the spectacle of sunrise over Mobile Bay.

Presently a small rowboat came across the waters. It tied up, and the oarsman came ashore. He gave good morning to Steven and sat down to talk. Now, Steven had a courtesy of manner that would make the courtiers of the old French courts look like stumblebums. Poor or rich, drunk or sober, he was of the school of chivalry. The newcomer, it developed, was of the same school; his polished manners also knew no bounds. Gracious conversation began. They told their confidences. It rapidly developed that Steven was the son of a Confederate general. And by an odd coincidence the man from the rowboat was too. Companionship grew.

Steven told how he had fled North to wrest his fortune from the dam-yankees. The other man had been even more thorough. He had spurned the very continent where such things as Appomattox could happen. He had pre-empted an island off the mouth of Mobile Bay and lived there alone. He was an Unreconstructed Rebel, and had built himself a hermitage. One day a month he rowed to the mainland for supplies, liquid and staple. This happened to be the day.

Eventually the saloon and ship chandlery, before which they were sitting, opened. Our man invited Steve to join him in a little something. Steve explained his position, and our man became his enthusiastic host from then on. They filled themselves and also the demijohn the oarsman had brought along. Eventually they loaded it into the boat and left for the island—for by now Steve had been invited to spend a month, and had accepted. They alternately rowed and paused to sample the demijohn. Above the rowing and the sampling was the constant hum of erudite conversation, confined largely to the War Between the States and its intolerable ending.

In the midst of this, Steve espied a smudge of smoke on the horizon. They sat and watched. Soon the vessel was nearly abreast. Then the two friends recognized her as a battleship, flying the hated flag of the United States of America.

Now, it seems that that man from the island always placed a fowling piece in his boat when he set out on a trip. Steve, eyes agleam, seized the gun and dropped a load across the bows of the battleship, calling upon her, in a loud voice, to heave to. The gun's pop attracted no attention whatever. Steve reloaded and fired at the foredeck, and again, at the bridge. He drew attention that time.

The battleship hove to in a hurry, a gig was swung down, and a rough bos'n's mate placed the men in the rowboat under arrest and took them to the battleship. Steve demanded that they be brought before the captain. This was done. The Confederates demanded immediate surrender of the battleship.

Now this, I understand, is all in the records of the Navy Department in Washington. I am sorry I have not had access to those records, so that I might give you the name of a captain in the United States Navy who possessed not only rich manners and a quick command of a situation, but also a sense of humor. The captain invited the Confederates to be seated. He politely offered them cigars. With courtliness he begged for a discussion of terms before he should turn over his sword. If I remember the story correctly, three bottles of champagne were ordered up and served. The conversation was heavy with elegance, and gradually became lightened by a certain bonhomie that grows between respected adversaries. It ended there in the captain's cabin with the drawing of a formal truce between the Confederacy and the United States.

This treaty of peace was signed and sealed in duplicate. Under the terms, the battleship was allowed to proceed to Mobile, but not to sail near their island, and the captain was permitted to retain his sword. The captain escorted the Confederates on deck. They were piped over the side with all the dignity that naval formality can bestow, and assisted into their rowboat, which they found almost dangerously loaded with cases of champagne and other ardent beverages. A launch was waiting to tow them back to their island, and at a signal it shoved off. Steve stood in the forepeak of the dory, seized the old fowling piece, which had been restored to him, and fired a salute. The battleship fired a salute in return.

Thus, in 1905, ended the last battle of the War Between the States.

Josie Pearl lived 35 miles from the town of Winnemucca, Nevada. Lived all alone in a little tar-paper cabin, surrounded by nothing but knee-high sagebrush and empty distance. There really wasn't any road to it—merely a trail across the desert. Your creeping car was the center of an appalling cloud of dust, and the sage scratched long streaks on the fenders.

Josie Pearl was a woman of the West. She was robust, medium-sized, happy-looking, and much younger than her years, which were 60-some; there was no gray in her hair. Her dress was calico, with an apron over it; on her head was a farmer's straw hat, on her feet a mismated pair of men's shoes, and on her left hand and wrist—$6000 worth of diamonds! That was Josie—contradiction all over, and a sort of Tugboat Annie of the desert. Her whole life had been spent in that weirdest of all professions, hunting for gold. She was a prospector. She had been at it since she was nine, playing a man's part in a man's game.

She was what I like to think of as the Old West—one day

worth $100,000, and the next day flat broke, cooking in a mining camp at $30 a month. She had packed grub on her back through 20-below Nevada blizzards, and had spent years as the only woman among men in mining camps, yet there was nothing rough about her—she didn't drink, smoke or swear, and her personality was that of a middle western farm woman.

She had been broke as much as she'd been rich, but she could walk into any bank in that part of the country and borrow $5000 on five minutes' notice. She had run mining-camp boardinghouses all over the West. She had made as much as $35,000 in the boardinghouse business and put every cent of it into some hole in the ground. She had been married twice, but both husbands were dead now. She never depended on men, anyhow.

She had found her first mine when she was 13, and sold it for $5000. She had recently sold her latest mine and was well off again, but she was staying on in the desert.

Her cabin was the wildest hodge-podge of riches and rubbish I'd ever seen. The walls were thick with pinned-up letters from friends, assay receipts on ore, receipts from Montgomery Ward. Letters and boxes and clothing and pans were just thrown—everywhere. And in the middle of it all sat an expensive wardrobe trunk, with a $700 sealskin coat inside.

She slept with a 30-30 rifle beside her bed, and she knew how to use it. In the next room were a pump gun and a double-barreled shotgun. And a dog. But Josie Pearl was no desert hermit, and she was not an eccentric. Far from it. She had a Ford pickup truck, and when she got lonesome she would go and see somebody. She had a big Buick in town, but didn't drive it much because it made her look rich. She would put on her good clothes and take frequent trips to Reno and San Francisco. She knew the cities well, and was no rube when she got there.

She talked constantly, and liked people to like her. She had educated three girls, and grubstaked scores of boys and found them jobs. She had nursed half the sick people in northern Nevada. She was known all over the western mining country.

She said gold brought you nothing but trouble and yet you couldn't stop looking for it. The minute you had gold, somebody started cheating you, or suing you, or cutting your throat. She couldn't even count the lawsuits she'd been in.

People had been doing her dirt for 40 years. But here's a strange thing: every person who had ever done Josie Pearl dirt had died within a couple of years. She wasn't dramatic or spooky about it, but she thought she had put the hex on them. She had been trimmed out of fortune after fortune by crooked lawyers, greedy partners and drunken helpers. Yet she still trusted everybody. Anybody was her friend, till proved otherwise. On one hour's acquaintance she said to me, "You get your girl friend and come out and stay with me two days and I'll take you to a place where you can pick nuggets up in your hand. I'll make you rich."

Which I consider exceedingly generous of Josie Pearl. But if I got rich I'd have lawsuits, and even one lawsuit would put me in my grave, so I started back to town—goldless and untroubled. But on the way, a stinging little flame of yellow-metal fever started burning in my head. Me? Rich? Maybe just one little old lawsuit wouldn't kill anybody.

THE GRASSHOPPER is a ridiculous creature. His legs are out of joint and his eyes are funny. But in 1936 the grasshopper was to the Dakotas about the same thing as a hurricane to Miami or a tidal wave to Galveston. In the Northwest the grasshopper opened and closed every conversation. He held second place only to the great drought itself. You couldn't say the grasshoppers destroyed everything the drought left; rather, the two galloped down through the sun-parched summer nose and nose, and it would be hard to say whether the last blade of grass died of thirst or was gnawed down by a hopper.

Have you ever seen a freshly plowed field, just after the soil is turned? Well, that's what a cornfield looks like after the hoppers are finished. They not only strip the blades—they eat the stalk and burrow down into the ground and nibble away the roots. They leave nothing whatever on the surface. They do the same with grain and grass and vegetables.

I wanted to take a picture of a hopper-devastated corn-field, but I didn't want a bare field, because you couldn't prove there had ever been any corn there. I wanted a field that had leafless cornstalks still standing, and I drove for a full half day—about 150 miles—through South Dakota before I could find a field that had even the stumps of cornstalks left.

The motorist's first engagement with a grasshopper horde gives him a queer feeling. They don't make a black cloud in the sky. They just sit thickly along the road, and you don't see them until your car stirs them up. Then all of a sudden they smack and bang all over the car. I was continually dodging and blinking.

That first batch lasted for about three miles. I stopped at the next town and bought a grasshopper screen to cover the radiator. Nearly every car out there had one. If you didn't have one, the grasshoppers would stick in the radiator until no air could get through, and your engine got hot. You were liable to find grasshoppers in your hotel room, or in your shirt in the morning, or hopping around the tables in the best restaurants.

The old-timers told me that grasshopper plagues usually lasted three or four years, and they were worse in dry years. This was the third and worst year of the current cycle. There wasn't much you could do about them, apparently. The Government had used Paris green. That killed them, all right. But as one farmer said, "For every one that dies, a thousand come to his funeral." It was like trying to bore a hole in water.

WILLIAM ANDREW JOHNSON was a happy old man with a distinction; he was, so far as he knew, the only living ex-slave of a President, and he was mighty proud of it. William was 79. He was freed when he was still a boy, yet his whole attitude toward life was shaped by the fact that he had been born into slavery.

When Andrew Johnson had gone to Washington to be President he had not taken William with him. "But when I was little, Mr. Andrew used to hold me on one knee and my sister on the other, and he'd rub our heads and laugh." William chuckled to himself.

William had a keen disappointment in the spring of 1936. President Roosevelt came to Knoxville to dedicate Norris Dam. William got it into his head he wanted to shake hands and tell him he once was a slave to a President. So he went to some of his white friends—big men in the Chamber of Commerce—and asked if they would fix it up. They told William they would try, but they didn't think anything could be done. Later they reported back that such a thing was impossible. William was mighty upset about it.

Of course, it wasn't impossible at all. William had just used poor judgment in picking his fixer-uppers. He should have known better than to ask a Chamber of Commerce man; he should have asked a newspaperman. If my idea of President Roosevelt was correct, the whole thing would have been as simple as this: a reporter would have told him that William wanted to shake hands, and the President would have said, "Sure," and they would have brought William up, and the President would have pumped his old brown hand and given him a big smile, and in all this world there wouldn't have been a happier or prouder mortal than William Andrew Johnson.

And that's pretty nearly the way it happened, too. I think the happiest I have ever inadvertently made anybody was when my column about William resulted in his being invited to Washington, where President Roosevelt gave him a cane and the keys to the city.

At San Salvador, the capital of El Salvador, I saw a boy who had wandered into the jungle when he was a baby, and for about three years lived alone like an animal.

He was first heard of in the fall of 1933. When there were rumors that a humanlike animal had been seen sneaking through the bushes in the low-lying jungle country along the Pacific Coast, an expedition of farmers was organized and they finally captured the "monster." He fought and bit and screamed. They took him to a farmhouse and shut him up in a room, but in a few minutes he was out and gone. He escaped three more times before they got him to the police station at Sonsonate. He was naked and filthy, and his hair and fingernails were long. He stared always at the floor. He was terrified of people, and would attack and bite without provocation. His only speech was a grunt or a scream.

No one knew for sure about the boy's origin. The theory was that the child lost his parents in a Communist uprising that occurred in that part of Salvador in the 1930's, and that he then wandered into the woods and went it alone. He was obviously a full-blooded Indian. During those years in the jungle he had probably slept in trees and caves. His arms were long, his chest thick, and he could swing through trees. He apparently had lived on live fish, tropical fruit and herbs. He had no fear of animals. He caught and killed poisonous snakes with his bare hands, even after he learned to talk.

After his capture he was kept for a month in the Sonsonate police station, where they studied him. He acted like an imbecile. He would not eat cooked food. They fed him raw meat, fruit and *tortillas*—threw it in onto the floor—but he wouldn't touch it until the people had left. Then he'd crouch in a dark corner and tear at the food. They watched him through slits in the wall.

Finally they took him to a government experimental farm a few miles from Sonsonate, where there was a school. And gradually they discovered he wasn't an idiot, but a very smart boy. His imitative instincts were acute. The first example they had was when a school official made a telephone call; a few minutes later the boy was found ringing an imaginary telephone and repeating the teacher's conversation.

After the teachers were sure the child wouldn't run away, they let him out at night by himself. Many times he went back into the jungle, swung through the trees, played on the riverbank, roamed alone throughout the night. But he always came back. He grew to prefer a bed to sleeping on the ground, and to prefer cleanliness, and he wanted to wear clothes. Slowly his sullenness vanished. And at last they

knew for sure he was a genuine, living, breathing Tarzan.
They were still calling him *Tarzancito*, which means "Little
Tarzan."

He had now been six years in "captivity." He had become
a part of our civilized world, and was going to public school.
Doubtless his jungle years were growing dimmer and dimmer
in his memory. He was in the fond and capable hands of
Colonel Alfonso Marroquin of the Salvadoran army, and was
living with the soldiers in the barracks of the First Regiment
of Infantry, in the heart of San Salvador. The Colonel had not
legally adopted the child but had given him his own name—
the boy was officially Ruben Marroquin. He was excellent in
mathematics. He loved football, and still had the strength
and litheness of the jungle.

When I met him, he shook hands and smiled, and seemed
to have a tremendous desire to be nice and do the right thing.
But it was his voice that astonished me most. It was a frail
little voice, of great gentleness, high but not sharp—rather,
it was soft like a whisper. It seemed to express a great appreciation for everything.

I WENT to lunch with some fellows in Toledo, Ohio. The
restaurant was a big one—there must have been 150 men and
women eating lunch. A waiter came up and said to me,
"What'll you have?" I didn't say anything for a couple of
seconds, of course, and then suddenly the waiter turned
toward the kitchen and yelled: "Hey, this rube won't order.
Come here."

Waiters all over the place threw down their dishes and
came running. They grabbed me and dragged me clear across
the restaurant, kicked open the front doors, and whisshhh—
there I was right on the sidewalk, thrown out of the place!

That's the way things went in that restaurant all the time.
It was a madhouse. Something was always happening. The
whole business—and a prosperous business it was—had been
built up on the policy of insulting the customers. The waiters
all wore galluses and kept their hats on and talked all the
time. If you were getting bald, they called you "Curley." If

you were completely bald, they would polish your head with a rag. If you spilled something, they'd bring a big baby bib and tie it around your neck. To set the table they just brought an armload of silver and threw it at you. If you ate left-handed, as I do, a waiter would stop dead in his tracks and point at you and yell to the whole house, "Hey, look at this rube, he don't even know which hand to eat with. Haw! Haw! Haw!"

The head man said to me, "A new customer always gets rolls and a cup on his first visit here." And just then a waiter came running and yelling, "Rolls and a cup for the new customer." He had an empty cup and two rolls of toilet paper on a plate. Everybody laughed, including me, although I didn't see anything funny about it. During our soup course the waiter came around and said solicitously, "Is there enough water in that soup, or would you like me to put my thumb in it?" Once in a while a waiter got up and walked on the tables. And from the kitchen there was a constant bedlam of dishes breaking, pots falling, women screaming, bells and whistles going off, moans, shouts and thumpings. All during the meal a waiter kept going around the restaurant like a newsboy, yelling, "Here ya are—*News-Bee*, *World-Telegram*, *Daily News*—read Ernie Pyle's column—read all about it!" He was holding high in the air a big roll of toilet paper.

When we started to leave I could hardly lift my topcoat from the rack, it was so heavy. Waiters came running from everywhere. They felt in the pockets and yelled, "We've caught a thief! We've caught a thief!" And then they started unloading the pockets. They took out knives and forks, salt and pepper shakers, jars of sugar, bottles of ketchup—I didn't know my pockets could hold so much—and all the time yelling, "Boy, did he try to make a getaway!" Everybody in the place was howling.

The place was known as Bud & Luke's. It was run by two brothers, Eugene and Glenn Fowler. They had started it as a side line 11 years before, when they were auto salesmen and not doing very well. At first they were too busy to do a decent job of waiting on people, and had to cover up their poor service with a little kidding. The kidding seemed to take hold, and now it had grown into this colossal buffoonery.

I asked Bud (or maybe it was Luke) if anybody ever really got sore. He said, yes, once in a while. They would always try to smooth things over, but if the guy didn't warm up, then they would really let him have it. Nobody had ever got sore enough to fight, however. More people got sore because they came for a ribbing and didn't get it.

They threw a customer into the street only about once a week. These throwouts were generally arranged ahead of time (as mine was, I learned later). I think the funniest one was when a couple of boys from the *News-Bee* called up and arranged to have an out-of-town guest thrown out, and the waiters got mixed up and threw out one of the arrangers.

I wish that every state historical society in America would send a delegation to Montana. They might also invite a few writers of history textbooks to go along. And if they would then practice what they learned, I'll bet that 20 years from now we Americans would know a lot more about American history. Montana makes its history a thing of joy, instead of a stodgy sermon. Every so often along the highways—maybe 20 miles apart, sometimes 50 miles—you'll see a neat little sign: "Historical Point—1000 feet." You coast along and pull over to a wide graveled area, and there is a handsome signboard. Its historical message is easy to read, and it *says* something—for instance this one a few miles east of Shelby:

THE OILY BOID GETS THE WOIM!

A narrow-gauge railroad track nicknamed the "Turkey Track" used to connect Great Falls, Montana, and Lethbridge, Alberta. When the main line of the Great Northern crossed it in 1891, Shelby Junction came into existence. The hills and plains around here were cow country. The Junction became an oasis where parched cowpunchers cauterized their tonsils with forty-rod and grew plumb irresponsible and exuberant.

In 1910 the dry-landers began homesteading, they built fences and plowed under the native grass. The days of open range were

gone. Shelby quit her swaggering frontier ways and became con-
crete-sidewalk and sewer-system conscious.

Dry-land farming didn't turn out to be such a profitable endeavor,
but in 1922 geologists discovered that this country had an ace in the
hole. Oil was struck between here and the Canadian border, and
they all lived happy ever after.

In other states you never see a car in front of those stone
monuments with their dull bronze inscriptions. But in Montana you hardly ever pull up to a historical sign without finding a car or two already there, with people out copying down
the inscription, and chuckling. One grave fellow got up in
the Malta Lions Club and introduced a resolution asking the
state highway department to tear the signs down and replace
them with something "dignified." Unfortunately, the Lions
didn't string him to a tree, but they did shout him down.

NOT ONE in 10,000 of us job-holding mortals would dare do
what the Partridge family did. E. Harve Partridge had always lived in Spokane. He married young, he never went to
college, and by the time he was 25 he had two daughters.
At 41 he had been a reporter on the Spokane *Chronicle* for 18
years. His daughters were 16 and 17.

Each year the Partridge family would take its little vacation. But early in the spring of 1936 a bigger vacation dream
began to stir in the Partridge breasts. They decided to take a
steamer trip to Alaska. Then one evening at supper Harve
Partridge said, "Why don't we buy a boat and sail it to
Alaska ourselves?" The kids were wild about the idea, but
Mrs. Partridge said, "Don't be foolish. You've never been in
anything bigger than a rowboat. We couldn't sail it by ourselves."

One week-end Harve Partridge took a bus to Seattle—300
miles away—and saw a small cabin cruiser for $900. He
steered it for an hour around the bay, wrote a check, and took
the next bus home. The Partridge family was going to sail to
Alaska.

The three months of preparation were as much fun as the
trip itself. They bought $12 worth of nautical charts, and a

parallel rule, and a compass that cost two and a half. Every evening the whole family got down on the living-room floor and, using a footstool for a boat, with the compass on top of it, worked out nautical courses and steered them. The upshot was that they went to Alaska and back, all by themselves. When they started, Skipper Partridge had steered a boat exactly four hours, and the others, never.

Not one of the landlubbers was seasick, though they wallowed through waves ten feet high. Sometimes it was so rough they couldn't cook. They chugged within 60 feet of whales. The girls went out in the little lifeboat and with axes chopped off hunks of floating icebergs for their refrigerator. They drove ahead for hours through thick fog, and hit their destination right on the nose. They were tossed around in terrific tide rips. So innocent were they that they didn't know what a tide rip was till after they'd been through one. They navigated the swirling currents of dangerous, rocky narrows. Partridge learned to fix a broken clutch at sea. Frequently they sailed all night, through rain and darkness. They put faith in their nautical book learning and it brought them through.

On the way back the eldest daughter, Jean, was ordered by the skipper to take the wheel at night, lay out her own course, take them through a narrows in pitch darkness, and wake her father when they got safely on the other side. She did.

The Partridges sailed 2500 miles in three weeks, spending $300. When they returned they sold the boat for as much as they'd paid for it.

AT FORT YUKON, Alaska, I met a remarkable woman. Nine years before, her world had come to an end in that mosquito-infested village; she had had more than she could take. Two of her boys had just been buried—mysteriously drowned in the Yukon. Her husband had quit cold on the family. Everything was on her shoulders, and they had grown too weary under the burden. It was time to quit. Nobody cared anyhow.

She led her four children down to the riverbank. "Come on, let's go for a little ride in the canoe," she said. It would be easy. Over the side with them, and herself over last. You live only a minute in the Yukon River; the cold water stops your heart. They were ready to step into the boat when an old man with long whiskers came and tapped the woman on the shoulder. "Come walk up to my cabin," he said. "I want to talk to you." She barely knew the man, but she went. And the man said, "I know you don't want to go onto charity. You can make a living on the trap line. It won't be easy, but you can support yourself and the children."

So Mrs. Maud Berglund turned trapper. She bundled her four children into a gasoline boat, and the old man went with them. For two weeks they chugged up the Porcupine and its tributaries. The baby died on the way. They buried him, and went on. They didn't stop until they were 280 miles beyond Fort Yukon, which is itself north of the Arctic Circle. Then they camped and built a log house.

When I met them, the three little girls were young women. They were still trapping.

Only nine times in nine years had Mrs. Maud Berglund and her daughters been back to the "metropolis" of Fort Yukon. Eleven months of the year they lived alone among snow and wolves and moose and mountains. Just after the spring ice-break they would come down river with their winter's catch of furs, sell them, and return with a year's supply of staples. The round trip, allowing for two weeks' stay in Fort Yukon, took just a month. They made the trip to Fort Yukon in two open motorboats, with a small scow that they pushed ahead of them. They had to bring their 22 Husky dogs with them, for nobody lived in Berglundville but themselves.

Mrs. Berglund had a one-room log cabin in Fort Yukon. The 22 dogs were staked out behind it, and what a howling they set up when strangers came around! I was lucky enough to catch the Berglunds there, and I spent an evening and a forenoon with them.

"This is just a stopping place," said Mrs. Berglund, apologizing for the cabin. "So we don't try to keep it nice. Our home is 'up there.' I wish you could see it. We have made a real home of it."

Mrs. Berglund was a handsome gray-haired woman—fine of feature, refined of speech, easy and gentle in her manner. The rough life seemed not to have touched her personality at all. But her three daughters were children of nature. They were deeply tanned; their hands showed hard work; their shoulders and legs were strong like a man's. The youngest had been carried over the trap line by dog sled for two years before she was big enough to make it herself. All their education was given them by their mother. They knew no life but that of the trapper. They had never been south of Fort Yukon —never seen a village with real streets or brick buildings. They had never drunk or smoked, or danced or played cards. They didn't know much about men. But they had to shoot only once at a running moose, and they could freeze their feet without crying.

Their hobby, their amusement, their recreation, their joy were all in one thing: their dog teams. Each girl had her own team, her own sled, her own rifles. They would talk dog to you until you were black in the face. They loved their dogs above all else.

Although they did not know our world, the girls were smart and zestful. After the first few minutes of bashfulness, their conversation flowed out like a torrent, and their eyes shone; out came guns and wolfskins to show you, and moose antlers, and stories of little incidents in excited snatches. Those three girls were the freshest in spirit of any woman I had ever seen.

I asked them, "Do you ever look at pictures of cities?" One of them said, "Yes, we've seen pictures of New York and places like that. But I don't think we'd ever want to go there. We've got too much freedom up here."

In reply to my question, Mrs. Berglund said they didn't get lonesome much any more. "When we first went up, we would get in black sloughs for days. But the radio has helped that a lot. Now, when we get low we go turn it on, and we're soon out of it." They also had bright gasoline lamps, and books and magazines up there. But the girls didn't care much for reading; they turned on the radio instead.

Every year they picked and canned berries and wild fruit. And they caught salmon with a fish wheel, and dried it and stored it for winter feed for the dogs. When the fall freeze-up came they cut ice from the river and stored it in the ice well. They would kill a moose apiece and fry the steaks and then freeze them.

In the late fall, when the snow was on and the season opened, they started their real winter's work—five months of lonely running of trap lines. They had more than 200 miles of lines, and 400 traps.

John Roberts and one of the girls started out together. Mr. Roberts was the long-whiskered old man who had tapped Mrs. Berglund on the shoulder and helped her get started. He had trapped with them ever since, and though he was now aged and shaky he could still shoot as straight as a G-man and tramp behind the dogs all day. Mrs. Berglund and the two other girls went in the opposite direction, setting traps as they went.

Every 15 miles or so they had a log cabin about ten feet square, with a door so low you had to crawl in. They tried to reach a cabin each night, but sometimes they didn't. Every cabin had a stove and a couple of bunks. Candles were used for light. Frequently a branch line of traps was laid at right angles to the main line. In following the branches they would separate, so a good part of their winter was spent in traveling absolutely alone.

"How do you kill the trapped animals that aren't already dead?" I asked Mrs. Berglund.

"We have to shoot the wolves, lynx and wolverine," she said. "The others are smaller, and we rap them on the head with a club."

But killing the marten got under Mrs. Berglund's skin. "They cross their little paws above their heads, and look up at you so pitifully, it's all I can do to hit one of them," she said. "When I first went up, I said I was going to save pelts and have myself a fine marten coat. But I don't want one now."

The Berglunds never went out unarmed, yet they had never

been injured by a wild animal. Wolves had never bothered
them, though they had had narrow escapes from charging
moose. All four of them seemed to be in awe of a moose's
killing powers.

"One jumped right over my sled and hit me with his hoof,"
said Evelyn, the middle girl. "The gun was lashed to the sled
and I couldn't get at it in time to stop him, so I just ducked.
Believe me, I had it out by the time he came back."

Home from the trap line late one night after ten days'
absence the Berglunds walked up to the cabin and found a
bear inside. He had upset things pretty badly, enjoyed a
good meal and then lain down on Mrs. Berglund's bed. They
made a gasoline torch, and one of the girls held it while
Mrs. Berglund shot Mr. Bear. The girls said bears would
attack you if surprised; but a moose would attack you any
time.

The Berglund women had all frozen their hands and feet
many times, but had never had any serious aftereffects. Fortunately, they had never had any critical illnesses or injuries.
But Mrs. Berglund knew all the home remedies, and she said
that even if one of them was to break an arm or leg they
could handle it all right. She gave me a little jar of cottonwood salve for my mosquito bites. They made it by crushing
the green buds of cottonwood trees and boiling them with
moose grease. The salve had a woodsy smell, and it stopped
the itching. They also used it for cuts and sores.

The Berglunds got mail only by chance. The postmaster at
Fort Yukon would give it to an Indian traveling north, who
in turn would give it to another, and so on, until it finally
came to the Berglunds. A letter received in Fort Yukon in
September might not reach them until April.

The first year they were up there they caught an Indian
robbing their trap line. Mrs. Berglund told him to get out of
that country, and said that if she ever saw him around there
again she'd put a bullet through him. "And I would too,"
she said, and meant it.

Living in the Arctic isn't any bed of feather mattresses, no
matter what some people say. In summer the mosquitoes buzz

in poisonous, tormenting clouds. Sometimes you can run your cupped hand along your cheek and come away with hundreds of them in your fist. In the fall, when the mosquitoes die, the gnats come to life. Mrs. Berglund said they are worse than mosquitoes—they get in your eyes, up your nose and in your hair—they make life a misery. And when the gnats go, then comes the winter.

At 60 below, your fingers freeze while you're unhitching a dog. You must move with the caution of a man with a bad heart; to breathe hard is to frost your lungs. You dare not perspire; your clothes would freeze on you. To get your feet wet is to lose them. To touch a piece of metal is worse than a bad burn. And don't think you don't feel the cold, either. "You shiver," said Evelyn, who was born to it, "until you just can't shiver any more."

But they kept on trapping. Nine years in the Far North, alone. Four women and an old man. Fighting, as we all do, for life. Some years they barely made their grubstake, but on the whole they were keeping well ahead of the game.

Just before our boat left, Mrs. Berglund told me a secret. "Mr. Roberts and I are going to be married," she said. "Nobody will ever know how big his heart is, or what he's done for us. He was the only one who sensed what I had come to that day nine years ago down by the riverbank."

You don't burn up with this thing called love, I guess, when you're knocking at the gates of threescore and more. But there is a deep thing called gratitude, and there is another thing known as human companionship, and the two put together sometimes do just as well as love, I guess, or maybe even a little better.

CONSTRUCTION engineers are great fellows, and they are smart. They know all about stresses and strains. You admire them a great deal while sitting around a table looking at their blueprints. But just wait till you are 700 feet up in thin air, standing rigid and paralyzed in a rickety little cage, suspended only by a piece of wire. At that moment you wish all construction engineers were in hell, and you know very well, figures or no figures, that a one-inch steel cable isn't strong enough to support a big guy like you who weighs 115.

On the south shore there was a little frame building which served as field office for the great Golden Gate Bridge. We went in there to get our safety helmets. When we came out we couldn't see any bridge at all, because the fog was so thick. "Well, we'll go up anyway," the bridgeman said. "Maybe it won't be so thick up above." We walked out along the temporary pier under the bridge, to the immense south tower, three blocks out in the water. Then we got into a wire cage and started up.

This cage was like an elevator, except that it didn't go up anything. No shaft at all. It just went up through empty air, like a bucket on the end of a rope, and the top of the ride was nearly 200 feet higher than the Washington Monument. As long as we were in the fog I was all right, because I couldn't see. But pretty soon we came out above it, and then the fright closed in over me. We went up and up and up. The fog and snatches of bridge and shore and city widened out below us. The elevator began to swing up and down. I knew instantly what that was: it was the cable fraying, and only a strand or two was left holding us. At two places on the way up we passed little shelves where the elevator sometimes stopped to let workmen out. When you came to one of these shelves the top of the elevator would hit it, and the cage would bump and jiggle around. It was enough to make a man want to lie down on the floor and cry.

Finally we were up there. Then we had to step across an open slice of sky about a foot wide (wide enough to fall through, all right), and then climb a steel ladder for 20 feet, cross a catwalk, climb another ladder 15 feet, and then we were out on top of the world. Oh, God, who ever talked me into this?

The top of the tower was as big as eight or ten rooms. There were little shops and control houses, and men in helmets were sitting around eating lunch. The view was wonderful, if you dared look. The fog was vanishing now, and the whole immense bridge was there below us, in both directions, and there was the Golden Gate with little ships going through it, and over yonder was Sausalito, and back here was San Francisco, and out there was the ocean.

Around the edge of the top was a strong wooden railing. Sense told me I could pound on it all day with a sledge and not make a dent, and yet I knew that if I leaned on it, as the bridgeman was doing, it would collapse. Furthermore, I knew that if I stumbled I wouldn't fall to the floor. No, I'd fall up about five feet, and then out about five feet over the rail, and then 750 feet down. That's the way I fall at the top of a high tower. Consequently, I stayed about six feet from the edge, with one arm wrapped around the doorway of one of the control houses.

The bridgeman said I was doing all right; a lot of people kept their eyes shut all the way up in the elevator, and a lot backed out when the elevator stopped—they just couldn't step across that foot of open space. And others who had gone on up would get so scared they would lie down on the floor and turn white and sweat and tremble. I was doing all right, he said. I was very careful, however, to step softly, like a cat, so as not to set up any vibrations that would collapse the tower. He said it was built so that an earthquake wouldn't collapse it, but you never can tell.

He asked if I wanted to walk down the catwalk that ran beneath the two cables, from the tower clear down to the bridge floor in the center. I sure would have liked to, but unfortunately I had an urgent appointment and couldn't wait. So we climbed down the ladders and waited for the cage, and went swinging and jerking down to sea level again me getting braver with every foot of the descent.

There was a young fellow in workman's clothes on the elevator. I said to him, "How long did it take you to get used to these high places?" He said, "When I started I was on the graveyard shift, from midnight till eight. It was so dark I couldn't see what was under me. By the time it got daylight I was all right. But I was so glad to get a job I'd of clumb the Eiffel Tower." Personally, I would rather starve to death.

I had the privilege of being one of the few outsiders to

cross the finished bridge before it was opened. But it didn't scare me. No, sir. We rode across in an automobile.

Nobody has seen all of America until he has driven through the redwood forests of northern California. You get an eerie feeling there where it's so dark, with those great trunks rising around you so thick and so straight. They don't seem like trees at all, but more like spirits or werewolves—something half human and half ghost. Everybody I've ever talked to about it has felt that way. You wouldn't be surprised to see an immense, gnarled wooden hand reach out and snatch you away into nowhere.

We have been many times to California. You could not count on the fingers of both hands the number of our trips out there. But always we have avoided coming right out and admitting that we liked California. We would say, yes, it might be all right if you could get back East once a year. Or we would make fun of their sunshine claims, for we had seen California in flood. Or we would join the intellectuals and hoot at all the Iowa farmers in Los Angeles. But maybe as we grow older we grow more honest with ourselves, or maybe we just reach a stage where we aren't ashamed of agreeing with the majority. Whatever it is, I am at last ready and willing to admit that I think California is wonderful.

Sure, it has spots I don't like. You couldn't hire me to live in agricultural Bakersfield, nor in far-north Eureka, nor in the sham of Hollywood. But you don't have to live in those places. There are hundreds of miles of startling seacoast, aching to be lived upon. There are thousands of magnificent little valleys, placidly waiting for man to come and despoil them with his enjoyment. There are deserts where those with a feeling for sand and wind could find peace. And there are mountains for the virile, and forests for the woodsy people, and fog for those who hate the sun. Yes, in full honesty, we admit that California does have everything. And we were sad at leaving because, in the way of all things, no man knows but that this backward glance over the shoulder may be his last glance forever.

MRS. MIKE

THE STORY
OF KATHERINE MARY FLANNIGAN

A condensation from the book by

BENEDICT AND NANCY FREEDMAN

Tʜɪs enthralling account of a 16-year-old girl from
Boston who married a Canadian Mounty and followed
him into the wilderness is a narrative of adventure, but
also a warm and glowing love story.

MRS. MIKE

HE WORST WINTER in 50 years, the old Scotsman had told me. I'd only been around for 16, but I was willing to take his word for the other 34. The train windows were plastered with snow, and outside great clouds of snow were being whipped along by a 60-mile gale.

"You'll be telling your children you were in the blizzard of 1907," the old man chuckled. "I was speaking to the conductor a while back. It's 40 below and dropping."

We'd left Montreal 18 days before, 18 days spent mostly in pulling the engine out of drifts. I was being sent to Uncle John in Calgary, Alberta, because of my pleurisy. Not so long before Alberta had been part of the great Northwest Territories, and my mother had had her doubts about letting me leave Boston to go into such a wilderness. However, the doctors said the cold dry climate would be good for my lungs. We looked it up on a map and Alberta seemed awfully empty. A couple of thin blue rivers, a couple of crooked lakes, and the map maker was through. My mother found the circle that was Calgary and said: "You'll bear in mind, Katherine Mary O'Fallon, that's as far north as I want you to go. Don't be letting your uncle take you up into this." She waved in the general direction of the North Pole.

We drew into Calgary at last. I put on the red plaid dress I'd been saving for the occasion and the big blue hair ribbon by which Uncle John was to recognize me. A few minutes later I was standing on the platform, and a tall dark lean gentleman with eyes just like my mother's was smiling and saying, "Katherine Mary?"

I put my arms around him and kissed him. "I hope you're my Uncle John," I said.

"Yes, I'm your Uncle John." Then he looked at me hard. "Just like your mother," he said.

42

Uncle John had a big coon coat for me. I put it on right over my other coat, and climbed into the cutter. My uncle threw a buffalo robe over my knees, picked up the reins, and we were off. It was like flying. We startled up the snow on every side, and the wind blew a challenge.

It took us two days to get to Uncle's ranch. We were almost there when I noticed a difference in the air. It seemed warmer, and the sky flushed a deep rose. The glow spread over everything. "Uncle John," I said, "my face feels warm."

Uncle smiled. "It's going to chinook," he said.

"What's that?"

"You'll see soon enough, Kathy."

That night at Uncle John's ranch I went to bed with a four-point Hudson's Bay blanket but by morning I had thrown it off. All day it blew hot and warm and the red glow deepened in the sky.

"Uncle," I asked, "what's happened? Overnight it's spring."

"It's a current of air from the west, warmed by the Japanese Current. When it reaches the prairie, the thaw sets in."

In 24 hours the snow was gone. The bare earth appeared with little grass blades pricking at it. What I had thought was field melted, and we saw the ice in the Red Deer River break and disappear. The larger chunks were carried past like white rafts. Everywhere, from all things, there fell a constant drip: from branches, from roots, from boulders, from eaves.

The river rose rapidly. In some places water ran over the prairie. There were thousands of cattle grazing along the riverbanks and Uncle John and the ranch hands were gone all one day driving them to safety. When they came trooping back that night, they were tired and silent. I put some coffee on the stove. It was hot and black, and the men relaxed.

"How many you reckon we lost?"

"Hundred head, maybe."

"MacDonald's lost more," Uncle John said.

"What happened?"

Uncle John gulped down more coffee. "Stock drowned. Ice

jammed. Blocked the river. Flooded the prairie. We were working in three feet of water, and it was rising all the time."

I felt sick. I closed my eyes, trying to shut out the picture of thousands of beasts helpless in the flood. Only that morning I'd seen them in the arroyos, red and white patches of them going on for miles.

"Happens every year, miss," one of the men said. "Most times we get 'em out. Sometimes we don't. It's the chinook does it."

So this was the North. . . .

I was in the kitchen making berry pies out of some dried currants I'd found there when there came an awful knock at the door and in strode a tall young man in a bright red jacket. He carried a man on his back.

"Holy St. Patrick!" I cried. "Is he dead?"

The young man laughed and dumped his burden down on the couch. "Smell him," he said.

I did. The odor reminded me of John L. Sullivan, the fighter, who used to board at our house in Boston.

"Who is it?" I asked.

"Johnny Flaherty—your uncle's cook. He needs some black coffee. You'd better be putting it on."

I whirled around. I was five feet, four and one half inches, but I had to look up, way up. "I thank you kindly for bringing him back, and I'll thank you to be on your way again, for I'm taking no orders from an English soldier."

"An English soldier, am I? And what gave you that idea?" He frowned down at me, and he was very good-looking.

"With that red coat, you're either off to a fox hunt or you're a British peeler."

"You little chit—look at the size of you and you insulting the uniform!"

That made me mad. He could have noticed my naturally curly hair or my eyes, instead of my size.

"Well, if you're not an Englishman, who are you?"

"I'm Sergeant Mike Flannigan, of the Northwest Mounted."

I never could really have thought he was an Englishman, not with the lilt he had to his speech.

Johnny Flaherty moaned from the couch.

"Miss O'Fallon," the Sergeant said patiently, "will you get the poor man some coffee?"

The big Mounty had no more than just succeeded in getting Johnny Flaherty to bed when Uncle John came in. He greeted Mike cordially, then his mouth clamped into a line. "Johnny home?" he asked.

Mike nodded.

Uncle John walked into the next room. Presently we could hear them in there going at it. Uncle John would start quiet and end shouting profanity and then Johnny would shout too. I was embarrassed that Sergeant Mike was there to hear such language but every time there was an extra loud oath, he'd throw back his head and laugh. I got so mad at him that I put two sets of spoons on the table and no forks. He noticed and laughed harder.

I stopped squarely in front of him. "What do you find so amusing, Sergeant?"

"A young lady like yourself in Alberta Territory."

My uncle came back presently, and the three of us sat down to dinner. For dessert I served one of the currant pies I'd made. Uncle John took one bite and a strange look came into his eyes. He laid the fork down and pushed back his chair. So did Mike.

"Well, John," said Mike, "when you teach Kathy how to shoot you won't be needing any ammunition." He grinned at me.

"Why not?" I asked.

"Well, you can use the currants in those pies you baked."

I took a big bite of pie myself. It was as if I had pebbles in my mouth. I made a fake gulp and tried to hold my mouth naturally as if I had swallowed them.

Mike said good-bye. I didn't answer because I couldn't. He took my hand and leaned toward me till my hair brushed his cheek.

"Spit 'em out," he said softly, "and next time, cook 'em."

ONE DAY when Mike came out to the ranch he stood in the doorway smiling and holding out a present. I opened the package and lifted out a pair of heavy mackinaw pants. "But they're men's," I protested. "Put them on. I'm not taking you hiking in *that*." And he pointed scornfully at my blue polka-dot dress.

We tramped along a stream, past the foothills and up into the mountainous country. I liked the way Mike walked. I liked the freedom in his body. I kept up with him too because he had just said that he hated to walk with women who minced along. Mike led the way along the path. Up ahead he stopped and held a brier that would have snapped back and struck me in the face.

"You walk like a boy." he said and I knew that was meant as a compliment.

We came to a stream bed in a forest of silver trees. I noticed one or two and finally a dozen trees that had been felled in the oddest manner. The stumps were not sliced straight across as a saw would leave them, but were whittled into a conical shape, the tip ending in a sharp point.

"Beavers," Mike whispered. "Their dam's just ahead."

We crept forward a few feet more. Mike pulled me down beside him on a rock ledge, and I stared at the blockade of wood, stones, twigs and mud that dammed the stream and turned it into a large pool.

We were silent a long time, waiting and watching. At last a beaver bobbed up to the surface of the pool. He swam across, using his tail as a rudder. He scampered up on shore, walking on his hind legs. He was carrying stones and pebbles in his paws.

"He looks like a little man," I whispered.

"That's what the Indians call them, 'the little people.'"

Suddenly Mike jumped up. He was looking upstream, and his face was angry. Not far away I saw what looked like a fishing pole set low over the water. It had a clamp on the end of it. A beaver had swum into it. The trap had sprung, swinging the pole high into the air. And there the beaver hung by its forepaws, whimpering. A large hawk swooped low, and I cried out. Mike wheeled around.

"Get back!" I saw then what he did not want me to see. The eyes of the beaver had been torn out of their sockets. Mike broke the pole and laid the animal on the ground Then he carried me into the edge of the wood where I couldn't see. A moment later I heard a shot, and Mike came back. He bent over and touched my hair, very lightly.

"The hawk did it, and the beaver was still alive!" I sobbed.

"Kathy, don't think about it," Mike said. "It isn't like this, as a rule. Almost all the fellows set traps under water, that either kill the beaver or let it get away without mangling it. These spring poles are nasty contrivances, and not many use them."

He took both my hands in his and I forced a smile. My face was streaked with tears, but he reached down and kissed it.

FOR A WEEK I had been after Uncle John to get his permission to go to the square dance at the O'Malleys' barn with Mike. And all I could get out of him was, "I'm thinking it over."

When Mike came to pick me up, Uncle John was still thinking it over. He said he'd let me know his decision when we came back.

We laughed together as we saddled our horses.

"Your Uncle John," said Mike, "never says anything straight on. Always hits it sideways."

It was quarter to one when we got back. Not once during the whole evening had Mike made a move to try to kiss me. Uncle John was sitting up.

"Mike," he said, "this is going too far."

"I know it is, John," Mike agreed, "and I want to talk to you about it right now." He looked down at me. "You stay where you are." I stood listening, expecting to hear Uncle John bawl Mike out. But it was Mike who was doing the talking. He was asking Uncle John if he could marry me.

In an instant I had my arms around his neck.

"Mike, do you?—do you?—"

"Yes," he said, and put my hands down. He turned to Uncle John. "Well, John?"

"I can't give my consent, Mike. You'll be going back to your wild North, and you can't take a delicate girl like Katherine Mary into a country like that."

Mike looked from me to my uncle. "There's two ways of thinking, when it comes to that. To my mind, the country would harden her, make a strong woman of her."

There was a silence.

Finally Uncle said, "There's no man I'd rather give her to than you, Mike Flannigan, and you know it well. But she was put in my charge by her mother. And her mother would not approve. She's only 16 and she is not well. I'm thinking she should go back to Boston."

"Have I nothing to say about this?" I asked the two of them.

Mike looked at me reproachfully. "Your uncle's too good a friend for me to be talking a matter like this behind his back."

"And what am I? I hope at least that you think as much of me as of my uncle."

"Kathy, of course I do."

"Well, then. If you love me, you tell me right here and now. And if you want me to marry you, you ask me, and then maybe I will and maybe I won't."

Mike came over to me. He spoke low so my uncle couldn't hear. "I love you, Kathy. I always have, and I think you've always known it. I'll make you happy, girl. I'll give my life to it. I want you for my wife."

"I'm going to marry him," I said to my uncle. But my uncle was no longer there.

"We are to be married here at the ranch next Sunday," I wrote to my mother. I knew she wouldn't have the money to come on for the wedding—and Mike already had his orders to return to his station at Hudson's Hope, 700 miles by dog sled from the end of the railroad at Edmonton. The trip would take two or three months. I was worried about those 700 miles to Hudson's Hope, but I pushed the fear down inside of me.

"I'm awfully happy," I wrote.

I was. Awfully happy and awfully in love.

WE SET OUT from Edmonton as part of a dog-sled caravan of traders, trappers and Hudson's Bay Company men. From the first day it was cold, sometimes 50 below zero. No amount of covers could keep me warm sitting on the sled and I'd have to get off and run until I was warm.

As we neared Athabaska, the weather changed. There was a tension in the air, and heavy clouds piled in the east. The sun was already low when a circle of pale silvery light sprang up around it. A little later, within this giant loop, four smaller shining circles appeared. In each circle a small unreal but gleaming image of the sun shone.

"Sun dogs, they're called," Mike told me. "I've seen as many as 16 surrounding the sun, like puppies around their mother. It means a blizzard."

It did. We were stuck in Athabaska two days before we could go on.

I began to hate the cold and snow. After two months of it, I also hated the loneliness and the vast emptiness of this barren and frozen country. One day the going was especially slow, and Mike was up ahead with the runner. Another mile, and he dropped back to my sled.

"How goes it, Minx?" he asked, and squeezed my hand.

I laughed and said, "Fine." But the smile went out of me, for the cold was cutting at my insides with every breath.

He gave me a sharp look and then began telling me what a good rest we'd have that night at a friend's house in Taylor Flats, but the pain was around me like a winding sheet. I sighed and buried my face into the furs, and then I think I slept.

The motion stopped. I sat up and looked around. We were in a clearing. Ahead of us was a house. Mike picked me up and set me down inside, and the sudden heat almost choked me. I remember being put in an iron bedstead, and Mike feeding me soup and then lying down beside me.

The next morning I was better but I had to rest in bed all

day. Toward evening I got up and met the Howards, the rough, hospitable family that had taken us in. There were six of them, including four grown sons.

For dinner Mrs. Howard served beans, dried eggs and dried prunes. During the meal I was startled by a low wailing cry that rose to a shriek. No one seemed to notice it or even look up. Then it came again, a low minor wail that built and built until the final shriek tore through you. The cry was taken up and answered again and again in a maniacal crescendo of sound. It was a wolf pack, crying for food.

I shuddered, and then I could bear it no longer. I followed the curve of the rising inflection, and when it reached its shrill wailing peak, I screamed too. The men looked at me aghast, but I screamed and screamed.

Mike leaped to his feet and took me by the shoulder. "Katherine Mary, stop it!" He spoke with a sternness I'd never heard before, and I did stop. But I began first to laugh and then to cry, hysterically.

And then suddenly I knew what it was all about. It hadn't been the wolves. Their cry had loneliness in it, and that was why I had to scream and cry with them. I was lonely, too, because I missed my mother. My family, my sisters—and even my mother's canary—were in my thoughts, but under my feet these two months had been only the trackless white of this dead and frozen land, empty with loneliness.

Later, when Mike and I were alone, I put my arms around his neck. "I'm happy, Mike," I whispered into his jacket. "Really, I love you and I'm happy. I don't know why I act like this."

But Mike's face was full of misery and an unhappy determination. He pushed my head against his shoulder and stroked it.

"I'm taking you back in the morning, Kathy," he said at last.

That night Mike and I lay awake with our own thoughts. And in the morning he took me on, not back. It was then that I really became his wife, for I knew that this white land and its loneliness were a part of Mike. It was a part I feared, that I didn't know or understand. But I told myself, "If you love Mike, you'll love the things that go with him."

The country, as we approached Hudson's Hope, became more beautiful. We traveled up the frozen riverbed, and hills large and small rolled away on either side. Finally we left the river and traveled to higher ground.

"When we reach the top you'll see the flag," said Mike.

There was a flag in front of every Hudson's Bay Company in the Northwest. It meant hot food, rest, fresh supplies, conversation, people; a little oasis of humanity and comfort in the white void. Only this time it would mean more; it would mean home. When the flag came into view, I took Mike's hand without saying a word. There on a plateau was the company store and around it a group of trappers' cabins that hid themselves among the drooping, snow-laden trees. Below, the hills rolled away, carrying white armies of poplar and pines on their backs. To the north the Peace River ran the gauntlet of dark bluffs. It was beautiful.

We stopped at the store, and the storekeeper, a big brawny giant of a man, pounded Mike affectionately and asked him in. "Son of a gun, son of a gun," he kept saying, and he called roughly to his Indian wife, who then shyly prepared and served us a hot meal.

After we had eaten, Mike took me to our house which stood in a forest of pine beyond the store. There was a large front room and two bedrooms. There was a combination stove and heater, the kind they all had in this country. Over the bed was a buffalo skin. The chinks in the wall were stuffed with moss, and through a side window I could see the cabin which served as Mike's office and the Hudson's Hope court and hospital.

"Mike, do people really come to you when they're sick?" I asked.

Mike said slowly, "We're 700 miles from civilization or a doctor."

"But do you know anything about it?"

"Not much. I bought some books in Calgary."

I looked at this man that I had married. There was more here than a red coat. Evidently he was a big man up here.

ONE DAY I was in the house making sandwiches to take to Mike at the office when my door opened and there stood a brave in full Indian dress. He nodded solemnly at me, then stalked to the best chair in the house and sat down. Behind him followed aunts, sisters, uncles and cousins. Each gave me a nod or a grunt and then they sat in my chairs. When the last chair was occupied they began seating themselves ceremoniously on the floor.

"Holy St. Patrick!" I said aloud.

But I couldn't just stand there with my mouth open. I had to do something. I was Sergeant Flannigan's wife. I had a position to keep up in the community. I thought of a speech, saying I was not settled yet but that we'd all have a nice party soon. But, looking into the rows of swarthy, stolid faces, I was convinced that the only thing they'd understand was food. I began cutting the sandwiches I had made for Mike into enough pieces to go around, and put on tea.

It was the strangest and silentest tea party ever given. When they had eaten all the sandwiches and had all the tea they could drink, the gentleman who had led the procession rose, grunted at me three times; then they all left. I had to keep looking at the crumbs, and the spot in the corner where one old crone had kept spitting, to assure myself that I hadn't been dreaming.

Including the Indians on the reserve, the population of Hudson's Hope came to about 135 people, but when we arrived most of the men were away trapping. One day a group of sleds suddenly appeared over the hill.

"Mike, Mike, look!"

We watched the men and teams surging over the plains below us. More and more sleds spread out over the valley until there must have been 50 men racing each other over the waste. The sleds were piled with dark furs.

From the other direction came the women, running to greet them. A tingling thrill of anticipation was in me. These women had not seen their men for seven months. But as the two groups neared each other, the women stopped running. Here and there a man ran forward and caught a woman to him. But when that happened, the man was always white, and the woman always young.

For the most part a woman would walk to the man's side and he, many times without a word to her, would throw heavy pelts from the sled into her arms. I watched, horrified, as one Indian unhitched one of his dogs and harnessed his wife to the team. Presently, the woman strained with the beasts, and the sled moved slowly after the others.

"Indian women are toughened to it, Kathy." Mike explained. "That's all they've known for a thousand years."

When winter ended I looked forward to getting out of my heavy mackinaw pants and into skirts once more. But I was never to wear skirts in this country; for spring and summer, and all during the mosquito months, I wore overalls as a protection against those vicious swarms of insects. Mike tacked a fine cheesecloth over every window. The mesh of ordinary screening was not small enough for those tiny, whining pests.

At my suggestion, Mike spent a good deal of time instructing the Indians in the use of cheesecloth, explaining patiently that they would have less sickness if they fastened this thin stuff over their windows and across the entrances of their tepees.

"This will make a big difference in the lives of those Indians, won't it?" I said.

"It should," Mike said.

It struck me this wasn't a very enthusiastic reply.

The next week I called on Oo-me-me, the wife of the Indian chief. She greeted me with smiling eyes, but no cheesecloth was in evidence. In the corner of the room a baby lay in a nest of rags. It waved its chubby legs, driving a flock of mosquitoes and flies into the air. On one leg was an open cut, angry and red. When the leg stopped twitching, the insects settled down on it again, biting into the raw flesh. I pointed to the bare windows. "The netting that Sergeant Mike put up, where is it?"

Oo-me-me smiled and left the room. Presently she returned with half a dozen skirts, mostly velvet and velveteen. Each dress was edged with a thin strip of cheesecloth.

Up here," Mike said, "there are no signposts or traffic cops. During the day you've got the sun, and at night the stars. From them you'll learn to tell time, direction and, to some extent, the weather.

It was my first astronomy lesson in the clear black night of Hudson's Hope, and the stars crowded in on us, a million times brighter, closer and more real than the stars of Boston. I remembered the verse from my mother's Bible, "And God made the firmament. . . ." This was the first time it had really looked like a firmament.

"The Indians call it the sky-curtain," Mike told me.

We lay on our backs on a blanket, gazing up into the sparkling holes in the sky-curtain. I suddenly realized that I was healthy and strong, so healthy and strong that for weeks I had forgotten all about my chest and my cough and my pleurisy.

And so I thought this would be a wonderful time to tell him, now that I was well, and the sky was full of stars, and his ear was close against my lips.

"Mike," I said, "we're going to have a baby."

He jumped a little. "Is it true?"

"I've known for some time," I said.

"Well, you certainly kept it hidden from me," he said.

I laughed. "That wasn't hard."

"You imp," Mike said joyfully, "you have the cunning of three lions."

I'd been working in the garden all morning. I was a little tired and didn't want to overdo because of the baby. I leaned the hoe against the house and sat on the steps. A wind had sprung up, lifting the grass in rhythmic waves like the waves of an ocean. The air was heavy and full of haze. The sun seemed half obscured, but it shone with a strange, flaming orange. I took in a deep breath. Smoke, that's what it was.

Not haze. There was a fire somewhere. I decided to get Mike. As I ran toward the office, I heard one of the dogs behind me. But it wasn't a dog. It was a giant cat with a tawny coat. I braced myself to meet it. The animal's tongue lolled out over its teeth, its eyes were glazed. It veered slightly and raced on. I fell against a tree, bewildered. A small striped badger scurried after the lynx, and I caught my breath. Only one thing could make the wild things of the forest take suddenly to the paths of men.

The smoke was thicker now and hot ash and cinders sifted down on the path. Mike was running to meet me. He grabbed me tight against him.

"Get to the river, Kathy. Stay there till I come for you."

He gave me a push. "Hurry, Kathy!"

I watched his red jacket disappear in the direction of the Indian reserve. "Dear God," I prayed, "don't let anything happen to him."

Women, dragging children, pulling children, holding children, were already crowding the riverbanks. Some had waded into the river and were standing waist-deep. The children cried and whimpered. I went down to the bank and walked into the river. The water was cold, and I waded up and down the edge until my ankles were used to it.

"Mrs. Mike!" Someone was calling me. It was Lola, the 'breed wife of one of the trappers. She held a baby in either arm. A third dragged at her skirts, crying, and I took him in my arms.

It was terribly hot. I waded deeper into the river. Lola followed. Through the smoke we could make out the tiny black figures of the men, laboring to stop the fire at the lumbered-over spot behind the company store, but the fire had entered through the back door and the building broke into flames; fire poured from every chink and opening. The river was the next natural barrier.

The wild things, hesitating at the brink of the river, hesitated no longer. A red fox dived into the water from the cliff above. The wind brought us the smell of his scorched coat. He swam until he was just within his depth, and there he stayed completely submerged, with only the top of his nose showing. There were 20 or 30 dogs around, but they paid no attention to him. Moose, deer, otters, mink—even bears and wolves—appeared in the river.

Flames shot up along the river like a ragged fringe. I closed my eyes, but I couldn't shut away the brightness. The child screamed terribly. I lowered him until the water was at his chin. Hot ashes were falling and burning me, but my body was numb with cold.

I tried to guess how long I had been in the river. Was it day or was it night? I did not know. I could not see the sky. I only knew the torturing heat and the smoke.

I covered the baby's nose and mouth and ducked both of us under the water. The child struggled, but I kept my hold until there was no breath in either of us. We came up, gulping, but the air hurt us. I lost count of the times we came to the surface. The child still struggled, so I knew it lived.

I don't know when I realized the air no longer hurt to swallow. I only knew that for some time I hadn't cooled our faces in the water and the river was silvery now with no brightness in it.

Mike picked us up. With his hunting knife he cut the clothes from me. The next thing I remembered I was dressed again, this time in Indian skirts and a man's shirt. I was lying on the open ground wrapped in a blanket and a smudge was burning at my head. It was day, the next day, Mike said. The baby and I would be all right. His face was black, with streaks of skin showing where the sweat had run down. The red coat had gone and the shirt under it. He applied a compress to my face and throat. "You were just chilled and tired, and you got second degree burns on that pretty face of yours."

I sat up and threw my arms around him.

"Mike, were many—" I stopped. The drawn look on his face told me.

It had taken 15 hours to get the fire under control. He had only 47 men and he needed a hundred to stop the fire at the river. The women and children from cabins east of the shore

were cut off before they could get to the river. The man he
had sent to warn them never reached them. Almost 40 had
died, a third of the village.

"It's not your fault, Mike."

"I don't know," he said slowly. "I should have sent two
men. One would have gotten through."

"You couldn't spare them."

"No."

I put my hand over his big one.

IT WAS witches' country, black, burnt over. Most of the familiar landmarks, including our own home, had burned completely. Trees stood hollowed, empty of their life, with only
stark charcoal wrappers left. It was hot underfoot; the fine
ash burned through our shoes.

The graves were dug all day. Thirty-seven wooden crosses
we made and whitewashed. We cooked mush in the cabins
and tepees that were left. The fire had skipped around like a
child playing hopscotch. Without reason it had taken, and
it had spared. Mike fell asleep while he ate. I shook him and
he finished. Mustagan, the Indian chief, had asked us into
his cabin. He shook hands with Mike after the custom of
white men. "The Sergeant, him save the people of Mustagan."

That was all, but it was enough.

NOT LONG AFTER the fire, while we were still engrossed in re-
building our house on a new site, a letter arrived transferring
us from Hudson's Hope to Grouard. We started almost at
once, for the fire had left us nothing to pack. Everyone came
down to the river to see us off; and although they faced a
long hungry winter, one by one, 'breed and Indian, each left
us a gift of food for the trip.

One day, after we had been weeks on the trail, Mike helped
me out of the canoe. The ground felt unsteady under my feet.
"Here we are," he said. We mounted a porch that squeaked
and moaned with every step. Mike knocked and the door
opened a grudging crack.

"What do you want?" The voice was high-pitched and querulous.

"It's Sergeant Flannigan, Mrs. Mathers. I've brought my wife to you."

We had hoped to reach Grouard in time for the baby, but the first warning pains had started after we'd gone to bed the night before. Mike had heard that there was a former trained nurse in Peace River Crossing, a Scottish woman named Mrs. Mathers. We had traveled all night to get here.

The door opened farther, and at first sight I didn't like her. She was a woman of 50, with a lot of flesh, loose and gray. The house looked like her—big, rambling and untidy. It smelled of stale food.

She led me to a bedroom and handed me a flannel night-gown which from the size of it was hers. She watched me as I slipped it on.

"You're not built right," she said.

"What do you mean?" I felt frightened.

"You're just not. Too small all over." She brought her face against mine. "I doubt if we'll take that baby out of you alive."

Mike stood in the doorway. "Get out!" he said, and his lips barely moved.

For a moment Mrs. Mathers stood and looked at him as though she hadn't heard right. Then she started for the door. "My own house," she muttered. Mike closed the door after her.

"Of all the fool, ridiculous things to tell a girl!"

He took my hands in his and kissed them. "Listen, Kathy," he said, "I didn't know she'd be like that. I'll get Mrs. Carpentier to come up from Grouard and look after you." He smiled. "Mrs. Carpentier is a good witch. You'll love her, Kathy. She's Cree, married to a 'breed trapper. Been midwife to every woman within a 100-mile radius."

Two nights later my pains began in earnest. Mrs. Carpentier was somewhere on the trail. Mrs. Mathers sulked in the next room, and it was Mike who sat with me. When the pain was worst, I held onto Mike's hands.

It was one of these times, when I lay exhausted, gasping for breath, that she came. I didn't notice that the door had opened. She was just standing there, looking down at me. Sarah, I thought, it's Sarah from the Bible. She spoke to me. Her voice was like an undertone of river water, slow, strong and clear. I sighed and closed my eyes.

Something fragrant, slightly pungent, was in front of my nose. It smelled of the woods. I opened my eyes to see. She was holding a glass for me to drink. "Root medicine," she was saying. "Make nice baby come fast. Squaw root for help squaw with baby." Then I lost the words, everything.

Mike was kissing me. "Darling, it's all over. We have a girl."

I smiled at him. I could hear Sarah moving. After a long time I was able to turn my head and watch her as she rubbed oil on the tiny mite of a baby. Sarah was big, big as a man. Six feet tall and strong. There was a grace and dignity in her, and a kindness and a knowing that 60 years had brought. I thought of what Mike had called her, the good witch.

I smiled at her. "You must have had a lot of children."

"Seventeen of my own. Many others, maybe hundreds, I brought into the world. I never lose mother, and I never lose child, except once . . . in this house." She paused. "He was dead baby I take from Mrs. Mathers."

Mike's hand tightened over mine.

Sarah left for Grouard two days after the Baby, Mary Aroon, was born. On the day she went I showed her the name Sarah in my Bible.

"Mrs. Carpentier," I said, "I want to call you Sarah. May I?"

She ran her finger over the name in the book.

"It is the name between us," she said.

In a week I was strong enough to make the trip. Mike brought a cart and padded it with blankets. I lay in it and bounced the long way to Grouard.

As we neared Grouard two men came riding up the trail to meet us. Constable Cameron had seen the smoke of our last campfire. He pulled in his horse, and saluted.

"Constable Cameron, sir. And this"—pointing to the slim youngster of 13 who rode behind him—"is Timmy Beauclaire, and I think, Mrs. Flannigan, he has a present for you."

"A puppy," the boy said. He pulled it out of his jacket. "Like it?"

"Very much," I said, and before I knew what I was doing, I showed him the baby, bundled in her fur bag. "Like it?"

He nodded, and we both laughed. He handed me the puppy. "I'll call it Juno," I said.

As we drove on we saw a little white cemetery on a hill bright and sparkling with crosses that were whitewashed and salted against the rains. Cabins began to appear, and presently we came to the Hudson's Bay Company store. Just beyond was a most curious building, a gigantic cage made of saplings stuck in a circle in the ground and bent in on themselves.

"Our jail, Mrs. Flannigan," Cameron said.

We drove up to a little cabin in a hollow. There were half a dozen people standing in front, waiting for us. There were tall trees bending over the house. And there was a garden of the strangest, most beautiful flowers I had ever seen. This was home.

Sarah was the first to greet me and help me out of the cart. She took the baby from my arms and led me into the house.

"You sit down, rest first," she said. "I have soup ready and tea. Plenty of time meet everybody."

I sank back into a chair, but I wasn't tired, just taking everything in—my new home, my new friends . . . and the flowers. I could see them through the window, row upon row of colors, soft and bright. And not one of them could I recognize. I wondered who had planted such lovely flowers.

Sarah was introducing my guests. There was Sarah's husband, shy silent Louis Carpentier, and the MacTavish brothers, James and Allan, and a man they called Old Irish Bill, and Timmy Beauclaire's family, his two sisters, Madeleine and Barbette, who were already busily playing with the baby, and his mother and father, Constance and Georges Beauclaire.

Georges Beauclaire grunted something, shook my hand and left, clearly relieved at the chance to join the men outside. He was a heavy, broad-shouldered man, rough and awkward in his movements, though with a certain good-natured big-bear grumpiness about him. Beside him Constance Beauclaire seemed delicate, shadowlike, and almost as young as their daughters. There was a foreign grace about the way she stood and walked, and her soft eyes had a veiled, preoccupied air that you find in people who live in the past. When her husband left, she drew up a chair and silently took my hand. The light fell more fully on her face, and I saw the strength and character I had missed. I saw a small, proud mouth, a slender straight nose, rare in the North, and deep, brooding eyes of an unearthly blue. This was no trapper's wife.

"Katherine Mary," she repeated my name softly, and it sounded unusual and elegant in her liquid French speech. "I would have wished to know you ten, 20 years ago. You will never understand, I hope, what it is to be one white woman, *the* one white woman." She smiled. "You must tell me about Winnipeg and Montreal and Boston. They are not the cities I remember, but they will do."

When the guests had gone, I went to the window and looked at my enchanted garden with its rows of flowers that never grew in a garden before.

"It's been lovely," I whispered to Mike. I turned to the garden. "Who planted it?" I'd forgotten to ask.

Mike seemed uncomfortable. "They say it was Mrs. Marlin. She wasn't here tonight. She's not very—she's not very well." Then abruptly he said, "Look, Kathy, don't get upset about those flowers." He started to explain something but I never heard it. I'd fallen asleep in his arms.

The next morning every single flower lay dead and withered on the ground. "Mike," I sobbed, "look!"

"I know, Kathy." He pulled one of the poor faded things up and it came right up out of the ground. It was just a blossom, cut and stuck in the earth.

"She's not right in the head, this Mrs. Marlin," Mike said

unhappily. "She thought it would be a pretty welcome, Kathy," he said. "They're mostly wild flowers. They grow in the woods and swamps. She must have spent all day finding them."

I pressed his hand tightly. Suddenly I knew the enchantment hadn't gone. They had all been so sweet to me, even crazy Mrs. Marlin, who had spent a day in the swamps so that I might have a pretty garden for an hour.

CONSTANCE bent over the crib and lifted the baby into the air. Mary Aroon laughed, and Constance laughed back. I had never seen her laugh freely before. She smiled across the room at me. "She is very like my Suzanne."

"Suzanne?" I said. I knew she had another son besides Timmy, and then of course the two girls, Madeleine and Barbette, but I hadn't heard of Suzanne.

"It was a long time ago." She laid little Mary gently in the crib. "My first family."

I didn'.t understand. "Your first family?"

She looked at me with her great lavender eyes. "Katherine Mary, you are so young."

She told me her story. She had come over from France as a young girl. Her family had been wealthy. She had gone to convent school on the Riviera. Then her father speculated and lost everything. He decided to go to America. On the boat going over, the entire family—father, mother, and five brothers and sisters—died of smallpox, leaving Constance alone and penniless. In America she got a position as a housemaid. Then one day, when she was out walking, someone called her name. It was Georges Beauclaire, who had been her family's groom. She was intensely glad to see him, for it seemed that part of her family had been restored to her. She married him that afternoon, and went with him to Canada to make a fresh start from nothing. That had been 25 years ago.

When she had finished, Constance got up and walked to the window.

"Katherine Mary, women up here speak of their first family, their second family, their third family. Counting the baby I lost our first winter, I've had four families. Nine children. All but four are out there." I knew she meant the little graveyard we'd passed on the way in.

"What happened?"

"Measles, scarlet fever, once it was typhoid. The winters are hard up here. There is no doctor, but I raised four. You saw my girls. Paul is married; he lives in Edmonton. And Timmy you know."

She turned from the window. "A nice family. It's enough for any woman. But sometimes I think of the others."

That night Constance asked us to go with her to the Mission for midnight mass. It was peaceful walking in the crisp cool air. Timmy and Ned Cameron went with us.

The Mission was the largest building in the region. It had a stockade surrounding it, and inside were gardens.

"There are 80 children living here now," said Mike. "They raise their own food. They took the prize last year in hard wheat. Bishop Grouard is a fine man, Kathy. Grouard's named for him. This Mission was the first building here."

The service had started, and we slipped in quietly. The benches were split logs. Candles made little pools of light, and shadows wavered on the rough-hewn walls. The Bishop stood like a sturdy old oak. Thick hunter's boots showed beneath his black cassock. But when he prayed it was a gentle conversation.

I looked up into the face of the Mother of Sorrows. She was carved in wood. The work was crude. It must have been done with a hunting knife. But the face was not cold, like expensive marble faces. A great beauty was there that made you forget its awkwardness and the strangeness of its proportions. The purity of the expression haunted me, the sorrow of the eyes, the sweetness of the mouth. I knew it. I had seen it before. . . I turned toward Constance Beauclaire, and her eyes were resting on Timmy. "Mother of Sorrows," I thought.

MIKE wanted me to take a girl from the Mission to help with the house and the baby. Sister Teresa at the Mission had a number of older girls to suggest. She showed me through the large recreation hall, where 30 or 40 children were playing, and introduced me to the big girls who were minding the babies. Then she opened a door at the back of the room. Wails and sobs came from the dark interior, and I drew back.

"It's punishment row," she explained.

Three small children were sitting on a bench crying their eyes out, and a big Indian girl of 15 sat beside them looking pensively at the floor.

The big girl looked up at me and smiled. Something about her face appealed to me instantly.

The Sister was looking at her, reproachfully. "Anne," she said, "has acted in a very foolish way. We rarely find it necessary to punish the older children." She turned toward the door.

Suddenly I said, "I'd like to take Anne." I turned to the girl. "Would you like to live with me?"

The girl looked at me earnestly. "Yes," she said, "please."

The Sister cleared her throat. "I think it would be best to discuss the matter with the Mother Superior."

The Mother Superior greeted me gravely. "Mrs. Flannigan," she said, "Anne is intelligent, charming and completely capable. Anne has a fault, however, a serious fault. We have no reason to believe that Anne has been immoral. But she imagines herself in love. We discovered they were even meeting inside the Mission walls."

"You know the boy?"

She nodded. "He's Jonathan Forquet. It's quite impossible. His father was Raoul Forquet, a half-breed who led an uprising against the government." There was a pause. "Jonathan is wild; he was raised in squalor by an Indian mother. When I asked him to leave Anne alone he answered, 'She be my *klootch*.'" The Mother Superior paused. "I wonder if you realize what the word *klootch*, as Jonathan used it, implies? Tragedy for our Mission-trained girls. Our girls read and write. Can you turn them into pack animals, to live in tepees, to haul and lift all day for a man who kicks and beats them? You see why Anne cannot marry him."

"Yes," I said, "I see."

When I told Mike what the Mother Superior had said, he just laughed and said, "I don't think we'll have any trouble."

But he was wrong.

From the first, everyone took to the girl. Her Indian name, we learned, was Mamanowatum, which means "Oh-Be-Joyful," and that is what we called her.

One day I went outside to shake the rugs. I could hardly believe my eyes. There on our doorstep was a pile of the most beautiful skins I'd ever seen. Beaver, mink, otter and lynx were stacked in a neat, gleaming pile. Oh-Be-Joyful came out, gave a little cry and gathered the skins in her arms, burying her head in the soft pelts. She whispered into the warm fur in her Cree language.

"Oh-Be-Joyful," I said sternly, "where did these furs come from?"

She looked at me with such happiness that I was troubled.

"From Jonathan," she said, and when she said it the name was the most beautiful I'd ever heard.

"Who's Jonathan?" I asked, to gain time.

"He called Jonathan Forquet. He is maker of canoes. In the almost summer he make the cut beneath the lowest branch of birch tree and another above the roots. With his knife he make the line between, and with the flat side of his knife lifts the birch bark and takes it away in one piece, without breaking. This I have seen him do."

"When did you see him making canoes?" I asked. "When you were at the Mission?"

She understood. We looked at each other a long time.

"They did not wish me to be joyful," she said.

"No, they didn't wish you to be a *klootch*."

Her black eyes studied me. "Mrs. Mike, I am *klootch*. The word, she mean woman, Indian woman."

"Oh-Be-Joyful," I said almost angrily, "are you happy here?"

"I love you," she said.

"Then you must promise me that while you stay here with

us you won't see Jonathan, or I'll have to send you back to the Mission. They will keep you for three years yet. We can take the pelts over to the company store. They'll give them to Jonathan the next time he's in."

"No," she said. Oh-Be-Joyful began to sob. I ran back and put my arms around her.

"Do you really love him so much?"

"Yes."

I felt confused. I wasn't so sure that the Mother Superior had been right. And I wasn't at all sure that Oh-Be-Joyful was wrong. I'd once heard an Indian refer to me as the Sergeant's *klootch*. If having a baby and a little home made you a *klootch*, it wasn't such a bad thing to be.

"What's he like?" I asked her.

She caught my hand and pressed it. "He tall and straight as young fir tree. He walk in the ways of our people. He hunt alone, no brother sit at his campfire. He is silent like the woods, and when he speaks it is with knowing. Yet great fierceness is in his soul. I want much, but never him speak love to me. Now today he lay furs before the door as my father lay furs before the tepee of my mother. Should I send them back to the lonely campfire?"

"Oh, dear," I said. "I wish Mike were here."

I packed up a lunch and took it to his office. There was a great deal of loud talk coming from the office, so I decided to wait outside. I took out a sandwich and started to eat. Through the window I glanced in. A swarthy 'breed with a dirty yellow handkerchief knotted around his head was saying, "He try kill me every night."

"Now wait a minute," Mike said. "Why should Jonathan want to kill you, Cardinal? Were you stealing from his trap lines?"

At the name Jonathan, I choked on my sandwich.

"I tell you, no," Yellow Handkerchief was yelling. "Him make up this damn lie."

"You're sure it's a lie?" Mike asked.

"You think I steal from trap line?" Yellow Handkerchief roared. "You think I thief? Then good-bye!"

"Now look here, Cardinal, let's not be so touchy. If your life's been threatened, I'm on your side; but I've got to know how matters stand before I can take any steps."

"How they stand?" Yellow Handkerchief was beside himself. "That snake Jonathan Forquet come every night to my house and shoot at me with bow and arrows."

"And how close does he come?"

"Damn close. Last night arrow she hitting between my fingers."

"He might be just trying to scare you," Mike said.

"He try kill me," Yellow Handkerchief said with conviction. "Him say to me, 'I kill you, Cardinal, you dirty dog, you steal from my traps.' It is a lie, but he shoot anyway."

"All right," Mike said. "I'll bring him in."

"Okay, okay, so long you put him in jail."

"I'm not promising that."

The door opened so suddenly that it almost knocked me off the step. Mike looked at me sternly. "Kathy, what's the idea, sitting out here in this rotten weather?"

"I had to talk to you about Jonathan. Is he really a killer?" Mike laughed.

"Listen, it's no laughing matter. Jonathan dumped a whole bunch of skins on our porch."

Mike looked concerned. "He wants to take her off, huh?"

"Yes," I said. "You've got to talk to him, tell him to keep away, and put the fear of God into him so he'll do it."

"Jonathan doesn't scare easy," Mike said.

"That's too bad for him. Then you'll have to put him in jail as Mr. Cardinal suggested."

"Good God, Kathy, I can't put a man in jail because he's in love!"

"But he's dangerous. Suppose he kills Mr. Cardinal, how would you feel?"

"Kathy, you're working yourself up over nothing. In the first place, I don't believe Jonathan is a potential killer. I think that Cardinal *did* rob his traps. He's got a reputation that smells like dead fish, a whole stinking trail of it, from here to Calgary. And Jonathan took this way of scaring him off. Trap-stealing is the most serious crime in the Northwest. You can see why. It's a man's livelihood."

"Then why didn't he come to you?"

"He is Indian, that's why."

MIKE had set out the next morning to find Jonathan and bring him in. It was long past suppertime when he returned. At first I didn't realize there was someone with him, standing silent in the dark.

"Come in," I said. The Indian boy followed closely behind Mike. I slammed the door shut against the wind.

"Kathy," said Mike, "this is Jonathan Forquet."

Jonathan nodded courteously, but there was no smile on his lips. His long dark eyes swept over the room. They came to rest on Oh-Be-Joyful, who stood in the farthest corner, hardly breathing. His face did not soften. He gave her no sign, but he looked for a long minute.

I led Mike into the kitchen and closed the door. I turned on him, blazing mad.

"Mike Flannigan, what on earth are you thinking of, bringing that boy here? Didn't you see the way he looked at Oh-Be-Joyful? Oh, you're crazy, just crazy!"

"Kathy, I brought him here because I didn't know what else to do with him. And I think," he added slowly, "that that's what you would have wanted me to do."

"Oh, Mike, if they hear about this at the Mission, they'll take Oh-Be-Joyful back. They'll think you're deliberately encouraging it. And you are."

He grabbed me tight by each shoulder. "Listen to me, you little minx. I brought Jonathan here so you could put a meal into him. The boy is starving. When I found him, he was peeling the bark from a jack pine and sucking at the sap."

I couldn't believe it. "But if he could shoot at Cardinal, why didn't he shoot food for himself?"

"He was hurt," Mike said. "That's why it took me so long to bring him in. He walked along with me quietly enough, and then all at once just crumpled up on the snow. I opened his shirt and found his whole body terribly bruised. He must have been kicked 50 times in the side."

"You think Cardinal beat him up?"

"Yes," Mike said. "I visited Jonathan's trap lines, and there are signs of a scuffle. When he found his traps had been meddled with, he lay in wait. Cardinal came to take a look at the traps, and Jonathan caught him and probably demanded the stolen skins. Cardinal must have knocked him out. I think one blow did it. If there'd been any real tussle, his face would look like his body. It's an ugly picture, Cardinal standing over an unconscious boy and kicking him. But I can't prove it—Jonathan won't talk. It's that devilish pride of his. He wants revenge, and he doesn't want me spoiling it by sending Cardinal to jail."

Jonathan sat through dinner in silence. He ate with his left hand. It was stiff, and he had difficulty raising it, but the other hand hung at his side, unusable. He ate slowly and very little. When he had finished he looked to Mike and me and said gravely, "I have eaten in the house of my friends."

"Yes," Mike said, "you have."

Oh-Be-Joyful smiled secret smiles to herself and moved busily around the room. I noticed Jonathan watching her with pleasure.

"She is too young," I whispered. "You will let her stay a while with me." I waited.

The words came so low from him I scarcely heard them. "It is well."

There was a rapping at the door. Mike opened it, and Cardinal stepped inside. When he saw Jonathan he grinned in a very unpleasant way and clapped Mike on the shoulder.

He planted himself before Jonathan. He stuck his neck out, bringing his face very close to Jonathan's. The boy did not move.

"So!" Cardinal said. "Sergeant Mike, we did good to arrest this fellow, no?"

"Jonathan is not under arrest," Mike said.

"Him murderer!" Cardinal cried. "Him try to kill me all the time." Again he brought his face close to Jonathan's. Jonathan watched, apparently indifferent, but Mike was mad.

"I thought I told you to stay away, Cardinal. You're not doing any good here." He turned to Jonathan. "I knew you had shot at Cardinal. I brought you here to get your side of the story, not to arrest you. But I warn you, there's to be no more shooting. I want your word on that."

"His word! What you think he is? Some damn good school-boy? Him murderer, murderer."

Jonathan looked fiercely ahead of him at nothing.

"Jonathan," Mike said, "if you shoot at Cardinal again, I'll be forced to arrest you."

Jonathan's gaze rested almost gently on Cardinal. "Then my next shot, she be my last."

It was obviously a threat, that next time he would shoot to kill. Cardinal turned pale, and when Jonathan had gone he fell heavily into a chair. The next morning we heard that Cardinal had left the region.

WINTER was long and quiet. The men were away from the village trapping. The women stayed in their houses. I was busy making friends with Mary Aroon. She had an uncanny eye for spotting things I needed, and yelling till I gave them to her—the end of my red pot holder, my green taffeta ribbon, or my spool of coarse thread. I expected another baby some-time in July. I was determined that this one would be just as strong and healthy as Mary Aroon. The bitter pessimism the women of Grouard had adopted didn't touch me. I wasn't resigned to losing six children to raise three. Every one of mine was going to grow up!

Sarah made me come to her regularly for medicine. In the little shed next to her cabin that served as her workroom she had remedies for all the ills and afflictions of man. It was a witch's den, a den of white magic. There were bearberry leaves drying on a plank, starweed soaking in a bucket of water, peels of slippery-elm bark stacked in a corner, stalks of trumpet weed crushed in a stone bowl—remedies for sore throat, for rheumatism, for snake bite, for headache, for a broken leg.

On one of my trips to Sarah's I encountered Mrs. Marlin.

"Mrs. Marlin!" I had never seen her to thank her for my flowers.

When I did so now she lifted a thin hand to her face and looked at me wonderingly. She had a fragile exotic beauty that comes of the mixing of many races. Her eyes were deep blue, yet the sockets they were set in were slightly slant as though a Russo-Chinese prospector had met the French-Indian *klootch* that was her great-grandmother. The effect was somehow inharmonious. It was an alien loveliness that delighted the eye but disturbed the soul.

"Flowers?" She paused. "I remember. I planted garden for you, Mrs. Mike. It is pretty, no?"

I stood looking at her, trying to think of something to say.

"They die?" she said. Then, nodding her head, "They die. I knew. What I touch . . . it dies."

She spoke the words quietly, but they were like a curse.

LATE that spring Cardinal was reported as having been seen up north in the Blackfeet country. Once again he had been up to his old game of trap-robbing—or rather, a refinement of it. This time he was substituting poor fur for good. It was all Mike needed to know.

I watched Mike strap his things to his horse. He would ride to Peace River Crossing, pick up another Mounty there, and make the rest of the trip north by canoe.

"When will you be back, Mike?"

"Two months, Kathy, for sure."

I reached out a hand and steadied myself against the porch rail. In two months the new baby was due.

I went into the house and closed the door behind me. I leaned my head against the pantry shelf and cried silently. Months didn't mean anything to him. He'd said it just like that . . . "two months."

"Kathy!" It was Mike calling. I rubbed my tears away and took a deep breath before I answered him. "Here," I called, "in the pantry."

He came in and took me in his arms and held me tight.

"Mike, promise me you'll be back."

He spoke softly, his lips against my hair. "I promise. Don't worry, Kathy. I'll be with you. I'll be back. If I wasn't sure that I would be, nothing could drag me away from you now, understand?"

He smiled at me with those blue eyes, and ruffled my hair with those big hands. Then the pantry door banged to, and I was alone.

Mike kept his promise. He was back in six weeks, with Cardinal riding beside him, the same dirty yellow handkerchief knotted around his neck. They put him in the strange cage that served as the jail.

After dinner that night Mike sat in the big arm chair with Mary Aroon on his lap. I curled up on a buffalo robe with my head on his knee. Just then the door burst open, and Cameron stumbled in.

"He's dead! Murdered!"

"Who's dead?" Mike said.

"Cardinal. He's sitting on the bench with his head thrown back against the bars. I thought he was sleeping. But when I got close, I see he's been stuck right through the throat. And the knife still in him."

Mike got into his jacket. "Have you ever seen the knife before? Do you know whose it is?" he asked.

"It's got Jonathan Forquet all over it, plain as though it was written. Hunting scene carved on the handle. It's Jonathan's work, all right."

"All right," Mike snapped and gave a quick look at Oh-Be-Joyful. "Let's not jump at conclusions." Mike opened the door. "Come on, we'll take a look at things."

Oh-Be-Joyful continued to stare at nothing long after they had gone.

"Jonathan didn't do it," I said. "He wouldn't kill a defenseless man." But I knew that by tribal law Jonathan had the right. "Besides, he's too clever to leave his knife there." But at the same time I thought: "Isn't that just like Jonathan to boast silently with a knife, to leave it as. a taunt?" I tried to reason myself away from the thought.

Oh-Be-Joyful said suddenly, "When they bring the knife, it will be Jonathan's."

Later, when Mike and Cameron returned, Jonathan walked between them. The three men entered without a word. Mike reached into his pocket and brought out a carefully wrapped object. He held the paper by a loose edge, and the weight of the knife brought it tumbling out of the wrapping onto the table.

"Oh-Be-Joyful," Cameron said, "look at the knife."

Oh-Be-Joyful looked first at Jonathan. But he made no move, gave no hint. Her eyes traveled slowly, unwillingly to the knife, then back to Jonathan.

"Well, it's his, isn't it?" Cameron asked.

She looked beseechingly at Jonathan, but he only smiled at her. She turned to me. "Mrs. Mike!"

I stepped up and put my arm around her. "It's all right, Oh-Be-Joyful." I looked defiantly at Mike. "You don't have to answer if you don't want to."

Turning to the boy, Mike asked, "Is it yours?"

Jonathan did not hesitate. "Yes," he said.

Mike said, after a pause, "Sometimes you make knives to sell, don't you? Is this one of those?"

"No, it is mine." Jonathan regarded us with a crooked smile. "You think I kill Cardinal?"

"I don't know. Somehow I don't think you'd do it that way. In fact, if you tell me you didn't do it, I'll look elsewhere." Mike paused, but Jonathan said nothing. "Otherwise I'll have to hold you on a murder charge. That will mean spending the summer in the cage."

He waited for a reply.

"All right," said Mike at last. "You're under arrest."

"No!" Oh-Be-Joyful sprang between them. "He did not do it," she said to Mike.

Jonathan looked at her almost tenderly. "You good *klootch*. You do not want me spend summer in cage with mosquitoes, with bull fly."

"Tell them you did not kill him."

Jonathan looked at her thoughtfully. "Did I not?"

Oh-Be-Joyful stood with her head down, and her tears dropped on the floor.

I watched the northern lights dance outside my window. They flashed and quivered, forming arcs and ribbons of colors. Sarah and Oh-Be-Joyful were hovering over me and Sarah kept telling me to relax. It was July and my time had come. I had been very unhappy about Oh-Be-Joyful. In these weeks Jonathan's arrest had lain like a shadow between us. I had tried to tell her how I felt, but she wouldn't let me. When she was not in the house, I knew she was standing before the cage, pressed against the bars.

After a while Sarah brought me something to drink and again I smelled the pungent odor of the woods. I lost consciousness. When I opened my eyes next, my son lay in my arms. Mike was standing over us. He put a big finger down to the tiny bundle, and baby Ralph grabbed hold. With the movement he grabbed hold of my heart too.

Suddenly there came a high, piteous wail. I clutched Mike.

"No, Kathy," he said. "It's nothing. Poor Mrs. Marlin is out there wanting to see your baby."

"She shall see him," I said. "Sarah, let her come in. Please. I want to show him off."

Sarah uttered an Indian grunt of disapproval but opened the door. Mrs. Marlin stood on the threshold, her voice uplifted on a keening note, her body rocking in sorrow. Oh-Be-Joyful held up the baby for her to see.

I sighed a little and watched with half-closed eyes as Mrs. Marlin timidly approached Oh-Be-Joyful. Something about her caught my attention. She moved slowly as one in a trance. Only her eyes were awake and alive. The avid, hungry way they fastened on my baby frightened me. I tried to tell Mike, but I wasn't quick enough. With a darting gesture of the hand she took the baby from Oh-Be-Joyful. She backed toward the door, the baby in her arms. Mike jumped and strode toward her. In her fear she clutched the baby tighter.

"Mike, don't!"

My words stopped him. "Yes," he said, "you're right."

Oh-Be-Joyful looked questioningly at me. I nodded to her. I watched the girl approach. Mrs. Marlin crouched against the wall, ready to spring, to rush them all. Oh-Be-Joyful stopped within five feet of her. She smiled and held out her arms. "Give me the baby."

The woman shook her head. "Mine," she moaned. "Mine." She cradled my son close in her arms, crooning to him. "My baby dead. You are my baby."

Mike edged a little closer and she began to moan again. Her voice was a broken murmur. "Dead, all dead. Baby dead, father dead. Everything I touch dead." She sang it to the tune of an old French nursery rhyme. Suddenly she turned on us.

"I tell him go away, leave alone. I'm widow of American, not *klootch* for every dirty 'breed put hands on. But when him drunk, come roaring into my house. Then he go trap line, don't come no more. I got baby in me, his baby. I think, when he come back, him marry me in church maybe. When pretty soon Sergeant Mike bring him, put him in cage I go see him tell him. He throw back his head and laugh at me. My knife she lie in my belt. I take, I stick, like I stick my pig, in the throat. I go home, get much sick. My little baby gets dead. Dead, dead, dead." She sang the words as a lullaby to my baby.

"Cardinal," Mike said.

"Cardinal," she repeated and spat.

"Where did you get the knife?"

"Knife?" She no longer remembered what she had told.

Mike said, "He laughed at you. You stabbed him with the knife. Where did you get it? Think. Jonathan Forquet stacked wood for you this winter."

She began to cry. "He said I could have it."

"Yes," said Mike, "you can have it. If you give me the baby, you can have it."

"To keep?" she asked.

"To keep."

She handed him the baby.

Not long after this we lost Oh-Be-Joyful. The Indians had given a great feast celebrating the first fruits of the corn. I lent Oh-Be-Joyful a suit of white caracul which Chief Mustagan had given me as a present when we left Hudson's Hope.

On the evening the feast ended, Mike and I stood watching the ceremonial dance. On toe and heel a line of girls danced forward to the line of boys. Then the line of girls swept back, and the young men surged forward, step, hop, step, in exaggerated rhythm. Oh-Be-Joyful, dancing in her white furs, was transformed with joy and beauty. Jonathan was dancing with the men. Fiercely, exultingly, he leaped and crouched in the prescribed positions of the dance.

Suddenly the line broke. The women wove among the men. As Oh-Be-Joyful passed them, boy after boy called to her. But she stopped in front of Jonathan and, lifting the scarf from her head, threw it around his shoulders. They stood where they were till the drums had stopped. I didn't see him ask the question—but when Jonathan walked across the village, Oh-Be-Joyful went with him.

They had seen little of each other since his release. It was as though he wanted to punish her for not knowing that he would kill Cardinal, but not murder him. Rather than help her to the knowledge he would sit in the cage, proud and haughty. He wanted his woman to understand him directly, soul to soul. It was a strange conception of love, strange and mystic.

But now he had forgiven her. At the edge of the wood they stopped and Jonathan caught some branches from her path. They swung back into place, and she was gone. She had followed her maker of canoes. He would build her a tepee of willow; they would lie on balsam and on furs.

Oh-Be-Joyful, Mamanowatum. It was the last we ever saw of her.

THE CHILDREN were in bed, and Mike was laying out his favorite game of solitaire. He never won it. It was winter again. For me there had been little to do except read, or take the children out on the sled Mike had made them out of an old wagon he had found in the back of the store.

Just then an Indian woman came in. "Sergeant Mike," she said, "my baby sick. My baby choke."

I brought Mike's jacket and coat. I hated these nights
when pain and death took Mike away: sickness, a woman
stolen, or a man shot. The shadows from the firs seemed
longer, darker, they moved more violently.

I had just gone to bed and was drowsing off when I heard
someone knocking. Mike wouldn't knock. I got out of bed and
into a bathrobe. There was someone at the window—Mike.
"Don't open it, Kathy," he called. "I don't want to come
in. Wiya-sha's baby just died of diphtheria. I'll sleep in the
office. If this is an isolated case, it will only be for five or six
days."

"You're sure it was diphtheria?"

"Pretty sure. Listen, darling. Don't worry. About the only
precaution you can take is to swab your throat and the kids'
out with iodine. If you need me, just hang a sheet out the
window."

By morning broken cries and lamentations drifting in from
the village awakened me. Mary Aroon was frightened and
began to cry. I shut all the windows and locked the door.
"It's the wind," I told Mary Aroon.

I drew pictures for her, and she colored them with her
crayons. I washed the breakfast dishes and I splashed the
water and rattled the dishes and tried to hum an Irish lullaby, but now and then a wild, despairing cry reached us, and
always the moaning underneath. I found myself straining
to hear it. Maybe it *was* the wind.

I put on Mike's breakfast. Then I looked out at the office.
There was no sign of him. But there was a flash of movement
over by the group of birch. It was a man running. He was
naked. Naked in below-zero weather. As I stared, he flung
himself into the snow, buried his hands in it, pressed it to
him like a covering. A woman ran to him, half-raised him.
She pulled him to his feet and supporting him, they walked
a few uneven steps. Suddenly he sagged in her arms; his head
fell across her shoulder. She lowered him to the ground, and
with her hands under his armpits dragged him past scrub
brush and trees until they were hidden. I went back to the
stove.

Then Mike was at the window knocking.

"Kathy," he said, "it's everywhere. They're lying four in a bed. Those who have food can't stand up to get it. Get out your biggest pots and cook up some beef and rice. When it's done, signal with the sheet and I'll come get it. Put it out on the porch."

I opened the door a crack and set out his breakfast. I told him about the man in the snow.

"Poor devil, fever. Sometimes they do that."

I asked him what he was doing for them.

"Nothing. I passed out all the quinine I had. Now I'm giving them alcohol. It's a stimulant, and that's what's needed. But food is the best. If we can keep their strength up."

He was gone. In an hour he came back for the soup. I passed out the three pots I had made. I dragged them across the floor and set them on the porch.

"Did you swab out the kids' throats?" Mike asked.

"Yes."

"Well, do it again." And he carried the pots off toward the reserve.

The day dragged on. No one came near the house. Mary Aroon and Ralph took their naps early. They'd played hard and were ready for them. I got out my work basket and tried to keep busy. I had determined not to listen, but the low drone was hypnotic. It was grief. They were crying for their dead.

The room darkened and I looked up. There at the window, with her back to the sun, a woman stood looking at me. Her hair was undone, and the wind whipped it against her face and body. She lifted her bundle against the glass of the window. It was a baby. Dead and already stiff.

"Please," I shouted to the woman, "go back home."

She remained motionless, holding out her baby as though that answered me.

"What do you want?"

The woman swallowed. She tried to speak. The effort made her choke. She spat in the snow, saliva with queer gray flecks in it. She pushed the dead baby toward me. Her mouth formed a word, formed it again and again. At last I understood. "Medicine."

"Go to Sergeant Mike."

Her eyes dulled, and she shook her head slowly. She's been to Mike; poor Mike, the liquor must have given out too. The woman still watched me. I was the white woman. I was expected to do something. I couldn't stand it.

"I can't help you. Go away, go away!"

She turned obediently and walked off my porch. She walked unsteadily and when the choking seized her, she fell forward in the snow, across her child. The wind lifted her hair, it crawled uneasily about her.

I turned away from the two dead people in my front yard.

RALPH WOKE crying. The glands under his jaw were swollen. His throat looked red. I hung out the sheet. By the time Mike came, there were large grayish patches on his throat.

"Mike," I said, "do something."

Mike kept hot towels on the baby's throat, and he had me boil water on the stove so the room would be moist.

"Feed him all he'll eat, Kathy."

"No, I want some medicine," I said, and shuddered at the word. That other woman, she'd wanted medicine too.

"There's an antitoxin," Mike said, "but it takes two or three months to bring it in, and it has to be fresh."

That night Mary Aroon held onto her throat and cried. I tacked up her pink tree and the purple and red hen where she could see them. I put her gingham bear on her pillow and fed her.

Ralph's body twisted. He was fighting for every breath. Every organ in him strained for air. The hoarse rasping sound gave way to a gurgle. Ralph struggled and lay still. Mike bent over him. When he raised his head, I knew. I guess I'd known before. He put his arms around me, but I broke away.

"No!" I said. "No, no!"

Seven hours later we lost Mary Aroon.

"Kathy," Mike said.

"But she's never been sick a day in her life!"

He tried to lift me up, but I clung to her, still promising her the puppy, a rag doll, stories.

"Kathy," he said. "Darling. You can't do any good here. Constance Beauclaire's girl, Barbette, she's been sick since yesterday. Go to Constance."

I packed a basket, I put in the right things; but all the time anger throbbed in me, a terrible anger against this country, this Grouard.

"Mike," I said, and I was careful not to look at him, "if we'd been in a town—"

"Don't, Kathy."

We walked to Constance's house.

The fire had gone out. I shivered. Barbette lay on a bed at the far end of the room. Constance was on her knees beside her. She got up slowly and smiled a weary smile.

"Yes," she said. "The food. You brought food. We will take it into the village .There is no need here."

Barbette was dead. I leaned against the door. It seemed natural that it should be so.

Mike went out. He was back in a minute with a couple of sticks.

"If you're going into the village, Kathy, I want you to take these. The dogs are dangerous. They haven't been fed for days."

I nodded and went out with Constance.

The first house I walked into, they were all dead but an old woman who sat on the floor, her head covered by a blanket, mourning. I put half a loaf of bread beside her and went out.

A dog turned on me. I struck it on the nose and it backed off, whining. Another dog, lean and gaunt and ragged, crawled up on his belly. The two watched, their saliva dripping, as a young man dragged the body of a girl out of a window and then hoisted her onto the roof of their cabin.

I looked at the roofs of the other cabins, and for the first time saw the rows of feet. There were other bodies lashed to the trees. It was our method of refrigeration.

The young Indian slid down from the roof and turned into the empty house. I put the other half-loaf of bread inside the door. He shook his head. "Where her shadow go, I follow."

The soft Cree words hurt his throat. He choked. Why had I not seen how gray his face was? He stumbled and half-fell onto a bed of skins. I rekindled the fire, went to him, but he motioned me away.

"Mrs. Mike! The dogs. They break in maybe."

"I'll wedge the door."

"Yes," he said, "for I must lie here many days. Sergeant Mike, him have one, two, maybe three men help him. We die too fast . . . is not enough." It was important for the Crees to keep their bodies intact. It would not do to appear in the next world mauled and torn by Huskies.

I came to a tepee where three children lay tossing. I hauled water. I set it to boil. I wrung out compresses. I forced soup down swollen throats. Sometimes the little dark faces blurred and it was my own two I was fighting for.

A child twisted into a terrible knot and died. The mother covered her head and moaned. It was morning. The dead in the trees looked down at us. Pain, tiredness, nothing touched me. Once a little pair of arms reached out to me and I thought: "Why these?" Something hurt in me when I looked at the two children who were going to live, that were getting better.

An old man came by, carrying the body of an old woman. A moment later there was a cry. A dog was tugging at the small shrunken corpse. The old man pulled and fought, but it was torn out of his hands. The growling dog began rending and tearing it. The old man, sobbing, flung himself on the dog, beating it with feeble hands. By the time I reached him, the old man was mangled.

Sometime after that, Sarah found me. She took me back to Mike. Part of the way she carried me.

The cribs were gone. I never asked Mike what he had done with them. Mary Aroon's crayon drawings were gone, too. I waited until Mike was out and then hunted the house over for them. I guess I was glad that I didn't find them.

Mike was gone every day. He and Tim Beauclaire and old Georges buried half a village that week. It was mostly the children that went, and the old people.

The second night Mike had taken me up the hill. We had walked between the rows of white crosses. A new row had been added. Cut into the wood I read the name, Mary Aroon Flannigan, and next to this, Ralph Flannigan. My two babies lying on this bare, windswept hill! I knelt down and laid my hands on the snow.

Mike touched my shoulder.

I got up and followed him home. I wanted to reach out to him, but I couldn't. At first I didn't know why, and then I realized that I was blaming him. Did he feel it? He was sweet and kind and patient, only he'd look away from me. And when he thought I was busy with something else, he'd stare at me. There was a bitterness I couldn't force back. He'd known. He'd lived in this country. Every winter he'd seen children die in epidemics. And he knew that in all the Northwest there was no help. He hadn't had the right to bring a wife into this country, to have children.

For two months we sat in the same room and exchanged scarcely a word. In the daytime he kept away from the house. I wanted him, I longed for him, I couldn't stand the loneliness. Sometimes I counted the minutes out loud. Then he'd come.

"Hello, Mike," I'd say.

"Hello, Kathy."

While I fixed dinner, I went over the things I was going to say to him. But when I was sitting facing him, my heart pounded and I would jump up for the salt or the milk. Anyway, what was there to say? Everything led back to the same labyrinth of pain and bitterness.

After dinner I'd sit and listen to him play the accordion. It was an old one he found in the store. He brooded in his music. He was lost to me as surely as the children were. Night after night I listened to his music, hating it. The sound of that accordion drove me mad.

One night when I saw him reach for it again, I knew I was

going to stand up and scream. I didn't because they brought a man in just then on a door. I washed the blood off his face before I saw his eye was almost out, just hanging. I cut the jacket and shirt off him. Mike worked over his face. And somehow Sarah was there and putting on poultices. It was Randy Nolan, new in the territory. When I looked at him again, his eye was in place, and Mike was bandaging it. One of his ribs was broken off and sticking out through the flesh, and across the others were long bloody slashes. An arm hung at an odd angle from the socket.

It wasn't the first time we had seen what a grizzly can do to a man.

The first week he was unconscious most of the time. The second week he lay moaning. Then he began to talk to me when I came into the room. He thought I was wonderful to take him in and care for him. He didn't know the gap it filled for me. He had a sister in Boston, and I would have slaved day and night just to hear him tell about the concert he'd heard at Symphony Hall, and what the latest thing in clothes was, and that almost everybody had a motor car now, and they went awfully fast, 25 miles an hour.

One day Mike came in with a wire. It was from Randy's sister. She wanted him to come to Boston as soon as he could travel.

A plan formed in my head that excited and frightened me.

"It would be the best thing in the world for him" I said to Mike as we were sitting in front of the fire that evening. "He needs medical treatment."

Mike looked at me for a long time. "He can't go by himself."

"I know." I talked very fast. I didn't look at him. "I thought I'd like to take him out. I haven't been out for almost four years. I'd take him clear through to Boston, and—"

Mike got up. "If you have to do this, Kathy, go ahead God knows, maybe it's best."

THERE wasn't much to do. I packed my clothes and the first-aid kit. Mike made a stretcher for Randy. One day Mike got up from his work and walked to the window. He stood looking out.

"Damn it, I don't want you to go."

"But—"

"Listen, we haven't even talked it out. You haven't told me how long you're going to stay yet, and I have a feeling—"

He shrugged. "What's the use? You're going, aren't you?"

In the morning everyone was at the dock. At the last Sarah came up to me.

"Mrs. Mike," she said, "come back."

Mike lifted me into the boat. I turned and waved, but the faces blurred. And the shouting, calling, and the well-wishing reached me as noise from which I could not separate a word. All the time I was thinking: "How could she know?"

It took us two days of hard travel, first by launch and then by horse and wagon, to reach the railroad. But at last there it was. In the midst of nowhere stood an engine, a caboose and a single car for passengers.

Mike carried my things into the car and put them on the seat. Then he pulled out some bills and stuffed them into my hand. Suddenly I realized he was saying good-bye.

"Kathy, I love you. I—" His arm went around me, clumsy and uncertain. And then he was outside. The train jerked forward. My last picture of him was standing alone, against the whole Northwest.

I stared out at the wet dripping country, my heart aching with the things said and things unsaid.

My sister, Anna Frances, was at the Boston station to meet me.

"I want to stay a long time," I told her.

The next day she and my mother gave me a homecoming party. Boys and girls whose faces I vaguely remembered crowded into my mother's living room. Someone played "Alexander's Ragtime Band" on the piano. We danced and my sister served sherbet and small delicate cakes.

Afterward my mother stole into my room. She put her arms around me. "Katie," she said, "you're lonely."

"Mother," I said abruptly, "I love him. I always will."

My mother smoothed my hair "Perhaps he could come to Boston."

I shook my head. "In Boston, Mike would be just a cop."

"Katherine Mary," my mother spoke in a firm voice, "the last thing I would ever do is to interfere in my daughters' lives. You were married somewhere off in the wilderness to a man I never met, and you've lived hardly like a woman, stuck in a little cabin with not two dresses to your name, and no doctor to care for your babies when they lay dying. It's not good for you, Katie, and it's not right. I believe a woman should stick by her husband. But this time it's different. And I'm not letting you go north again to loneliness and the graves of your children!"

"I don't want to," I murmured.

Night after night we went to plays, operettas and musical comedies—*Peg o' My Heart* and *The Pink Lady* and *Quaker Girl* —and one night my mother and I climbed up to the balcony to watch Sarah Bernhardt.

It was wonderful, but it was no use. I knew now how alien this life was to me. Even my mother and sister were irrevocably separated from me. I kept seeing Mike as I'd seen him last, alone against the Northwest. It was the country I was homesick and longing for, the country that made him *Sergeant Mike Flannigan*. I'd been unjust, I'd been wrong. I knew it now, and I had to tell him.

"Mike," I cried as if he were there to hear, "take me back. I'll never leave you again."

HE MET ME at the train. He had put bells on the dogs. Wrapped in a buffalo robe was a little new Juno the second, whose eyes were hardly open yet. And the big Juno, the team leader, had almost broken the traces to get at me.

And now I was beside Mike in the cutter. Mike! His voice was low and choked up. He'd start to say things, and then he'd stop and just look at me. Then I'd forget what I was saying and just look at him. I tried to tell him how wrong I'd been. But he kept kissing me, over and between and through all the words.

"We'll start over, won't we, Mike?"

He held me. "Sure."

The snow shone and sparkled. The sun struck here and there among the fine particles, touching them with cold fire. I didn't think how beautiful it was. I thought how many times I had watched it before. And now for the first time it was familiar; I recognized it just as I recognized the way the air smelled.

Mike had been watching me, and now he said, "How does it seem to be home, Kathy?"

That's it, it was home.

We got there late the next day. Icy branches arched like crystal domes above the cabin.

I jumped out of the sled and ran up on the porch, but Mike got to the door first.

"Listen, Kathy. It's in a bit of a mess."

"Don't be silly," I said. "It can all be straightened out." Mike looked dubious, so I prepared myself for the worst and pushed the door open.

The house was scrubbed, polished and shining. I looked at Mike to see if he had been joking, but one glance at his face convinced me that he hadn't. Everything was in its place, and on the table was a steaming hot dinner.

Just then I heard the back door close. We ran to the kitchen in time to see Sarah striding off. We called to her, and she raised her arm above her head to show she heard. But she wouldn't call back or even turn to look at me. She understood. This return was Mike's and mine.

AUGUST 1914, and war. Timmy Beauclaire came to say goodbye and to ask Mike to look after his pony. His brother, Paul, in Edmonton, had already enlisted.

By the end of the winter I had delivered five wires, "Missing in action," "Killed in action." One day Sarah came into the office.

"Make me a cup of tea, Mrs. Mike."

That very ordinary request frightened me, for in all the time I'd known her Sarah had never asked anything of anyone. She drank her tea. Then, abruptly, she said: "Constance's girl Madeleine, she have babies, she die."

"Madeleine died?"

"I take two babies from her. Boy and girl. She bleed. I make it stop outside, but inside she still bleed."

I watched Mike lay down his pen. "She had twins?" he asked.

"Yes. A boy and a girl."

No one said anything. We sat and drank tea.

Three hours later the telegraph began to click. Sarah raised her head and watched Mike closely as he copied the message.

"MARCH 27—MR. AND MRS. GEORGES BEAUCLAIRE . . . RE-GRET TO INFORM YOU . . . KILLED IN ACTION . . ." I turned to Sarah. "Does Constance know about Madeleine?"

Sarah nodded. "She was with her. By now she home."

"Why? Why does it happen like this? Why both together, and why to Constance?"

Finally I was there. I knocked and went in. She came toward me.

"Constance . . ."

I was going to prepare her, to say wise and gentle things, but all I could do was to hold out the telegram. She spoke through stiff lips. "Which one?"

"Paul," I said.

Next spring it was Timmy. Constance was preparing bottles for the twins. She turned to me smiling and saying, "Kathy."

I stood there where I had stood in the winter, by the corner of the table. Under my hand lay the first wire. It was un-opened and thick with dust. She had never touched it. I put the second wire on top of the first and went out.

Mike was staring out the window. Timmy's little cayuse stood in the pasture with her nose laid along the fence.

"Sarah was here. I don't know how the devil she knew, but she asked about Tim."

"Did you tell her?"

"She said, 'When they're little, sickness. When they're big, war.'"

THE WORLD outside, the noisy quarreling world that sent us the wires of death, sent us a new death. Born in the dirt of European trenches, in the fall of 1918 the flu had spread into the Canadian Northwest. And our people died, again without doctors, serum, or help.

I followed Sarah into the bedroom of the Beauclaire cabin. Old Georges sat huddled by the bed. It was many hours before Constance moved or spoke. She opened her eyes. "I'm dying, Kathy. But I'm so tired I don't care."

Sarah nodded. "She does not care. I know. At the end there are only the children. When they go . . . nothing."

We sat through the night. But Constance remained motionless. Her lips were parted, and her breath came and went too gently.

I watched it grow light. Mike came to take my place. Constance opened her eyes again, looked at all of us, knew us.

"Mike and Kathy, take the twins."

That was all. Georges threw himself across the bed, sobbing. I cried against Mike's coat for one of the dearest friends I ever had.

All the while I was conscious of Sarah moving about, silently doing the things that must be done. She passed me with a kettle in her hands. Her back was terribly bent, and her motions slow. I had never before seen how old she was.

I shook off my numbness. I opened the door and went into the twins' bedroom. Two little figures stood on the bed. One had a shirt over his head which Mike was trying to pull past his ears. "Here," I said, "you've got to unbutton another button."

"Then you'd have to take the whole thing off," he protested.

"There are times when it pays to start all over again, and this is one of them."

We hurried the children through the front room and out of the house. I went back to tell old Georges that he was to come to see them often, that they needed their grandfather. I don't think he heard me. His eyes were sunken and almost closed. I went out as quietly as I could.

That night Mike played he was a bear. And when we went to bed the house was in a litter, a wonderful exciting litter of cutouts and spilled jam and cookie crumbs. Mike caught me around the waist while I was cleaning up. "Well, girl?"

"Oh, Mike—" I couldn't say anything else because I was crying and getting kissed all at once.

IT WAS WONDERFUL having children in the house again. Long after they were in bed, Mike and I would sit discussing them and planning for the future. Mike thought it would be nice for Georges to be a Mounty, and I thought that maybe Connie would be a nurse.

It was one of these evenings when Jonathan Forquet walked into the room, holding in his arms a solemn-eyed baby.

"I come to my friends," he said.

It had been eight years, but he had the same proud way about him.

"Is Oh-Be-Joyful with you?"

He looked at me and answered slowly. "Can you not see that she is dead?"

Then I did see it. I saw it in the black eyes that looked hopelessly into my own.

"The sickness, it took her, Mamanowatum." He lifted the baby toward me. Jonathan watched me as I held her.

"Mamanowatum, she call her Kathy. She want this winter come show you girl-child. Now she no come never. Only I come, say, 'Keep baby.' No want Mission for keep her. They not like me."

Mike came over to me. "We'll keep her, won't we, Kathy?"

"Yes," I said. "Of course."

Jonathan nodded. "I come once, twice, in the year. Bring furs. You sell, Feed, make clothes for girl-child." He hesitated. Then he spoke in Cree: "Tell her of the joyful heart of Mamanowatum!"

Mike patted him roughly on the shoulder. We stood in the doorway and watched him walk into the night. "Mike," I said, "it's very strange . . . What does it all mean?"

"Well, there's a pattern," Mike said. "Oh-Be-Joyful was part of your life. Things like that don't just stop."

I knew what he meant. It wasn't something you could put into words, but you could sense it behind everything that happened. Oh-Be-Joyful had cared for and loved my children, and now it was I who was to care for and love hers. Mike was right: the pattern of a life isn't a straight line; it crosses and recrosses, drawing in and tying together other lives.

There was great excitement the next morning when Georges and Connie found out they had a baby sister. We told them they could celebrate any way they wanted. It wasn't hard for them to decide. They'd been after Mike for days to take them out in the snow.

Mike laughed. "Okay, Kathy, dress 'em up. I'll meet you on the porch." And he went striding off on some errand of his own.

When the last fur mitten was on, I sent them out to wait while I bundled up the baby and dressed myself.

It was a wonderful winter's day, clear and cold and dry, with the sun shining. I came up close to see what Mike was working over. It was our old sled. I thought he had burned it or hacked it to pieces, but evidently it had only been hidden.

"Warm enough?" Mike asked when we were at the top of the hill.

"Yes."

The twins were pulling at him, demanding a snow fight, but he still looked at me, unsatisfied.

I tried to tell him. "It hurts a little."

"What hurts you?" Connie asked. "A pin?"

"No," I said. "Happiness."

ON BEING

A REAL PERSON

A condensation from the book by

HARRY EMERSON FOSDICK

HARRY EMERSON FOSDICK, pastor of the Riverside Church in New York City, is internationally known as a preacher, as a professor at Union Theological Seminary, and as the author of *The Meaning of Faith*, and other books.

During the past 20 years more and more people have come to Dr. Fosdick for advice about their personal difficulties. To deal with unusual problems adequately, he studied the techniques of psychiatrists and psychologists, and in many cases asked their help. Thus he has been enabled to provide counsel concerning both mental and spiritual attitudes.

It's Up to You

THE central business of every human being is to be a real person. We possess by nature the factors out of which personality can be made, and to organize them into effective personal life is every man's primary responsibility.

Without exaggeration it can be said that frustrated, unhappy people, who cannot match themselves with life, constitute the greatest single tragedy in the world. In mansion and hovel, among the uneducated and in university faculties, under every kind of circumstance people entrusted with building their own personalities are making a mess of it, thereby plunging into an earthly hell.

Three elements enter into the building of personality: heredity, environment and personal response. We are not responsible for our heredity; much of our environment we cannot control; but the power to face life with an individual rejoinder—*that* we are responsible for. When acceptance of this responsibility involves self-condemnation, however, an alibi almost invariably rushes to the rescue. All of us resemble the lawyer in the New Testament story, concerning whom we read: "But he, desiring to justify himself, said . . ." A college president says that after long dealing with students he is unsure whether the degree B.A. stands for Bachelor of Arts or Builder of Alibis.

On the lowest level this desire to escape blame expresses itself in emphasis upon luck. Fortunate people "get the breaks," men say; personal failure is due not so much to mistake as to mischance. That luck represents a real factor in human experience is evident, and he who does not expect ill fortune as one of the ingredients of life is trying to live in fairyland. But nothing finer has appeared on earth than unlucky people who are real persons. The determining element in their experience is not so much what happens to them as the way they take it.

Glenn Cunningham, who has run the fastest mile on record, was crippled in boyhood in a schoolhouse fire. The doctors said that only a miracle could enable him to walk again—he was out of luck. He began walking by following a plow across the fields, leaning on it for support; and then went on to tireless experimentation to see what he could do with his legs, until he broke all records for the mile run.

Pilgrim's Progress came from a prison, as did *Don Quixote*, Sir Walter Raleigh's *History of the World* and some of the best of O. Henry's stories.

Bad luck is a poor alibi if only because good luck by itself never yet guaranteed real personality. Life is not so simple that good fortune suffices for it.

Many escape a sense of personal responsibility by lapsing into a mood of emotional fatalism. This is, curiously, one of the most comfortable moods in which a man can live. If he is an automaton, he is not responsible for anything.

On its highest level man's desire to escape responsibility expresses itself in ascribing all personal qualities to heredity and environment. This is a popular theory today. From intelligence quotients within to crippling environments without, it offers defenses for every kind of deficiency, so that no botched life need look far to find an excuse.

But consider the individual of superior inheritance and favorable circumstance. Must he necessarily be an admirable personality? Is *that* fate, willy-nilly, forced upon him? Certainly it does not seem so. The disastrous misuse of fine heredity and environment is too familiar a phenomenon to be doubted.

Handling difficulty, making the best of bad messes, is one of life's major businesses. Very often the reason victory is not won lies inside the individual. The recognition of this fact, however, by the individual concerned is difficult. At times we all resemble the Maine farmer laboriously driving his horses on a dusty road. "How much longer does this hill last?" he asked a man by the roadside. "Hill!" was the answer. "Hill nothing! Your hind wheels are off!"

The world is a coarse-grained place, and other people are

often unfair, selfish, cruel. Yet, after all, we know the difference between a man who always has an alibi and the man who *in just as distressing a situation* habitually looks inward to his own attitudes and resources—no excuses, no passing of the buck. In any circumstance he regards himself as his major problem, certain that if he handles himself well that is bound to make some difference. Anyone can recognize the forthright healthy-mindedness of the youth who wrote home to his father after an unsuccessful football game, "Our opponents found a big hole in our line, and that hole was me."

When we succeed, when by dint of decision and effort we achieve a desired end, we are sure we had a share in *that*. We cannot slough off responsibility when we fail. We cannot eat our cake and have it too.

The beginning of worth-while living is thus to confront ourselves—unique beings, each of us entrusted with the makings of personality. Yet multitudes of people wrestle with every conceivable factor involved in the human situation before they face their primary problem—themselves. Our commonest human tragedy is correctly represented in a recent cartoon: A physician faces his patient with anxious solemnity, saying, "This is a very serious case; I'm afraid you're *allergic to yourself*."

Our Many Selves

THE common phrase, "building a personality," is a misnomer. Personality is not so much like a structure as like a river —it continuously flows, and to be a person is to be engaged in a perpetual process of becoming.

The tests of successful personal living, therefore, are not neatly identical when applied to two persons in different situations or to the same person at different ages. Concerning one criterion, however, there is common agreement. A real person achieves a high degree of unity within himself. The often conflicting elements of personal experience, such as impulses, desires, emotions, must be coördinated.

Each of us deals continually with the underlying problem of a disorganized life. The ruffled man badly flurried because he has mislaid a pair of glasses, the hurried person trying to do something with too great haste and becoming flustered, the frightened person fallen into a panic, the choleric individual surprised by a burst of temper into loss of self-control— such examples from ordinary life remind us how insecure is our personal integration.

No virtue is more universally accepted as a test of good character than trustworthiness. Obviously, however, dependability is possible only in so far as the whole personality achieves a stanch unity that can be counted on.

Many of us frequently act "out of character." The general pattern of our lives may involve honesty, truthfulness and similar qualities—but not always. This is evident even with regard to a virtue like courtesy. How common is the person whose courtesy is unreliable! We all know him—polite today, morose and uncivil tomorrow; obliging and well bred in business, crabbed and sulky at home; affable with one's so-called "equals," gruff and snobbish with one's servants.

In a man with character, the responses to life are, in their quality, established and well organized; one can count on them. His various emotions, desires and ideas are no mere disparate will-o'-the-wisps. He has become a whole person, with a unifying pattern of thought and feeling that gives coherence to everything he does.

A "well-integrated" life does not mean a placid life, with all conflicts resolved. Many great souls have been inwardly tortured. Florence Nightingale had a desperate time finding herself, and wrote in her diary, "In my 31st year I see nothing desirable but death." Dwight L. Moody said, "I've had more trouble with D. L. Moody than with any other man I know."

In all strong characters, when one listens behind the scenes, one hears echoes of strife and contention. Nevertheless, far from being at loose ends within themselves, such persons have organized their lives around some supreme values and achieved a powerful concentration of purpose and drive.

The process by which real personality is thus attained is inward and spiritual. No environmental changes by themselves can so *push* a personality together as to bring this satisfying wholeness within. Even so fortunate an environment as a loyal and loving family cannot dispense a man from confronting himself. Thus Novalis said: "Only so far as a man is happily married to himself, is he fit for married life." As for material prosperity, that often disorganizes life rather than unifies it. Indeed, nervous prostration is a specialty of the prosperous. Wealth, by increasing the number of possible choices, is often far more disrupting than satisfying.

A MODERN novelist describing one of his characters says, "He was not so much a human being as a civil war." Every human being sometime faces a situation where on the one side is his actual self, with his abilities and circumstances, and on the other are ideal pictures of himself and his achievements; and between the two is a gulf too wide to be bridged. Here inward civil war begins.

To hold high ideals and ambitions is man's glory, and nowhere more so than in the development of personality. This faculty, however, can function so abnormally that it tears life to pieces.

No well-integrated life is possible, therefore, without an initial act of self-acceptance, as though to say: I, John Smith, hereby accept myself, with my inherited endowments and handicaps and with the elements in my environment that I cannot control, and, so accepting myself as my stint, I will now see what I can do with *this* John Smith. So Emerson put it: "There is a time in every man's education when he arrives at the conviction that envy is ignorance; that imitation is suicide; that he must take himself for better, for worse, as his portion."

Alec Templeton entertains millions over the radio with his music and amuses them with his whimsicalities. He is stone blind. The first natural response to such crippling disadvantage is an imagination thronged with pictures of the unattainable, and from the contrast between them and the actualities commonly spring resentment, self-pity, inertia. The human story, however, has nothing nobler to present than handicapped men and women who, accepting themselves, have illustrated what Dr. Alfred Adler called "the human being's power to turn a minus into a plus."

Tension between our existent and our desired selves often arises from high moral ideals, and nowhere is it more likely to be mishandled. Unselfishness and loyalty, for instance, are major virtues, but a daughter under the thralldom of a possessive mother can so picture herself as in duty bound to be unselfish and loyal that, without doing her mother any real good, her life is blighted and her personality wrecked.

Ethical ideals in their application are relative to the individual. One man may have a calm, equable temperament that need never be ruffled; another may have to say, as Dr. Stephen Tyng did to one who rebuked him for asperity, "Young man, I control more temper every 15 minutes than you will in your whole lifetime."

W_HEN self-acceptance is not achieved and the strain between the actual and the dreamed-of self becomes tense, the result is an unhappy and sometimes crushing sense of inferiority. One study of 275 college men and women revealed that over 90 percent suffered from gnawing, frustrated feelings of deficiency. They gave all sorts of reasons—physical incompetence, unpleasant appearance, lack of social charm, failure in love, low-grade intellectual ability, moral failure and guilt.

To be sure the feeling of inferiority can never be taken at its face value as an indication of real lack. The runner-up in a championship tennis match may suffer wretchedly from a sense of inadequacy. However, the importance of the problem itself is made evident by the unhealthy ways in which it is commonly handled.

Some deal with it by the smokescreen method. Feeling miserably inferior, and not wanting others to know it, the shy become aggressive, the embarrassed effusive, and the timid bluster and brag. One man, hitherto gentle and considerate in his family, suffered a humiliating failure. At once he began to grow harsh and domineering. Paradoxical though it is, when he felt superior he behaved humbly, as though he felt inferior;

when he felt inferior he began to swagger as though he were superior.

Others, like the fox in Aesop's fable, call sour all grapes they cannot reach. The frail youth discounts athletics; the debauchee scoffs at the self-controlled as prudes; the failure at school scorns intellectuals as "highbrows." A major amount of cynicism springs from this source. Watch what people are cynical about, and one can often discover what they lack, and subconsciously deeply wish they had.

Still others find excuses based on an exaggerated acknowledgment of their inferiority. So one student who was struggling with failure said: "I have thought it over carefully and I have come to the conclusion that I am feeble-minded!" Far from being said with despair, this was announced with relief; it was a perfect excuse; it let him out from all responsibility. Yet, factually it was absurd, and emotionally it was abnormal.

Among the constructive elements that make self-acceptance basic in becoming a real person is the principle of compensation. Deficiency can be a positive stimulus, as in the classic case of Demosthenes. Desiring to be an orator, he had to accept himself as a stammerer. He did not, however, conceal his humiliation with bluster and brag, nor decry eloquence as worthless trickery, nor resign himself to stammering as an excuse for doing nothing. He took a positive attitude toward his limitation, speaking against the noise of the waves with pebbles in his mouth until he could talk with confident clarity. To say that Demosthenes became a great orator *despite* his stammering is an understatement; the psychologist would add that he became a supremely effective orator *because* he stammered.

Some form of compensation is almost always possible. The homely girl may develop the more wit and charm because she is homely; the shy, embarrassed youth, with the temperament of a recluse, may be all the more useful in scientific research because of that.

Involved in such successful handling of recognized inferiority is the ability to pass from the defensive to the offensive attitude toward our limitations. John Smith accepts John Smith with his realistically seen limitations and difficulties, and positively starts out to discover what can be done with him. Captain John Callender of the Massachusetts militia was guilty of cowardice at the Battle of Bunker Hill. George Washington had to order his court-martial. Callender re-enlisted in the army as a private, and at the Battle of Long Island exhibited such conspicuous courage that Washington publicly revoked the sentence and restored to him his captaincy. Behind such an experience lies a basic act of self-acceptance—open-eyed, without equivocation or excuse—along with a shift from a defensive to an offensive attitude, that makes John Callender an inspiring person to remember.

In achieving self-acceptance a man may well begin by reducing to a minimum the things that mortify him. Many people are humiliated by situations that need not be humiliations at all. To have what Ko-Ko called "a caricature of a face," to lack desired ability, to be economically restricted—such things are limitations, but if they become humiliations it is because inwardly we make them so. One man developed an inferiority complex that haunted him all his life and ruined his career because he had curly hair of an unusual shade of red. Napoleon accepted himself—five feet two inches tall, and 43rd in his class at the *École Militaire*. He never liked himself that way. Considering his imperial ambitions, his diminutive stature was a limitation, but had he made of it and of his scholastic mediocrity a humiliation, he probably never would have been Napoleon.

Life is a landscaping job. We are handed a site, ample or small, rugged or flat, whose general outlines and contours are largely determined for us. Both limitation and opportunity are involved in every site, and the most unforeseeable results ensue from the handling—some grand opportunities are muffed, and some utterly unpromising situations become notable. The basic elements in any personal site are bound to appear in the end no matter what is done with them, as a landscape still reveals its size and its major shapes and contours, whatever the landscape architect may do. These basic elements, however,

.are to be accepted, never as humiliations, commonly as limitations, but most of all as opportunities and even as incentives.

One of the ablest women in this country, now the wife of a university president, was brought up in poverty. She recalls an occasion when, as a girl, she complained of her hardships to her mother. "See here," said the mother, "I have given you life; that is about all I will ever be able to give you. Now you stop complaining and do something with it."

Our most intimate and inescapable entrustment lies in our capacity to be real persons. To fail at that is to fail altogether; to succeed is to succeed supremely. Says Noah in the play *Green Pastures*, "I ain' very much, but I'se all I got." That is the place to start. Such self-acceptance is realistic, humble, self-respectful.

Getting Ourselves Off Our Hands

A certain "Charm" School, promising to bestow "personality" on its clients, prescribes in the first lesson that one stand before a large mirror and repeat one's own name in a voice "soft, gentle and low" in order to impress oneself with oneself. But obsession with oneself can be one of life's most disruptive forces. An integrated personality is impossible save as the individual finds outside himself valuable interests, in devotion to which he forgets himself. To be whole persons we must get ourselves off our hands.

Self-centeredness is natural in early childhood. Many, however, never outgrow it. At 50 years of age they still are living on a childish pattern. Moralists censure them as selfish, but beneath the ethical is a psychological problem—they are specimens of arrested development. A novelist says of one of her characters: "Edith was a little country bounded on the north, south, east and west by Edith." Edith suffers from a serious psychological affliction. Egocentricity is ruinous to real personality. At the very best, a person completely wrapped up in himself makes a small package.

Being a real person is arrived at not so much by plunging after it as by indirection. A man escapes from himself into some greater interest to which he devotes himself, and so forgets himself into consecutive, unified, significant living. Practical suggestions as to ways and means of getting out of ourselves must start close at home with the body. Many miserably self-centered folk need not so much a psychiatrist to analyze them or a minister to discuss morals with them as common sense in handling the physical basis of a healthy life. The modern man needs constantly to be reminded that he cannot slough off his biological inheritance. Our bodies were made to use in hard physical labor. Any man who has found his appropriate recreation or exercise where he can let himself go in the lusty use of his major muscles knows what a transformation of emotional tone and mental outlook such bodily expenditure can bring.

One of the most durable satisfactions in life is to lose oneself in one's work. This is why more people become neurotic from aimless leisure than from overwork, and why unemployment is one of the worst of tragedies, its psychological results quite as lamentable as its economic ills.

THE PROBLEM of finding external interests weighs more heavily on some temperaments than on others. The "extrovert" readily takes part in objective practical affairs, is emotionally spontaneous and outgoing, is relatively toughminded when he is disapproved by others. The "introvert" is sensitive to disapproval, is given to introspection and self-criticism, and in general is more aware of the inner than of the outer world. While everybody can recognize these two types, and each man can judge to which of them he himself is more closely akin, they do not constitute two mutually exclusive temperaments. Nor is the advantage altogether on either side. The balanced man is a synthesis of the two.

Abraham Lincoln had a tragic struggle with himself. In his early manhood he was not a unified and coherent person but a cave of Aeolus, full of storms, with the makings of neurotic ruin in him. In 1841 he said, "I am now the most miserable man living. If what I feel were equally distributed to the whole human family, there would not be one cheerful face on earth." He could easily have been an extreme example of the morbid "introvert," but he was not. He solved his obsessing inner problems by outflanking them. The amazing development of his latter years into great personality came not so much by centering attention on himself as by forgetting himself. His devotion to a cause greater than himself transformed what he had learned in his long struggle with himself into understanding, sympathy, humor, wisdom. We cannot call him in the end either "introvert" or "extrovert." He combined them.

THE PERSONAL counselor constantly runs upon self-focused lives, miserably striving to find happiness through "self-expression." Popularly, self-expression has meant: Let yourself go; knock the bungs from your emotional barrels and let them gurgle! As a protest against petty moralisms, this is easily explicable, and as a means of release to some individuals, tied hand and foot by senseless scrupulosities, it has had its value. The wise counselor wants self-expression too; but he wants it to be practiced in accord with the realistic psychological facts. Merely exploding emotions for the sake of the momentary self-centered thrill gets one nowhere, and in the end the constant repetition of such emotional self-relief disperses life and leaves it more aimless than it was before. Even in the sexual realm this is true. Says an eminent psychiatrist: "From the point of view of cure, the advice to go and 'express your instincts' is foolish. In actual experience I have never known a true neurosis cured by sexual libertinism."

Adequate self-expression is a much deeper matter than self-explosion. Its true exponent is not the libertine but the artist, the scientist, the fortunate mother absorbed in her family, the public-spirited businessman creatively doing something for his community, the teacher saying as Professor George H. Palmer did, "Harvard College pays me for doing what I would gladly pay it for allowing me to do." Such personalities, in eminent or humble places, really express themselves, and their common quality is not self-absorption but self-investment.

AT LEAST two practical consequences follow from such successful expansion of the self.

For one thing, it gives a person a saving sense of humor. In anyone afflicted with abnormal self-concern, a deficient sense of humor is an inevitable penalty. Only people who live objectively in other persons and in wide-flung interests, and who therefore can see themselves impartially, can possibly have the prayer answered:

> O wad some Pow'r the giftie gie us
> To see oursels as ithers see us!

The egocentric's petition is habitually otherwise:

> O wad some Pow'r to others gie
> To see myself as I see me.

Nast, the cartoonist, one evening in a social group drew caricatures of each of the company. The result was revealing —each one easily recognized the caricatures of the others but some could not recognize their own. This inability to see ourselves as we look to others is one of the surest signs of egocentric immaturity.

Aristophanes, in his drama *The Clouds*, caricatured Socrates, and when the play was produced all Athens roared with laughter. Socrates, so runs the story, went to see the play, and when the caricature came on he stood up so that the audience might the better enjoy the comic mask that was intended to burlesque him. He was mature. He had got himself off his hands.

An extended self also results in power to bear trouble. In those who rise to the occasion and marshal their forces to deal with it, one factor commonly is present—*they are thinking about someone else besides themselves.* So one young American officer in the first World War wrote home: "You can truly think of me as being cheerful all the time. Why otherwise? I have 38 men with me. If I duck when a shell comes, all 38 duck, and if I smile, the smile goes down the line."

A person who has genuinely identified himself with other persons has done something of first-rate importance for himself without intending it. Hitherto he has lived, let us say, in a mind like a room surrounded by mirrors. Every way he turned he saw himself. Now, however, some of the mirrors change to windows. He can see through them to new interests.

Using All There Is in Us

ONE WAY or another we must do something with all the emotional drives native to our constitution. Such emotional urges as curiosity, pugnacity, fearfulness, self-regard, sexual desire are an essential part of us; we can either be ignobly enslaved by them or master them for the enrichment of our personality.

Curiosity is an emotional urge in all normal people, and its manifestations are protean. Peeping Toms, prying gossips, inquisitive bores, open-minded truth-seekers, daring explorers, research scientists are all illustrations of curiosity. Some uses of it produce the most despicable persons, while others produce the most admirable, but there is no escaping it. From this fact, which holds true of all our native drives, a double lesson comes: first, *no basic emotional factor in human nature is to be despised;* and second, *each of them can be ennobled by its use.*

Pugnacity is one of the most deeply rooted emotional drives in human nature, and combativeness is necessary to the continuance and advance of human life. The fighting spirit expresses itself in hard work, in bravely facing personal handicaps, in the whole range of attack on entrenched social evils.

If, however, we give this indispensable emotional drive gangway, the results are shattering. A chronic hatred or even a cherished grudge tears to pieces the one who harbors it. A strong feeling of resentment is just as likely to cause disease as is a germ. If one is so unfortunate as to have an enemy, the worst thing one can do, not to the enemy but to oneself, is to let resentment dig in and hatred become chronic.

When Edward Everett Hale in his later years said, "I once had an enemy, a determined enemy, and I have been trying all day to remember his name," he gave evidence not only of right-mindedness but of healthy-mindedness. So, too, Lin-

coln, rebuked for an expression of magnanimity toward the
South during the Civil War, and told bitterly that he should
desire rather to destroy his enemies, was not only morally
but emotionally sound when he answered, "What, madam?
Do I not destroy them when I make them my friends?"

FEAR is another indispensable element in the human make-
up. Even in its simpler forms we cannot dispense with it; on
the streets of a modern city a fearless man, if the phrase be
taken literally, would probably be dead before nightfall.
And fear can be a powerfully creative motive. In a profound
sense schools spring from fear of ignorance, industry from
fear of penury, medical science from fear of disease. But fear's
abnormalities—hysteria, phobia, obsessive anxiety—tear
personality to pieces.

Human life is full of secret fears, thrust into the attics and
dark corners of personality. Fear of the dark, of cats, of closed
places, of open places; fear of responsibility, of having children, of old age and death; guilty fears, often concerned with
sins long passed; religious fears, associated with ideas of a
spying and vindictive God and an eternal hell; and sometimes a vague fearfulness, filling life with anxious apprehension—such wretchedness curses innumerable lives.

The disruptive effect of such secret, chronic fearfulness is
physically based. The adrenal glands furnish us in every
frightening situation with "a swig of our own internal fight-
tonic." A little of it is stimulating; too much of it is poison.
Habitual anxiety and dread constitute a continuous false
alarm, turning the invaluable adrenal secretion from an
emergency stimulant into a chronic poison.

To get our fear out into the open and frankly face it is of
primary importance. As infants we started with fear of two
things only—falling and a loud noise. All other fears have
been accumulated since. To find out where and how we picked
them up, to trace their development until we can objectively
survey them as though they were another's and not our own,
is half the battle. Often they can then be laughed off.

Sometimes, however, the fear we find ourselves confronting

is justified. In that case we are commonly defeated by the fallacy that dangerous situations are necessarily undesirable, whereas the fact is that there is *stimulus* in hazardous occasions. Love of danger is one of the strongest motives in man. When life does not present men with enough hazard, they go out looking for it. They seek it in their more active sports, in risky researches and explorations, in championing unpopular causes. To stand up to a hazardous situation, to let it call out in us not our fearfulness but our love of battle, is a healthy, inspiriting experience.

One of the sovereign cures for unhealthy fears is action. Dr. Henry C. Link gives this homely illustration from a mother: "As a young wife I was troubled with many fears, one of which was the fear of insanity. After the birth of our first child, these fears still persisted. However, we soon had another child and ended up by having six. We never had much money and I had to do all my own work. Whenever I started to worry about myself, the baby would cry and I would have to run and look after him. Or the children would quarrel and I would have to straighten them out. Or I would suddenly remember that it was time to start dinner, or that I must run out and take in the wash before it rained, or that the ironing had to be done. My fears were continually interrupted by tasks into which I had to put my back. Gradually my fears disappeared, and now I look back on them with amusement."

This story furnishes one explanation for the prevalence of emotional ills among prosperous and leisurely people. They have time to sit around, feeding their imaginations. In wartime they can listen over the radio to every news broadcast and commentator until, unlike a healthy soldier who has a job to do that he can put his back into, they become morbidly distraught over dangers concerning which they do nothing practical. In ordinary peacetime such people are the prey of endless imaginary woes, so that it is commonly true that those worry most who have least to worry about.

The dual nature of fear, as both good and evil, is nowhere better illustrated than in a man who dreads so much falling short of his duty that he dreads much less the cost of doing it. If one has anything positively to live for, from a child, or a worthwhile day's work, to a world delivered from the scourge of war, *that* is what matters.

Self-regard likewise is not to be despised or suppressed but educated and used.

When Charles Lamb said, "The greatest pleasure I know is to do a good action by stealth, and to have it found out by accident," he revealed how omnipresent is the wish for notice and attention that enhance self-esteem.

The cynic says that at the fountainhead of every so-called "unselfish" life are self-regarding motives. The cynic is right—but in his cynicism about it he is wrong. We all start as individual children, with self-regarding instincts. The test of us, however, lies in the objective aims and purposes which ultimately capture these forces in us and use them as driving power. A wise counselor, therefore, never tells anyone that he ought not to wish to feel important, but rather endeavors to direct that powerful wish into constructive channels.

From self-regard when it goes wrong spring vanity and avarice. Some people live habitually in the spirit with which Mascagni dedicated his opera *The Masks:* "To myself, with distinguished esteem and unalterable satisfaction." Yet we neither can nor should stop caring for ourselves. Our initial business in life is to care for ourselves so much that *I* tackles *Me*, determined to make out of him something worth while.

Probably it is in the realm of *sexual desire* that "sublimation" —redirection to a higher ethical level—is talked about most and understood least. Not all demands of the human organism can be sublimated. In satisfying physical hunger there is no substitute for food. When sex is thought of in its narrowest sense, it belongs in this class.

To the youth troubled by this elemental biological need, many sensible things can be said: that chastity is not debilitating and that sexual indulgence is not necessary to health; that interest in competing concerns is good therapy; that the general unrest accompanying unsatisfied sexual tension can often be relieved by vigorous action, fatiguing the whole body; that sexual desire is natural and right, to be accepted with gratitude and good humor as part of our constitutional equipment, and not sullied with morbid feelings of guilt at its presence; that nature, when left to itself, has its own ways of relieving the specific sex-tension.

Sex, however, is far more deepseated and pervasive in personality than at first appears. All the relationships of the family—maternal, paternal and filial—are grounded in this larger meaning of sex, all fine affection and friendship between brothers and sisters, and men and women, and all extensions of family attitudes to society at large, as in the love and care of children.

When one's life is thus thought of as a whole, sublimation of sex becomes meaningful. It is possible for one to choose a way of living that will channel one's devotions and creative energies into satisfying courses so that the personality *as a whole* finds contentment, even though specific sexual desires are left unfulfilled. So an unmarried woman, denied motherhood, can discover in nursing, teaching or social service an outlet for her maternal instincts that brings to her personality an integrating satisfaction.

That there must be some restraint on all our native drives is obvious. Picture a life in which all the native urges explode themselves together—self-regard, pugnacity, sexual desire, fear; obviously pandemonium would reign. The popular idea, therefore, that the restraint of basic emotional drives is in itself unhealthy is nonsense. The choice before us is not whether our native impulses shall be restrained and controlled but how in the service of an integrated life.

THE MULTIPLE possibilities of use and misuse in handling our native drives root back in the essential quality of all emotional life, *sensitiveness*. One of the most important subjects of self-examination concerns the way we handle this primary quality. Let a man discover what he is characteristically touchy about and he will gain valuable insight into his personal problem.

Many people are extremely touchy to criticism. Their

amour-propre squirms under adverse judgment. Sensitiveness to the opinion of others, without which social life could not go on at all, has in them been perverted into a disease.

Such abnormal persons take appreciation for granted and regard criticism as an impertinence. The normal person comes nearer taking criticism for granted and regarding appreciation as velvet. Emerson once made a speech that a minister sitting on the platform deeply disliked. The minister, in delivering the closing prayer, prayed, "We beseech Thee, O Lord, to deliver us from ever hearing any more such nonsense as we have just listened to." Asked afterward what he thought about it, Emerson remarked, "The minister seems a very conscientious, plain-spoken gentleman." Such healthy-mindedness is a necessary factor in a well-integrated personality.

Mastering Depression

ONE OF the commonest causes of personal disorganization is despondency. Some despondency is physically caused, but the moody dejections most people suffer are not altogether beyond their control.

A first suggestion for dealing with this problem is: *Take depression for granted.* One who expects completely to escape low moods is asking the impossible. To take low moods too seriously, instead of saying, This also will pass, is to confer on them an obsessive power they need not have.

A second suggestion is of daily importance: *We can identify ourselves not with our worse, but with our better, moods.* Deep within us all is that capacity. The ego, the central "I," can choose *this* and not *that* mood as representing the real self; it can identify itself with hopefulness rather than disheartenment, with good will rather than rancor.

All slaves of depression have this in common: They have acquired the habit of identifying their real selves with their low moods. Not only do they have cellars in their emotional houses, as everybody does, but they live there. While each of us has depressed hours, none of us needs to be a depressed person.

This leads to a third suggestion. *When depression comes,*

tackle yourself and do not merely blame circumstance. Circumstances are often so tragic and crushing as to make dejection inevitable. Nevertheless, to deduce from the presence of misfortune the right to be a despondent person is a fatal error. Life is an assimilative process in which we transmute into our own quality whatever comes into us. Walter de la Mare's lines have a wider application than at first appears:

> It's a very odd thing—
> As odd as can be,
> That whatever Miss T. eats
> Turns into Miss T.

Depressed persons can make depression out of any circumstances whatsoever. This truth is especially pertinent in a tragic era when the world is upset by catastrophic events. Not to be depressed by present calamities would reveal an insensitive spirit. Nevertheless, many today blame their emotional disorganization on the sad estate of the world, whereas their real problem is within themselves. As D. H. Lawrence wrote concerning one of his characters, "Poor Richard Lovatt wearied himself to death struggling with the problem of himself, and calling it Australia."

The fourth suggestion goes beyond self-tackling and says: *Remember others.* Emotions are contagious. One depressed person can infect a whole household and become a pest even to comparative strangers. If, therefore, Ian Maclaren's admonition is justified, "Let us be kind to one another for most of us are fighting a hard battle," good cheer and courage are among the most important kindnesses that we can show.

The fifth suggestion calls for deep resources of character: *Remember that some tasks are so important that they must be gone through with whether we are depressed or not.* Strong personalities commonly solve the problem of their despondency not by eliminating but by sidetracking it. They have work to do, a purpose to fulfill, and to *that*, whether or not they feel dejected, the main trunk line of their lives belongs.

The Ultimate Strength

To pull a personality together takes inner reserves of power—of power assimilated from beyond oneself.

As truly as a tree exists by means of chemical assimilation through roots and leaves, our own physical organisms sustain themselves by appropriated power. The entire cosmos furnishes the indispensable means by which we live at all. We are pensioners on universal energy, and our power is not fabricated in us but released through us.

This principle of released power does not stop at any supposed line separating man's physical from his spiritual experience. That our spirits are continuous with a larger spiritual life, and that in this realm also our power is not self-produced but assimilated, is the affirmation of all profound religious experience.

No more pathetic cases present themselves to the personal counselor than those whose only technique in handling their problems is to trust in the strength of their own volition. Soon or late they face problems to which such a technique is utterly inapplicable. When bereavement comes, for instance, bringing with it profound sorrow, to appeal to the will to arouse itself and solve the problem is an impertinence.

Such moments call for another technique altogether—the hospitable receptivity of faith.

Many people ask, "How does one get faith, if one does not have it? One cannot *will* to have faith." But faith is not something we *get;* it is something we *have.* Moreover, we have a surplus of it, associated with more curious objects than tongue can tell—faith in dictatorship or astrology or rabbits' feet, in one economic nostrum or another. That we have more faith than we know what to do with is shown by the way we give it to every odd and end that comes along.

Our trick of words—"belief" vs. "unbelief"— obscures this. No man can really become an unbeliever; he is psychologically shut up to the necessity of believing—in God, for example, or else in no God. When positive faiths die out, their place is always taken by negative faiths—in impossibilities rather than possibilities, in ideas that make us victims rather than masters of life; in philosophies that plunge us into Rabelais' dying mood: "Draw the curtain; the farce is played."

A friend once wrote to Turgenev: "It seems to me that to put oneself in the second place is the whole significance of life." Turgenev replied: "It seems to me that to discover what to put before oneself, in the first place, is the whole problem of life." Whatever one does put thus before oneself is always the object of one's faith; one believes in it and belongs to it; and whether it be Christ or Hitler, a chosen vocation or a personal friend, when such committal of faith is heartily made, it pulls the trigger of human energy.

Confidence that it is worth while constructively to tackle oneself, and the determination so to do, depends on faith of some sort. Distraught and dejected people almost inevitably ask: "Why should we bother to try to create an integrated and useful personality? Of what importance are we anyway?" These miserable folk perceive nothing worth living for, and the only cure for their futilitarian attitude is a positive faith.

Even though one goes no further than Robert Louis Stevenson in saying, "I believe in an ultimate decency of things," such faith has inestimable value. If one can go beyond Stevenson's affirmation, religion presents the most stimulating faith in human experience. It has said to every individual: Whatever you may fail at, you need not fail at being a real person; the making of great personal life include handicaps, deficiencies, troubles and even moral failures; the universe is not a haphazard affair of aimless atoms but is organized around spiritual purposes; and personality, far from being a chance inadvertence, is the fullest and completest way of being alive and the most adequate symbol we have of the nature of God.

Thus religion is a basis for hopeful adventure and a source of available power in trying to make the most of our natural endowments and become what we ought to be. And he who undertakes that task is on the main highroad of creation's meaning and is accepting the central trust of life.

Farmer Takes a Wife

By John Gould

When John brought his Boston bride home to the down-East farm, both he and Great-uncle Timothy felt she had considerable to learn before she'd be a full-fledged farmer's wife. This story of how they taught her is a refresher course in humanity, filled with dry wit, shrewd observation and down-East legend.

The author, John Gould, a Maine farmer born and bred, now publishes the *Lisbon Enterprise* at Lisbon Falls, Maine.

Farmer Takes a Wife

NEXT to scalding a hog, which is as complicated a process as I know of on a farm, there's as much getting ready to a wedding as anything. A new wife coming to the old place makes a difference. Among other things, Uncle Timothy and I had to pull the turnips in September instead of October, so they were small and we lost $200, just because I got married.

Not that I've regretted it. A fellow doesn't have much choice in the time of his wedding, and a girl brought up in Boston doesn't know about turnips—so it was a case of losing one or the other when she set the date. We pulled the turnips and I left Uncle Timothy alone in the big house while I went to Boston to get me a wife.

It was a successful wedding. We had six bridesmaids and potted plants all over the church. Some of the people who came up and kissed us afterward wanted to know where we were going to live. "John is a farmer up in Maine," my wife would say. The idea of a farmer from up in Maine getting married on Massachusetts Avenue must have astonished them. They took one last look at my wife with eyes brimming sympathy, and I haven't seen them since.

As we made our way out after a polite meantime, she said: "Some of those buzzards think I'm crazy to marry a farmer."

"You are."

She said, "I've married a farmer and I want to be a farmer's wife."

When, two weeks later, we got back to the farm, Uncle Timothy had everything in order and I began reading my mail. One letter was from my county agent and after I read it I told my wife, "I'm going to join the artificial breeding association."

"What?" she asked.

I said, "For the cows."

She said, "Oh."

This was an abrupt beginning for the educational program. So I explained that the dairymen were going to organize the Androscoggin Valley Artificial Insemination Association, and the advantages were numerous. "It only costs four dollars a year and that's the cheapest way to keep a bull I ever heard of."

"Some things are beyond price," she said.

I said, "Why, the bull's prorated telephone expense is more than that!"

"Who ever heard," she said, "of a bull using a telephone?"

So I told her about Oscar.

Oscar was no ordinary bull. He had several unusual escapades to his credit, like the time he charged the Ladies' Farm Bureau picnic and ate 127 cream-cheese and olive sandwiches. Another time he was being used as a demonstrator in a safety bull pen, but the only thing he proved was that 700 men and women can't all get up in the same pear tree.

The time he telephoned Aunt Hulda Banter, in Cleveland, stands out as his finest accomplishment. She was about to observe her 88th birthday, and her only child, Mrs. Nute (our neighbor), was minded to telephone congratulations. Mrs. Nute cranked for Central and yelled, "Now, git off'n the line everybody; I'm calling long-distance."

While she was waiting the connection, Oscar moved toward the house. He had already torn down his stanchion and put the hired man up on the scafflings. He bounded into the kitchen and shoved one foot through the cane bottom of a Boston rocker. Mrs. Nute went headlong through the sitting room to round up a posse.

Oscar limped, rocker and all, over to the telephone. In Cleveland, Aunt Hulda was excitedly holding her receiver to her ear and the operator was intoning, "Here is your party; go ahead, please."

Oscar sucked in a torrent of wind and blatted so the house shook.

To this day, Aunt Hulda believes she was struck by lightning.

We never raise 'turkeys. Grandfather used to, but he said they were foolish. When the dog ran at them they'd take off and fly up in the orchard—but not a one of them ever had the sense to fly back. They'd walk back and it would take all afternoon. But along in the summer Uncle Timothy would buy a decent-framed tom, and at the right time he'd ply him with corn. Sometimes he'd have the tom standing in corn to his hips. In mid-November my wife said, "I suppose I'm expected to cook a big Thanksgiving dinner like the Pilgrims had."

Uncle Timothy asked me confidentially if I thought a city girl could be trusted with roasting the turkey. My wife hadn't heard about Uncle's tom, so she said, "Have we got a gobbler?"

"We have," said Uncle Timothy.

"And your folks are coming," I said.

I'd asked them on the sly, because I thought it would give them a chance to see the kind of life their daughter married into. For that reason I'd been extra cautious about getting things together. I always keep my eye peeled for the right items for Christmas and Thanksgiving—trace up a batch of onions all the same size and keep out the smoothest turnips. There's always a special pumpkin or two and special squashes, and when we're grading apples we have a special box for the big ones. I like to take wooden bowls and make them up with mixtures—Spies and Jonathans, Yellow Delicious and Red Delicious, Bellflowers and Macs, big as a grapefruit. Then I set them where anybody can always get to them without reaching too far.

Uncle Timothy always has a little salt bag full of beechnuts to use in the turkey stuffing. I wouldn't be bothered gathering them, but he waits on the first frost and fights over them with the jays and squirrels.

He picked the turkey dry, so he wouldn't color up, and the bird looked as if he was marble. Then Uncle brought in a special wheelbarrow load of beechwood for the roasting and said everything was done that we could do outdoors.

I drove to the train to meet my wife's folks, and beyond complaining of the cold they seemed to like the looks of things. They hadn't supposed we lived so far out in the woods, they said, and I told them our farm had been cleared before anyone knew where the town was going to be. I've noticed it always astonishes city folks to find a farm home can have modern conveniences.

The next day we had Thanksgiving dinner, and my wife dished up a dandy. Uncle Timothy was proud of her and said so. He hovered around the stove every minute his turkey was inside, and every time he'd start to offer advice he'd think better of it, and he never said a word. The turkey was perfect. And tears came in the old fellow's eyes when he sat down to eat and my wife said, "Now save room—there's bag pudding and three kinds of pie."

"God love you," said Uncle Timothy. "It's brains makes you say that. Most women fill you up first and then bring in pie you can't find room for. Makes me think of Liz Dacey— she had a mince pie once that lasted her all winter. She'd insist everybody have more meat and potatoes, and then she'd say, 'Now, if anybody wants pie, I've got some, but the way you've stuffed I doubt you've got room.' I was there once threshing beans, and I told her I always had room for pie, and she bull-headed out in the back butt'ry and brought in a piece the right size for a peaked boy all run down with poor blood. It was froze solid, but I ate it for spite."

My wife's folks kept saying, "Aren't those potatoes delicious?" "Don't those onions taste good?" "My, that's the best squash I ever ate!" Uncle Timothy said that thick cream and new butter have a lot to do with smashed potatoes, that the time you pick a squash makes it taste the way it does, and that the way to grow decent onions was a secret betwixt him and God—and he wouldn't tell so long as God didn't.

AFTER THE WOMEN had done the dishes, we sat in the parlor and Uncle Timothy poured out some of his cider and told his story about Samoset, a real Indian who used to come around every fall and take Thanksgiving dinner with the family. Great-grandfather called him Samoset, but nobody ever knew his real name.

The first year Samoset came was the first year up here and things hadn't gone well. Great-grandmother had scarcely enough on hand to feed her own. But Samoset was welcomed warmly and was set where the embers on the hearth would play upon his back.

It was indeed a sparse Thanksgiving feast. A dry season had made potatoes like acorns and ears of corn like hemlock cones. The hens had got afoul a fox, and the old cow had straddled a rail and fixed herself for beefing. Great-grandmother saved a few hens, but the beef had spoiled a-curing. Eggs were for meat and apologies pieced out the vegetables.

Samoset took that all in and he stood up. He wiped his fingers across the seat of his doeskin pants, pointed at the table and made a very naughty noise calculated to convey an opinion that the food was abominable. Then he strode out the door and disappeared into the forest.

The folks joked the incident off and sat down to eat, with Aunt Deborah and Great-grandmother each insisting the other have the extra egg. And then there came a hullabaloo outdoors and up raced Samoset in the wake of two puffing squaws pulling a sled. In they came and they brought bundles of smoke-dried Merrymeeting ducks, joints of corned venison, pouches of fine meal, bunny skins tightly packed with nuts and dried berries, sticks of Kennebec turkeys and a great basket of odds and ends.

Oh, it was a grand Thanksgiving, and Great-grandfather said grace all over again and even the squaws sat at table and watched Aunt Deborah drip unashamed tears into her partridge pie.

Samoset came every Thanksgiving for a long time, but alone and without offering—because Great-grandfather began to master these lands and each year the woods were farther back from the house. Then one year he didn't come and no one ever heard of him again. Aunt Debbie said it was funny how you'd miss a man who never spoke to you, and all at once it dawned on everybody that the only time Samoset had opened his head was that first time when he made a noise with his lips.

It surprised us that my wife liked snow and carried her enthusiasm to the point of reading us snow poems from the newspapers and magazines. I therefore learned that poets make a lot of money on the first snow. I suppose cottony billows of fluffy down clinging to pine limbs do make a fetching sight.

They also break limbs off trees, pull down fences, gum up the tractor wheels, get down your neck and cover the parts to the mowing machine you were about to assemble after painting. I bear them no grudge—I simply wish to point out to the poets, as I did to my wife, that a lot goes on they don't know about.

My favorite snow poem was composed by Uncle Timothy one frigid morning:

> *The Snow! The Snow!*
> *Oh! Oh! Oh! Oh!*

I should explain that when one reads this aloud, the chattering of teeth is introduced between the second and third Oh's.

This type of presentation is patently superior to verses that stem from imaginary experiences. I think I could improve our poets. The first lesson would consist of a short workout with a crosscut saw among my timber. The silent mantle of immaculate beauty would be dazzling in its consummate loveliness and the poet would be contemplating neat measures about it. At that point two bushels off an adjacent hemlock would knock him flatter than a one-sided spondee.

For lesson two, I should instruct him how to catch a cow who has wandered from the drinking tub, and is 300 yards off in the field dragging her keel in the drifts. I would cause him to shovel out the mailbox (after the highway tractor has buried it ten feet deep). After that, I believe we'd either get no snow poems at all, or some so realistic my wife would wear mittens when she read them.

I remember at the time of the first snow my wife wanted to know what kind of a winter we'd have, and Uncle Timothy and I gave her the works. Along in the fall it is customary for rural sages to discuss the likelihood of a long hard winter. I simply prophesy heartily that we are in for the worst one in history, and prepare for it. I told my wife the coming winter would be the worst in 82 years. Uncle Timothy corroborated my foresight.

He said gypsy moths had laid their eggs high—positive indication snow would be 11 feet deep. He said the blackberry vines leaned southerly—evidence that they expected severe northerly winds. The pumpkin and squash vines had been unusually long, indicating they dreaded the coming winter and wanted to get as far away as possible.

Between the two of us we may have convinced her; but we felt her recollection of her first Maine winter would bear us out. I guess it did, because the next fall she said we'd have a long hard winter.

WHEN my wife said, "What do you want for Christmas?" Uncle Timothy said, "Nothing. Christmas is for children and them that have them. You might pray that I'll live long enough to see a kid's sock on the chimney again."

My wife put her hands on the arms of the rocker and leaned down to whisper, "I promise, Uncle, I'll bend every effort."

"It's been a long time," Uncle Timothy said. "When my brother David's children were little we used to have Christmases in this old house, with aunts and uncles from all around, and there was one old ripper of a blizzard struck one year and we figured wouldn't nobody come; but we sat 28 people down to the table. As I recollect, all 27 gave me suspenders. You might get me some this year, if you want to. I'm about caught up again."

Uncle Timothy announced he wasn't going to give anything, and we both knew he'd already been to town and come home with two big bundles he'd hid in the barn. My wife had broken into the bale of new yarn and had somehow figured out Aunt Sarah's double saw-tooth design, and had made him a pair of mittens about an inch thick. I knew Uncle Timothy would fill up and swallow when he saw them—he knew mittens from away back and he hadn't seen double-knit ones since his wife died.

I picked a couple of ducks, and we had a pheasant in the freezer for a Christmas-morning pie. Uncle Timothy insisted we go down to the church service, but he wouldn't go—said we could tell him about it and it would do him full as much good. The only time he ever went near the church was every spring, when he whetted up his axe and went down to split the wood for the church and parsonage. He never started on our own pile until he had the church and the minister fitted.

So all in all we made out a good Christmas, and I guess my wife was satisfied. Uncle Timothy told her, "There's been 218 Christmases on this old farm, and I think we done all right by the traditions. I guess, now you're here, it won't be the last."

He sat in his chair with his mittens on and didn't take them off until he went to bed.

WE'D BEEN busy all one day and I was watching my wife read a book. "Listen to this," she said, and she read a paragraph aloud. According to this book, the austere and forbidding geography of our New England countryside was enlivened purposely by our esthetic farmers through the use of red paint on our farm buildings.

I disagreed. I explained to my wife what I'd found out about paint.

The paint our early settlers used was made of red ocher mined locally and spread with either kerosene oil or skimmed milk. It was the only available paint; they used it because they could get it. If the local paint mine yielded yellow ocher instead of red, the local homes were yellow.

The esthetics of the matter are less interesting to me than the skimmed milk. They knew nothing of chemistry then, and were not aware that the 20th century would develop a casein paint.

As we were talking it over, Uncle Timothy recalled the painting of our first big barn. They brought red ocher in a cart and mixed it in a barrel with coal oil. Then they poured in skimmed milk, stirred, and painted. I objected that oil and milk won't mix, and Uncle Timothy retorted that nobody said they did. The pioneers just slapped them on simultaneously. They needed paint, so they made paint, and that's all there was to it.

Anyway, the big barn burned 50 years later and was painted just that once. Meanwhile it added color and sprightliness to the dismal landscape hereabouts. Actually it must have been pretty streaked, and my wife says it was probably a good thing we had the lovely countryside around here to relieve it. It was fun to watch my wife assume title to the legends in our family. We told them to her one by one, and soon we noticed she referred to them as old friends. That's the way I'd hoped it would be.

Once in a while Uncle Timothy overstepped and my wife had a job distinguishing valid history from his inventions. I showed her the place down in the woods where Great-grandfather got the wild goose. The goose was, at the time, in the mouth of a big dog fox. Great-grandfather let out a yell that made the fox drop the goose and take to the bushes, and then he brought the goose home. That's all there is to the story.

But Uncle Timothy said Great-grandfather was driving to town in the buggy and a flock of geese sailed low over the road. Having no gun, he grabbed the buggy whip, stood up, and whacked the leather seat cushion so it banged like a musket fire. Naturally, the geese all thought they'd been shot, so they fell in heaps up and down the road.

But we have plenty of valid antiquities. Like Great-grandmother's copper kettle. It was big enough to scald a hog in, and she was proud of it. It had a thousand uses in the settlement—they washed children, boiled soap, made maple sugar and just about everything else in it. One day Dr. Babcock came up and said he'd like to borrow the kettle.

Being a doctor, he was considered a suitable borrower, and he slung the kettle over his shoulder and walked away. But the next day Great-grandfather was up in the pines and he found Dr. Babcock sitting on a stump reading a book and off to one side the copper kettle slung on a witch's tripod. The kettle was bubbling and steaming, and the doctor had a good pile of wood worked up.

He had dismembered a cadaver and was boiling the meat

off the bones. In later years the skeleton hung in his office and he used it to demonstrate to patients the location of their hurts. Great-grandmother never liked her kettle afterward, and Dr. Babcock was allowed in the house only on the extremest of emergencies.

Probably nobody ever stopped to count the parts to a cream separator, but they run high. Besides the spouts and things, they have a million little conical disks that slip inside one another. To get disk 35 in where disk 28 should go is bad business. The milk wouldn't know where to go if the numbers weren't right. Whatever takes place in there is too fast for me to watch, and as long as cream comes out one hole and milk out the other, I don't much care. But one morning I cranked away and we had two buckets of milk and a cup of cream. From then on the separator refused to live up to the claims of the manufacturer.

A week or so later my wife said, "Les Houghton has a separator he'll sell, and I'm going to buy it."

"No, you ain't," said Uncle Timothy.

"Why not?"

"Because nobody but a fool ever buys anything from a Houghton."

"But he says it's all there and works easy and will separate."

Uncle Timothy put on his hat and went out to the barn to think it over, and when he came in he pulled up his rocker and sat down and said, "Look, I want to tell you about Maine traders. Les Houghton is just like a drunk that can't help drinking. He can't help trading. In fact, his father before him was known as the champeen trader in these parts. But the Houghtons got two eyes—one to look they ain't cheated, and one to look for people to cheat. They been at it so long everybody is waiting for ways to get even. You're new, and they got a chance to dicker without expecting something to bust in their faces."

My wife said, "I didn't know a separator could stir up so much fuss."

Uncle Timothy said, "Don't take it so hard. I think I know where I can get you a separator, but first I want to warn you against trading characters. Somewhere on this farm is something Les Houghton wants—and he's found out we need a separator."

She said, "I told him we did."

"Just so," said Uncle Timothy, "and he nosed around to see what we got he needs. Well, you let him alone. You know, one time Les's father, old Henry, went up to State Fair without a red cent, and he swapped his jackknife with a fruit peddler for a half-dozen peaches. Then he swapped the peaches for oranges and the oranges for something else, and inside a half hour he had a whiffletree and a length of chain. Then he swapped that for this and this for that, getting boot every time. He came home that night driving a pair of roans that would go 3200, hitched into a blue tipcart, with a bull tied to the tail gate. In the tipcart he had everything from a hay-knife to an icebox. He had churns, logging tools, beehives, storm windows, chairs, and a big brass cage for a parrot he kept a squirrel in all one winter. And he had $17 in his pocket, papers on the bull, a Holmes note on a McCormick reaper and eight jackknives, including his own."

Uncle Timothy got up, put on his hat and said: "Now, that's what a trader is, and the Houghtons is all traders."

Two or three days later he hitched up the mare and rattled up the road, and when he came back he had a separator. My wife was pleased. "Where'd you get it?" she said.

"Les Houghton."

My wife said, "Why, you double-crossing old coot!"

Uncle Timothy laughed. "I had the cussedest time finding out what it was we had that Les wanted. It was the hind wheels off the old manure spreader."

I said, "Did it take any money?"

"Three dollars. He held out for the wheels and $15. But his spreader ain't worth a cent without new wheels and they've got over 150 loads to get out."

The next morning we tried the separator and it worked fine. I had to smile when Uncle was telling her about trading characters, because I don't expect she'll ever meet a better one than Uncle Tim. The Houghtons are beginners by comparison.

In the middle of a night there came a thumping on our door, and Uncle Timothy called my wife to come see what he had. It was the first new lamb. Now my wife had never seen a new lamb before, and you can't blame her for what she did, but she made a cosset of it.

Anyone who has grown up with sheep knows that the worst thing you can do is make pets of them. Once you've got a pet lamb you can't make a move without stepping on it.

This night, while Uncle was down to the barn to find out which ewe was the mother, my wife rigged up a bottle of milk and fed the lamb. Uncle was furious when he came back. "You'll have a cosset, you'll have a cosset!" he yelled. And so she did. Uncle spent the rest of the night wrestling with the ewe and her offspring, but although the mother was in the mood the lamb wouldn't play. It already knew that milk came from another place.

So my wife spent the spring running around with a bottle of milk and the summer trying to avoid her eager stepson. For a time it was fun, but long before he went to market in the fall she had had enough. She learned what farmers feel about their animals—you like them and talk to them and give them every care, but they come and go and except for the dog you don't make pets of them.

Poets have always done well by the wind—and in general, I'm in favor of more poetry and less wind. My wife, at first, spoke cheerfully of the tangy, gusty weather, so we felt obliged to show her some people were of a different opinion.

Long ago Jim Coombs of Carter's Corner was becalmed with his sailing vessel down around the Solomons, and the crew sat around for two weeks without a breath stirring. About that time, Jim fished in his pocket and drew out a silver shilling. He tossed it overboard with a flourish and called at the sky, "Give us a shillin's worth of wind!" Almost immediately Jim's ship was in the middle of the worst hurricane he ever saw. When the storm abated, Jim stood on deck amid the wreckage and commented, "If I'd a-knowed wind was so cheap, I'd not a-bought so much."

Down-East wind is very cheap. Uncle Timothy claimed once that the wind blew his hat against the barn and held it there a week. Another time, a clapboard came loose and vibrated over a knothole, and the barn whistled *The Stars and Stripes Forever.* We admitted to my wife that the wind sails boats, turns windmills, and brings fresh showers to thirsting flowers. But we pointed out it is possible to have too much of a good thing.

The day we started laying new roofing, we nearly blew off the barn, and 30-foot sheets of tar paper would stick right out straight. Sometimes the barn door will slap shut in your face and smash a whole basketful of eggs. On windy days the telephone lead-in wire whines like somebody strangling a pussycat. Upwind surges of conversation keep us in touch with our neighbors. One day a woman up on the hill a quarter of a mile away combed out her hired girl and the girl got mad and quit—a dramatic exchange that held us spellbound for 15 minutes.

This particular day saw us fighting every inch of the way, and nobody around suggested it was merely gusty or tangy. Instead, when Uncle Timothy and I came in for supper, we were told, "Knowing how a windy day gets you down, I decided it was time somebody got blown some good—so I baked a mince pie."

Uncle Timothy washed up and then improvised:

> *I saw you toss the kites on high,*
> *And blow the birds about the sky,*
> *And bake for me a hot mince pie.*

ALL MAINE people are natural-born liars, which is not at all so hideous a distinction as being a trained one. My wife hadn't got used to this when Henry Jorgen came up to brood solace with me over the continued wet weather. Instead of commenting that we'd had enough rain for anyone with normal desires, Henry, who lives 20 miles from the ocean, said, "Got a sea serpent in my pasture."

My wife was just about to put in a doubting remark, but I knew Henry was merely emphasizing his displeasure at the weather, so I beat her to it and said, "A big one?"

"Not awful big," said Henry. "But pretty-colored.'

This method of making a basic fact memorable has nothing to do with injunctions against false witness. Henry, and people like him, has never been known to utter an untruth. He tells good wholesome lies because it's the most artistic way he knows of to tell the truth.

I think my wife is getting used to it. When Jerry Turner was bragging about his hens, she tried to take him down a peg one day by saying, "I hear your hens lay eggs as big as grapefruit."

Jerry looked her straight in the eye and said, "No, that ain't so—but my pigeons do."

If the sun should come up some morning with a derby hat on, I imagine few of my neighbors would bother to mention it to their wives at breakfast. I remember once Chris Wadell painted his silo with red, white and blue stripes, making it look like a big barber pole. The silo sat on top of the hill, and when it was just weather color it could be seen to the limits of the horizon. Now you could hear it, too. But not a man for miles around commented on the improvement, and it's likely Chris never expected them to. A man driving through one day asked Chris why he painted his silo that way. Chris said it was to preserve the wood.

I suppose I was guilty of some such foolishness when I made my bucksaw out of black walnut. Odd jobs that I'd saved up for a rainy day were being disposed of, and I came to making a bucksaw frame. I had some ash, but thought it would cut to waste; I had some oak, but bucksaws get left out in the rain sometimes and oak will soak water like a lobster trap. The maple seemed warped. I turned over a pine board and found a lovely piece of black walnut. I suppose I'd planned to use it for a silver chest. But it soon made a bucksaw and it was grand wood to work. When I had it strung together and had filed the saw, it was still raining, so I inlaid the handle with some cherry and basswood and carved rosettes at the top.

I was sawing wood with it a couple of afternoons later when Charlie Little came in to see if I wanted to buy a guinea hen, which I didn't. I laid the saw down to put another stick on the horse, and Charlie picked it up. He ran his thumb over the inlay, rubbed the walnut, plucked at a saw tooth with his fingernail and then reached over and sawed off a stick. He handed the saw back without comment, which indicated the matter had his approval, if not his understanding.

When you come right down to it, why should we expect anyone to comment on things like that? People usually do, and that's why housewives don't hang washings on the front lawn and why hardly anyone does his carpenter work in the parlor—the way Satchel-Eye Dyer did all his life. I suppose I've got the only inlaid black walnut bucksaw in the world, but I don't know if it's a distinction. I've set out to show it to my wife a number of times. I never have. I did tell her about Satchel-Eye Dyer.

"Nobody was ever named that," she said.

But he was. And I've always felt humanity needlessly ignored his history.

The first recorded incident in the life of this remarkable man was prophetic. It was when he was aged four. He got lost in the woods and a posse located him after two days of search. He was sitting on a stump in despair, and as the searchers came up behind him they heard him say, "Hello, God—my name is 'Delbert Dyer; I got lost in the woods. My mother has lost a fine boy." He ultimately proved in many ways the accuracy of his own estimate.

He married Nellie Overton and brought her home one afternoon to share his weal and woe. The next day the barn burned. He saved the stock, and had to turn the dining room into a tie-up. It took him three years to build a new barn, and in the meantime the animals eventually occupied three rooms downstairs, a bedroom up, and the sheep were in the back open chamber. In addition, Satchel-Eye used the parlor for a carpenter shop and occasionally shod a horse or two in the kitchen. When Dr. Dowd arrived to assist in Nellie's first accouchement, he said he might just as well have driven his mare and buggy right upstairs.

He peeled off his coat and sent Satchel-Eye for some hot water. Satchel-Eye appeared almost at once with the hottest water the doctor had ever used. It appeared that he had rigged a bellows on the kitchen range to assist in shaping horseshoes, and by giving a few pumps on the handle he had made water boil in a matter of seconds. Thus Sylvanus was born, and Dr. Dowd was given his choice of ten dollars or 200-weight of yellow-eye beans. Being to the manner trained, Dr. Dowd took one bag of beans and five dollars, and jokingly said, "When I come back next year, I hope you'll have either a barn for the stock or a house for your family."

When he came back the next year to witness the arrival of Rufus, the barn had been built, but now the house had burned. Nellie was waiting her time on a brass bed in the grain room, while Satchel-Eye spoke reassuring words to her and rocked little Sylvanus in his cradle with his foot. To improve his time he mended a bridle, which Nellie was steadying for him with one hand. This time Dr. Dowd took one bag of beans and abated the five dollars, telling Satchel-Eye to put it toward the saw bill for a new house. Dr. Dowd was a good man.

After the new house was built, Satchel-Eye continued to confuse his two buildings. One winter they made 25 beehives in the parlor, accumulating some good shavings for poultry litter. So the next spring Satchel-Eye started raising ducks. It seemed unnecessary to move the shavings, so they put the ducks in the parlor. They built a runway so the ducks could come and go by a front window and they fenced off the lawn for a range. The feed hoppers were on the piazza.

When the boys were grown, Satchel-Eye built a boat. Being 35 miles from the ocean, on a hill where brooks ran only in the spring, he had hardly any need of a boat. All the lumber was cut on the place, shaped in the parlor and fitted in the front bedroom. They had to take the front of the house down to move the boat.

They hoisted the boat up, backed a hayrack under it and

took it down beneath the barn. Someone asked Satchel-Eye one time why he built it and he said it was a handy thing to keep beans in.

Then they rebuilt the front of the house and hung it on hinges in case they should ever build another boat. This was handy, of course, and they made a practice of keeping things in there under cover. They'd come out and prop up the front of the house, back in the horses, and come out with a set of logging sleds or a manure spreader.

Some of Satchel-Eye's reactions to the world outside were memorable. He didn't leave the farm often, but he went abroad with his eyes open and came home wiser and always richer. Once he went to the State Fair and brought Nellie home $5 worth of spun sugar—the pink kind. He never saw any before and he knew Nellie hadn't. It filled the whole back of the wagon, and she piled it up in the pantry and said, "Thanks, 'Delbert. I'll try some after supper."

ANOTHER time he was up to the city and saw a box kite in a store window. He bought one and he and the boys studied it out. Then they made a big one with improvements and they flew it with five balls of binder twine. It hung off over the village for weeks, unless the wind shifted, and then they had a windlass they'd made with a grindstone crank to crank it home with.

They'd play around with boats and kites a while and then they'd fall to and work like beavers. People said they'd trot the horses down the field when they were loading hay, tossing up bunches as the rack went by, and get in seven or eight loads in an afternoon. They'd cut wood for two weeks and have enough for two years. Then they'd quit work all at once and maybe go fishing for three days at a time. They always brought back some trout, alive, in a bucket of water, and dumped them in the well. People going by would see Satchel-Eye sitting on the well-curb with a fishpole and think Simple Simon had moved in, but Nellie usually had trout to fry if she wanted them.

Nellie lasted only a few weeks after Satchel-Eye died, just

long enough to sell the stock and wind things up. Satchel-
Eye said, toward the end, that he'd had a good life. He knew
everybody thought him queer and he didn't mind a bit. He
said, "I always did just what I'd a mind to, the best way I
had of doing it. I figure things different, that's all. People are
so afraid of being laughed at that nobody has any fun."

THE FIRST TIME my wife blew the dinner horn was about half
past ten one morning, and she didn't have a thing ready to
eat. "I was practicing," she explained, as Uncle Timothy
came puffing up around the beehives.

There's something about a horn. People who don't know
one note from another, if you give them a trumpet, will set
their lips to it to see if they can make a noise. Long ago we
had a dinner horn that was the horn off some beefed steer, and
they say little Aunt Deborah, who was about two thirds the
size of a pint dipper could wind it so the basswood leaves
would shiver, up in the woods. Uncle Timothy says she could
blow it in the teeth of a gale and make the wind turn square
around. That was the kind of horn Roland and Robin Hood
blew, I suppose, and it could peel the bark off an oak at 100
paces.

But something happened to the old horn, and back before
my time they bought a fisherman's foghorn—the galvanized
kind lobstermen carry in their boats for heavy days. Anyone can blow this one; it has a metal reed in it. When we
started work a distance from the house, I showed my wife
this horn and said to blow it at dinnertime.

I thought the morning had passed rather swiftly. When I
came up, I found Uncle Timothy sitting on the chopping
block, and he said, "It's only half past ten." He said if he
couldn't eat right now, he was going to sit right there until
he could. "I fight appetite until I hear the horn—then I just
give up. I got to eat," he said. "My juices start if I hear a
horn blow."

But my wife was making a stew, and you can't hurry a
stew. She hadn't even started the dumplings. I got a hammer
and started nailing up some wire for a new duck pen, and

Uncle Timothy made a pretense of helping me. He didn't have his heart in it though. When the horn blew again he lit out, and when I got up to the house, he was eating. He stopped eating halfway of his plate and said to my wife, "Don't ever do that again as long as I live."

My wife laughed at him and said, "You know, Uncle, when I first came here I didn't like you."

Uncle Timothy grinned and said, "I'm just an old fool and I'm nine tenths glutton, so I don't know as I blame you a bit."

She said, "But I wouldn't swap you now for the world. The way to a woman's heart is through a man's stomach."

Uncle Tim looked sober for a time, and then he said, "You know, none of the Goulds ever amounted to anything, but they managed to find themselves some awful smart women."

BEES ARE an unpredictable chattel. Some days they are purry and pleasant, but other days they go around looking for trouble, and send many an innocent yelling to the house.

I'm not an educated beekeeper. We've always had bees, we get honey, and they swarm now and then, and I let it go at that. But Uncle Timothy decided it was time somebody took an interest in them, and he studied up on apiculture all one winter. The fruit of his study came when the first swarm appeared, and he found a bushel of bees on a Baldwin tree.

When I arrived on the scene he was peering into the distance. A new but empty hive stood at his feet. "They flew," he said, and that's all he'd say. I made no comment, but Uncle Timothy plainly inferred that I accused him of bungling. So he took to wandering around when he had time, trying to find a hollow tree with bees in it.

One day he came in and said, "I've found them bees that got away from me last spring. They're in a maple." We went and cut the tree down, split it, and opened up not quite a washtub of comb. Uncle Timothy was as pleased as a winning candidate. He gave me a little lecture, saying, "A man who understands bees can do anything with them."

Then he took off his pants. I never saw such dexterity. I was about to congratulate him on his skill at his years when

I found I had mine off too. I never had bees climb up inside my pants legs before, but it's a thing I've watched against since. I got eight different connections, and Timothy said he got five that could qualify. "Anything that goes in less than six inches don't count," he said.

We took the tub to the house, and my wife said it was quite a good haul. "Did you get stung any?" she asked.

"No," said Uncle Timothy, "nothing to speak of. Bees are very friendly if you know how to handle them."

She said, "I was just wondering why you two happen to have each other's pants on."

ONE October night I loaded up the truck and told my wife if she wanted to get up at 2 a.m., I'd take her for a ride to Boston.

"I don't know if I want to," she said.

I said, "It's been almost a year—and maybe Boston has changed."

"It's been a very short time, and I've changed," she said. "Besides, in my condition, I better stick around home."

"I asked the doc," I said, "and he said it would be all right."

"But I don't want to go to Boston. I like it here."

"Nobody likes to go to Boston, but they've got people up there who want to buy stuff from us, and we can't afford to be choosy."

So she decided to go.

Uncle Timothy was alarmed at first. He said, "I've got a date to be a great-great-uncle, and you can't do this to me." But when he heard the doctor had given his consent, he mellowed up. He told her what Hiram Ricker used to say, that he always went to Boston to find the biggest fool in the world. "When he found him," Uncle said, "he always turned out to be a man who'd moved up there from Maine."

So before daylight, we were bowling along on the Newburyport Turnpike. She had a surprise figured out—we were going to her old home and pile things on the front doorstep before her folks woke up. We had boxes of apples, a barrel of

potatoes, some turnips and squash, eggs and cream, a box of
butter and some broilers all dressed and ready for the pan.
Then we'd go to the market and come back for dinner and see
how the gifts pleased.

For my part, I was curious to hear what she'd say about
what she saw, because if you can't take the country out of a
boy, maybe you couldn't take the city out of a girl.

After stopping by to astonish her folks, we drove to the
market and unloaded. She stood in an unrevealing bear coat
of Uncle Tim's and checked out the boxes. She certainly
looked as if she'd never been out of the woods before. A policeman came by and asked her, "Do you park on the sidewalk at home?"

"Sure do, when there are any. Do you mind?"

"Not a bit . . . and now if you could spare an apple . . ."

He tucked a half dozen deep in his dignity and departed. A
meat clerk sidled up and asked, "Suppose it's pretty cold up
in Maine now?"

She said, "No, nothing to worry about yet. It's been down
to ten below a few times, but we don't generally see any cold
weather until later."

"I suppose you're still haying up there?" he said.

"Just on Tuesdays," she said, and the subject was dropped.

After we had dinner and got thanked for the donations, we
kissed her folks good-bye and started back. She slept most of
the way and the ride had no adverse effect whatever on Uncle
Timothy's Christmas happiness.

Uncle Timothy wanted to know, first, if we got our money;
and next if we saw anything worth looking at. My wife gave
him a pipe she bought and said, "Feller said it first about
New York, but it's just as true of Boston. It's too far away
ever to amount to anything."

Uncle Timothy turned to me and said, "No question about
it, John—she's been naturalized."

Peace of Mind

A condensation from the book by

DR. *JOSHUA LOTH LIEBMAN*

Rabbi of Temple Israel of Boston;
well known also for his nation-wide radio broadcasts

PEACE OF MIND

Once, as a young man, I undertook to draw up a catalogue of the acknowledged "goods" of life. I set down my inventory of earthly desirables: *health, love, talent, power, riches* and *fame.* Then I proudly showed it to a wise elder.

"An excellent list," said my old friend, "and set down in not unreasonable order. But it appears that you have omitted the one important ingredient lacking which your list becomes an intolerable burden."

He crossed out my entire schedule. Then he wrote down three syllables: *peace of mind.*

'This is the gift that God reserves for His special protégés," he said. "Talent and health He gives to many. Wealth is commonplace, fame not rare. But peace of mind He bestows charily.

"This is no private opinion of mine," he explained. "I am merely paraphrasing from the Psalmists, Marcus Aurelius, Lao-tse. 'God, Lord of the universe,' say these wise ones, 'heap worldly gifts at the feet of foolish men. Give me the gift of the Untroubled Mind.'"

I found that difficult to accept; but now, after a quarter of a century of personal experience and professional observation, I have come to understand that peace of mind is the true goal of the considered life. I know now that the sum of all other possessions does not necessarily add up to peace of mind; on the other hand, I have seen this inner tranquillity flourish without the material supports of property or even the buttress of physical health. Peace of mind can transform a cottage into a spacious manor hall; the want of it can make a regal residence an imprisoning shell.

Analyze the prayers of mankind of all creeds, in every age— and their petitions come down to the common denominators of daily bread and inward peace. Such pleas for spiritual serenity must not be identified with ivory-tower escapism from the hurly-burly of life. Rather, they seek an inner equilibrium which enables us to overcome life's buffetings. Peace of mind cannot be won by any brief or superficial effort. Association with noble works—literary, musical, artistic—helps to promote inward peace, but these alone cannot wholly satisfy the dimensions of the soul. Certainly we shall not find peace in the furious pursuit of wealth which slips like quicksilver through our grasping fingers. And finally, not even in the sublime sharings of human love—that emotion which most powerfully conveys the illusion of perfect happiness—is peace of mind reliably to be found.

Where then shall we look for it? The key to the problem is to be found in Matthew Arnold's lines:

We would have inward peace
But will not look within . . .

But will not look within! Here, in a single phrase, our wilfullness is bared.

It is a striking irony that, while religious teaching emphasizes man's obligations to others, it says little about his obligation to himself. One of the great discoveries of modern psychology is that our attitudes toward ourselves are even more complicated than our attitudes toward others. The great commandment of religion, "Thou shalt love thy neighbor as thyself," might now be better interpreted to mean, "Thou shalt love thyself properly, and *then* thou wilt love thy neighbor."

A prominent social worker received a letter from a society woman who wanted to join in his crusade to help the poor of New York. She spoke at some length of her imperfections and ended by saying that perhaps her zeal for *his* cause would make up for her shortcomings. He wrote a brief reply: "Dear Madam, your truly magnificent shortcomings are too great. Nothing could prevent you from visiting them on victims of your humility. I advise that you love yourself more before you squander any love on others."

Some will argue that this is a dangerous doctrine. "Human beings love themselves too much already," they will say. "The true goal of life is the rejection of self in the service of others." There are errors in this estimate of human nature. Is it *true* that we are spontaneously good to ourselves? The evidence points in quite the opposite direction. We often treat ourselves more rigidly, more vengefully, than we do others. Suicide and more subtle forms of self-degradation such as alcoholism, drug addiction and promiscuity are extreme proofs of this. But all the streets of the world are teeming with everyday men and women who mutilate themselves spiritually by self-criticism; who go through life committing partial suicide—destroying their own talents, energies, creative qualities.

Such actions constitute a crime not only against ourselves but against society. He who does not have proper regard for his own capacities can have no respect for others. By loving oneself I do not mean coddling oneself, or indulging in self-glorification. I do, however, insist on the necessity of a proper self-regard as a prerequisite of the good and the moral life.

THERE ARE myriad ways in which we show contempt for ourselves rather than self-respect. Our feelings of inferiority, for instance: how often we attribute to our neighbors superior powers; we exaggerate their abilities, and sink into orgies of self-criticism. The fallacy here is that we see in others only the surface of assurance and poise. If we could look deeper and realize all men and women bear within themselves the scars of many a lost battle, we would judge our own failures less harshly.

To one who goes through life hypnotized by thoughts of inferiority, I would say: "In actuality, you are quite strong and wise and successful. You have done rather well in making a tolerable human existence out of the raw materials at your disposal. There are those who love and honor you for what you really are. Take off your dark-colored glasses, assume your place as an equal in the adult world, and realize that your strength is adequate to meet the problems of that world."

Another road to proper self-regard is the acceptance of our imperfections as well as our perfections. Most men have two pictures of their two selves in separate rooms. In one room is hung the portrait of their virtues, done in bright splashing colors. In the other room hangs the canvas of self-condemnation, painted equally as unrealistically in dark and morbid shades.

Instead of keeping these two pictures separate, we must look at them together and gradually blend them into one. We must begin to know and accept ourselves for what we are—a combination of strengths and weaknesses. It is enough if we learn to respect ourselves with all our shortcomings and achievements; to know that true love of self neither exaggerates its powers nor minimizes its worth.

The great thing is that as long as we live we have the privilege of growing. We can learn new skills, engage in new kinds of work, devote ourselves to new causes, make new friends. Accepting, then, the truth that we are capable in some directions and limited in others, that genius is rare, that mediocrity is the portion of most of us, let us remember also that we can and must *change* ourselves. Until the day of our death we can grow, we can tap hidden resources in our make-up.

Every person who wishes to attain peace of mind must learn the art of renouncing many other things in order to possess other things more fully. As young children, our wishes were sovereign; we had only to wail and the adult world hastened to fulfill our every desire. We knew, at that stage of development, very little about the postponement of satisfaction or the necessity of renunciation. But as we grow older we learn that every stage of human development calls upon us to weigh differing goods and to sacrifice some for the sake of others.

The philosopher Santayana pointed out that the great difficulty in life does not so much arise in the choice between good and evil as in the choice between good and good. In early life, however, we do not realize that one desire can be quite inconsistent with another. The young boy may vacillate between a dozen different plans for the future, but the mature man will have to renounce many careers in order to fulfill one. The same truth exists in the realm of emotions. It is fitting for the adolescent to transfer his love interest from one object of affection to another, but it is tragic when the grown man still plays the role of the adolescent. The man trying to wear youth's carefree clothing, the woman costuming her emotions in doll's dresses—these are pathetic figures. They have not yet learned that human growth means the closing of many doors before one great door can be opened— the door of mature love and of adult achievement.

THE FIRST fundamental truth about our individual lives is the indispensability of love to every human being. By "love" I mean relatedness to some treasured person or group, the feeling of belonging to a larger whole, of being of value to others.

Our interdependence with others is the most encompassing fact of human reality: our personalities are made by our contacts with others. A boy may catch the contagion of courage from his father, or receive the misery of fear from his mother. In a spiritual sense, we digest our heroes and heroines and make their way of life part of our own emotional substance. Thus every saint and every sinner affects those whom he will never see, because his words and his deeds stamp themselves upon the soft clay of human nature everywhere. There is, therefore, a duty which falls upon all of us—to become free, loving, warm, coöperative, affirmative personalities. If we understand this relatedness with others we shall get on noticeably better with our family, friends, business associates—and ourselves.

Next to bread, it is simple kindness that all mortals most hunger for. In times of catastrophe and disaster it finds a natural expression, good to contemplate in men's actions. But too often it is lacking in our daily lives. Many of us are dictatorial or bad-tempered toward others—employes, sales-persons, domestic help. "I call no man charitable," said Thoreau, "who forgets that his barber, cook and hostler are made of the same human clay as himself." When we fail to be kind to all men, we destroy our own peace of mind. The jeweled pivot on which our lives must turn is the realization that every person we meet during the day is a dignified, essential human soul.

In the exchange of simple affection lies the true secret of marriage—which at its best is mutual encouragement. When we are accepted, approved, *needed* by those who know all about us and like us anyway, we have the first inkling of the peace that transcends understanding.

To love one's neighbors is to achieve an inner tolerance for the uniqueness of others, to resist the temptation to private imperialism. Among our renunciations we must renounce undue possessiveness in relation to friends, children—yes, even our loves. The world is full of private imperialists—the father who forces his artistic son into his business, or the mother who rivets her daughter to her service by chains of pity, subtly refusing the daughter a life of her own.

When we insist that others conform to our ideas of what is proper, good, acceptable, we show that we ourselves are not certain of the rightness of our inner pattern. He who is sure of himself is deeply willing to let others be themselves. He who is unstable in his own character must reassure himself by trying to compress others into his mold. We display true love when we cease to demand that our loved one become a revised edition of ourselves.

Every normal person experiences countless fears and worries. But it is possible to master these enemies of serenity.

It is true in a sense that man is blessed by his capacity to know fear. Fear is often the stimulus to growth, the goad to invention. Moreover, fear experienced in the presence of real danger is desirable. But are not most of our fears groundless? Scrutinize that large body of fears coming under the heading of "personal anxiety." Sometimes we are afraid about our

health; we worry about our hearts, our lungs, our blood
pressure, our insomnia. We begin to feel our pulse to find
evidence of disease in every innocent or meaningless symp-
tom. Or we become concerned about our personalities. We
feel insecure, bemoan our failures, and imagine that others
scorn or disapprove of us.

We must realize, of course, that our fears may disguise
themselves. Some deep self-distrust may appear as an un-
reasoning fear of high places, of closed rooms. Again, our
fears cunningly cloak themselves in the garments of physical
pain. The new science of psychosomatic medicine has
demonstrated that a whole gamut of illnesses, from the common cold to crippling arthritis, can often be traced to mental
rather than physical troubles. It is so much easier to be sick
than courageous! The ill health enjoyed by many chronic
invalids is no more than an elaborate disguise for deep-seated
fears.

Many such feelings of insecurity are hangovers from childhood when we really *were* inadequate and inferior, and knew
that there was a vast difference between our weakness and
the strength of the adult world. This difference disappears as
we grow, but our childhood is a blackmailer that makes us
pay over and over again for failures or mistakes that long
ago have been outgrown.

Are we obsessed perhaps with a fear of death or the thought
of punishment in an afterlife? Let us come to see that such
fear is a projection from some early experience when we were
punished by a parent, locked in a room, left alone. Are we
continually haunted by the disapproval of others, frightened
of social rejection? Let us look at these anxieties in the light
of maturity, see that our neighbors are no less fallible than
ourselves, and realize further that in the adult world we
should not expect to be coddled as we were in childhood.

A source of hope lies also in the fact that our moods are
temporary. This is a hard lesson to learn. When we are tired,
every pinprick becomes the stab of a knife. But it is natural
and normal to have depressed moods, and we should always
remember that we will come out into the light again. We

human beings are very tough organisms, able to withstand many shocks, to shed many tears, to live through many tragedies without breaking. Let us learn not to take the depression of the day or month as the permanent state of our life.

IT is natural to experience fear concerning our economic and social future. Countless people are frightened of unemployment or the collapse of their careers. These fears are very real. But firmly attached to them are highly neurotic residues. Americans particularly are engaged in a marathon race in which the runners are extremely anxious about those panting at their heels and envious of those ahead. This relentless race for economic success is the source of many breakdowns and premature cardiac deaths.

A yearning for achievement is an admirable attribute of human nature. Where, then, do we go wrong? We err in the excessive energy that we devote not to real accomplishment but to neurotic combat. A man may have a home, possessions, a charming family, and yet find all these things ashy to his taste because he has been outstripped by some other runners in the race for material things. It is not that he does not possess enough for his own wants but that others possess more. It is the *more* that haunts him and makes him minimize his real achievements.

The time has come to say: "I am no longer going to be interested in how much power or wealth another man possesses so long as I can attain sufficient for the dignity and security of my family and myself. I am going to set my goals for myself rather than borrow them from others. I refuse any longer to destroy my peace of mind by striving only for money; I will also judge myself in the scale of goodness and culture."

WE HAVE learned that unexpressed emotions ultimately have their vengeance in the form of mental and physical illness. This truth illuminates for us the problem of achieving peace of mind in the face of bereavement and grief. Dr. Erich Lindemann, in clinical work at the Massachusetts General Hospital with hundreds of grief patients, has uncovered the basic fact that to repress real feelings of grief may lead to morbid reactions later. Dr. Lindemann's patients included some who developed severe illness or depressions years after the loss of a loved one. Amazing cures of the mental and physical ills resulted when patients were persuaded to express the pain and sorrow that should normally have found outlet before.

How absurd is that notion which has gained currency in modern society that men and women must repress emotional outbursts. It is not those outbursts but the avoidance of them which scars the fabric of the soul.

The first law, then, which should be followed in the time of the loss of a loved one is: *give way to as much grief as you actually feel*. Do not be ashamed of your emotions; released now, they will be the instrument of your later healing.

The discoveries of psychiatry—of how essential it is to express rather than to repress grief, to talk about one's loss with friends and companions, to move step by step from inactivity to activity again—remind us that the ancient teachers of Judaism had an intuitive wisdom about human nature which our more sophisticated age has forgotten. The Bible records how open and unashamed was the expression of sorrow on the part of Abraham and Jacob and David. Our ancestors publicly wept, wore sackcloth, tore their garments, and fasted. It is unfortunate that in our time the expression of honest emotion has become taboo. Let us understand that the unrepressed experience of pain somehow has a curative function and that any evasive detour around normal sorrow will bring us later to a tragic abyss.

Armed with such knowledge, if we are courageous and resolute we can live as our lost loved ones would wish us to live—not empty, morose, self-centered and self-pitying but as brave and undismayed servants of the greater life.

It is not often that we are brave enough to come face to face with the thought of our own mortality. Yet man is not free in life unless he is also free from the fear of death.

As far as our own deaths are concerned, we should remember what science teaches about the process of dying. We
needlessly frighten ourselves with anticipated horrors which
never come to pass. As the famous physician, Sir William
Osler, put it, "In my wide clinical experience, most human
beings die really without pain or fear. There is as much
oblivion about the last hours as about the first."

Montaigne said a wonderfully wise thing about this:
"When I have been in perfect health, I have been much more
afraid of sickness than when I have really felt the sickness.
. . . Death is not to be feared. It is a friend."

No, death is not the enemy of life but its friend, for it is the
knowledge that our years are limited which makes them so
precious. Plato was right when he declared that infinite life
on this earth would not be desirable, for a never-ending
existence would be without heights or depths, without challenge or achievement. It is profoundly true that the joy of
our striving and the zest of our aspirations would vanish if
earthly immortality were our lot.

At the same time, we dare not ignore the hunger in the
human heart for some kind of existence beyond this narrow
span of life. There is an almost universal feeling that God
could not shut the door completely upon our slowly developed talents—that there must be realms where we can
use the powers achieved here. And one should not lightly
dismiss the thoughts of the philosophers who insist that
there is nothing inherently impossible about life in un-
dreamed dimensions; that just as infrared rays are invisible
to our eyes, so a creative, growing universe might well have
hidden unsuspected continents beyond the perception of our
senses.

Moreover, we should always remember that there are
other forms of immortality besides personal survival. Man
displays perhaps his most remarkable and his most unselfish
genius when he turns from the thought of individual immortality and finds inspiration in the immortality of the
human race. The more we concentrate upon the immortality
of mankind, strangely enough, the richer becomes our own

individual life. As we link ourselves to the heroes and sages and martyrs, the poets and thinkers of every race, we come to share the wisest thoughts, the noblest ideals, the imperishable music of the centuries. Poor, indeed, is the man who lives only in his own time. Rich is the man who participates in the riches of the past and the promises of the future.

Both science and religion teach us, at last, that the obstacles to serenity are not external. They lie within ourselves.

If we acquire the art of proper self-love; if, aided by religion, we free ourselves from shadow fears, and learn honestly to face grief and to transcend it; if we flee from immaturity and boldly shoulder adult responsibility; if we appraise and accept ourselves as we really are, how then can we fail to create a good life for ourselves? For then inward peace will be ours.

LOST
BOUNDARIES

Condensed from the book by

W. L. WHITE

Author of "They Were Expendable," "Report on the Russians," etc.

IN this true and fully authenticated story, W. L. White, one of the country's ablest reporters, focuses attention on a certain family in a New England town. The intimate revelations of the narrative have important implications in every section of the United States.

Mr. White's story will be made into a feature motion picture by Louis de Rochemont, originator of *The March of Time*, and a producer who has launched a new and vigorous trend in movie-making with such realistic film successes as *Fighting Lady*, *The House on 92nd Street* and *Boomerang*. The tale of the Johnston family seems destined to awaken the nation to one little-discussed phase of our national life.

BEFORE you learn what Albert Johnston was told at the age of 16 and why he was not told it before, you should know something about his background. It would be dull but accurate to say that, until he was told, we are dealing with a normal New England boy. From the time Albert was four, his father had been the leading country doctor in the little town of Gorham, New Hampshire, and here Albert had played over the hills, learned to ski, and camped out on long Boy Scout hikes. He made the high school honor roll, was elected president of his class, and took piano lessons—a normal American boy and Yankee both in his outlook and in his flat accent.

This was also true of his heredity, which had been for many generations thoroughly American except for two German great-grandparents, who, his mother said, accounted for the fact that Albert was darker than most of his schoolmates, with brown eyes, a high prominent nose and dark curly hair.

When Albert was 15 the family moved down to Keene, bigger than Gorham but like it a typical New England town, with its 200-year-old Congregational Church on the main square, its white spire high above the green elm leaves. His father, who had taken a year off to study Roentgenology at Harvard, was now working in Keene's leading hospital and Albert, who was planning on Dartmouth, was sent to nearby Mt. Hermon School.

One of Albert's schoolmates there was a Negro, and since Negroes in rural New Hampshire were a curiosity—except as occasionally a summer visitor brought along a Negro cook—Charlie Duncan, the son of Todd Duncan who sang in *Porgy and Bess*, was a surprise to Albert. Charlie, who was popular in Mt. Hermon, and who later became a leader of his Dartmouth class, was brilliant in his studies. He was also on the

148

ski team and a year ahead of Albert, who, toward the end of his junior year, was elected captain for the next.

But at this point there was a little incident. When the coach at first failed to include Albert in the group which was to represent Mt. Hermon at the big meet at Meriden, it was Charlie Duncan who told the team, "I think Peanut [Albert's school nickname] is a better skier than I am," and offered to give up his place. In the end the coach relented and promised both could go. So when Albert went home for the week-end he was still bubbling over this schoolboy honor.

This home is one of the most beautiful in Keene, occupying a large corner lot on one of Keene's finest residential streets, but on this particular week-end there was trouble, as the boy could sense. His father, who had seen the war coming, had early answered the Navy's call for volunteers, and had been promised a commission as Lieutenant Commander. Now there seemed to be some hitch. The Navy seemed to be out. Dad was all lathered up about it, talking a lot with Mom. Neither had told him what it was about. Dad had already had a couple of drinks. Probably the Navy had decided he was too old, or too fat, or something like that.

Albert couldn't see that it mattered much, and he decided he would take a bath and then call a couple of girls to see how things were for a date tonight. Certainly it didn't matter as much as the news that he was, after all, going with the ski team.

As he started the tub in the room which adjoined his parents' bedroom he began telling them of Charlie Duncan's offer to give up his place for him and he remembers how, as he praised Charlie Duncan, his father "beamed all up." And then said to Mom: "I'm going to tell that boy."

His mother almost screamed from the bedroom: "No! No! Don't do it! Don't ever do it!"

"I've got to do it," his father answered. Presently he came to the bathroom door.

"Turn off the water," he said. "Do you know something, boy?"

"No, what?" said Albert.

"Well, you're colored."

Albert still remembers the funny sensation that went through him, and for a minute he didn't say anything. Then he said, "Well, how come?"

"I'm colored and your mother's colored."

Albert had his shirt off, but he did not continue dressing for the date, because he knew he would not want to call a girl tonight. He walked slowly into his parents' room.

There his father explained that his own mother was colored, and also his father, although he didn't look it. His grandparents on Mom's side were colored, too, although they also didn't look it; in fact, all four grandparents were colored, but all could get by.

He must not tell anyone of this, because of what it might do to Dad, and the three younger children hadn't been told yet. They explained what "passing" was, and how Dad had had to do it, not because he was ashamed of being colored, but only to make their living.

Then his mother asked him, now that he knew, how he felt about it.

Albert said he felt proud of it, and that he hoped to do something for the Negro. And his father was so pleased he jumped up and shook Albert's hand, even though Albert was only 16. It was the first time this had ever happened in exactly this way, and of course it pleased Albert. But as his father and mother now began telling him the whole story of how it had happened, the story of both their lives tumbling out at once in their excitement, he kept feeling more and more dazed.

Thyra Johnston, Albert's mother, had lived in New Orleans until she was nine. Her grandfather, James Baumann, Sr., had been shipping commissioner of the Port of New Orleans. He had originally come from Germany, and in New Orleans had married a colored woman. Her father, Sam Baumann, had a job as a clerk in the New Orleans post office, but when the Democrats elected Woodrow Wilson in 1912, her father, fearing that segregation in New Orleans might extend even to the federal offices, obtained a transfer to Boston. He leased a duplex in Roxbury for his family and there the Baumann children, who were very fair, went through grade school and high school, the only Negroes in their class, and mixing with everyone. The family also had Negro friends among Boston's small Negro colony, but they kept these separate from the others.

In appearance Thyra Johnston has a creamy, soft skin, wavy light-brown hair, and light blue eyes. In high school she had taken the commercial course, so after she graduated she went to work as a stenographer for the Mellin's Food company. On her application blank she had put down "White."

Her father had always opposed her going out with dark men. When Joe Carter, the dark Negro halfback of Brown University, invited her to go with a group of his colored friends to the Brown-Harvard game, her father forbade her to go for fear she might be seen and recognized.

"My dad was fair and handsome," says Thyra. "He said he had brought us up from New Orleans to get us out of it. I liked Joe very much, but my parents felt that if I married a dark man I would be 'going back.'"

She met Dr. Johnston through some colored friends during a summer vacation trip to Chicago in 1923, while he was still a premedic student at the University of Chicago. He was a little darker than she, yet not so dark that he had any trouble buying orchestra seats to see the Duncan sisters in *Topsy and Eva*, although Chicago theaters were quite biased against colored people. The day before she left he asked her to marry him, which she did that Christmas in Boston.

Albert Johnston had been born in Chicago on August 17, 1900, and registered on his birth certificate as a Negro, although his father, who was agent for a Chicago real estate company and had to pass as white to hold this job, did not encourage colored people to visit the house.

In high school all of his friends, including girls, were white. "At first," he said, "I found colored girls distasteful, but presently found my own race more interesting than the white. As a colored student at the University of Chicago, I wasn't invited to attend social functions. But no one seemed to mind this social exclusion. We had our own fraternity house, and our own life."

Rush Medical College then had a quota of two Negroes per class of whom he was one, and the other was Ralph Scull, who was for years the only colored teacher at Rush. "I was well treated by both the students and the faculty," he remembers. "No one is prejudiced against you if they know you."

However, the two Negroes did not serve along with the rest of the students as junior interns at nearby Presbyterian Hospital, for fear the white patients there would object. Remembering this, Dr. Johnston now smiles. "I have since practiced medicine for 18 years," he says, "and have never had a colored patient."

After his marriage, medical school was a struggle, and when little Albert, Jr., was born, Thyra Johnston had to stay behind in Boston while the young father did his best to support himself, pay his tuition and send something to his family, by working nights in the post office and as a porter during vacations.

Upon graduation, before he could get his M.D. degree, it was necessary for him to intern at some first-rate hospital. Negro hospitals were not ordinarily so classed by Rush Medical, so Johnston wrote to what he thought were the most liberal hospitals in the country, hoping they would take him in. Several seemed anxious to have him until, on personal interview, they found he was colored.

Finally he was accepted by Maine General Hospital at Portland. They didn't ask about his color and a diploma from Rush proves nothing of its bearer's racial background— proves only that he has the brains to finish one of the nation's stiffest and best medical schools.

At Maine General, Dr. Johnston was well liked, and got along fine "as soon as I got over my fear that my racial identity would be recognized." After that he danced and played tennis with everyone as the other interns did.

Later they told him, "You know when you first came, some of us thought you were a Filipino, or maybe a Hawaiian or a Jew—we didn't know what you were." And Dr. Johnston smiled along with them. So long as they didn't care enough to ask directly, why should he tell?

When he finished his internship, this hospital chief offered him a job as pathologist, but the head of the board of registration, Dr. Adam Leighton, told him of an even better opening in Gorham, N. H., where an old friend of his, Dr. H. H. Bryant, had recently died, leaving a fine practice.

Young Dr. Johnston found it even better than he expected. Dr. Bryant's widow would sell his office equipment and good will for $1000. To finance this, he found he could borrow $2000 at the Gorham bank on the strength of the good impression he made, and he immediately stepped into a busy country practice.

But it was a practice which required some understanding and Dr. Johnston will never forget his first case, when after having driven all day on winding White Mountain roads through a sleet storm and arriving in Gorham exhausted, he was called out at 3 a.m., only to find his patient, a gnarled old Yankee farmer, sitting in the parlor smoking.

"What's the matter?" the doctor asked.

"Piles."

"How long you had 'em?"

"Eighteen years."

"Any worse now than they have been?"

"Nope."

The New Hampshire Yankees simply wanted to know if their new doctor was lazy, or if he really would come when called. After that he was called constantly, and, with money rolling in, he felt secure enough to send for his wife and family.

There was quite a little prejudice in the town, but mostly between the old Yankee stock and the French Catholics who were coming down from Canada. As for Negroes, it didn't come up. For as far as Gorham knew, there weren't any. Apparently no one suspected, yet it worried Thyra Johnston, who kept wondering what they were going to do when the children grew up.

"Maybe we won't have to do anything," Dr. Johnston told her.

Their colored friends down in Boston knew the Johnstons were "passing" for white in Gorham but they were used to this and did nothing to hurt them. Some of them didn't like the idea, but these, Thyra Johnston points out, were "mostly too dark to 'pass' themselves."

Before long they were growing into the town. The popular new doctor was presently elected to the school board, as well as to the Rotary Club and the Masonic Lodge. The Congregational minister had asked to enroll the children in the cradle class. Thyra Johnston became active in civic work and also in the bridge club, and was twice asked to take the presidency of the Gorham Women's Club.

As they made real friends—ones who might not care much, even if the Colored Thing did get out—they felt at last secure enough to move out of rented quarters into a house of their own. The three-story house they bought was on a hill, and included a large reception hall and two parlors. They lent its yard for the Christmas tree of the Congregational Church and the house for its Christmas social, and all of Gorham came. The church ladies made more money that year than ever they had before. It was just as crowded for their New Year's reception, and soon it easily was the gayest and most popular house in town.

There was one disturbing incident that summer when Thyra Johnston's father (no one would dream he was not all white) came up from Boston for a visit, and one afternoon while the rest of the family was swimming he fell into conversation with a stranger on the bank.

"See that lady down there?" the man had said to him. "They say she's a real mulattress."

"You must be very much mistaken," said Thyra's father, "because that lady is my daughter."

The Johnstons now knew that people must have been talking. But since the father reported the stranger had not said it in a hateful way, only as a matter of curiosity, they hoped it might not make too terribly much difference if it did get out.

The family had been in the new house three years when they went to Boston for a year so that Dr. Johnston, who had been offered a position as a Roentgenologist at a nearby hospital, could take a postgraduate course in this specialty at the Harvard Medical School—the first Negro so far as he knows ever to study Roentgenology there.

To avoid having the children run into old Negro friends in Boston they took an apartment in Brookline. Little Albert, who was now 11, went to Lawrence School and here first ran into race prejudice. There was a fairly high percentage of Jews there and, because he was darker than most, he was immediately asked "Are you a kike?" But it hadn't seemed to him important, any more than the time back in Gorham when his mother had become unaccountably angry because in teasing their French-Canadian maid he had called her a "Frenchman" and she had spiritedly retorted by calling him a "little pickaninny."

However, he was glad when the year was over and he could go back to school in Gorham. In high school he quickly made the honor roll and, although at first he was not good at skiing, he managed to take second place in slaloming. He was doing remarkably well in piano, too, When he played as his little brother sang "Bless This House" at the Congregational Church Children's Day service, it not only moved the people to tears, but when it was over they clapped right out in church.

Their minister, who had been a graduate of Mt. Hermon School in western Massachusetts, recommended this school for Albert. And just as the application came through, his father received his appointment at the Keene hospital as a result of his X-ray work at Harvard.

It was a struggle to leave Gorham, with the family now so securely settled, and Dr. Johnston so well known that even the dogs didn't bark when he came to the door. But it was a step up in his profession which he could not fail to take. In Keene some of the Congregational ladies called early, but it was not the same. Keene was a larger and therefore colder town, lacking the village intimacy, and for a while the Johnstons again worried about "the Colored Thing."

At Mt. Hermon, Albert's first roommate was a belligerent Irish boy (he did not stay long) who kept looking curiously at Albert's olive skin and asking, "What *are* you? A kike or a Greek or what? No? Well I bet you've got some nigger in you." This didn't bother Albert, but now and then he wondered how a little German blood could make such a difference.

After the Johnston family had lived three years in Keene they felt secure enough to buy the big house they had been renting on one of Keene's best residential streets. But meanwhile the doctor, who had been following the papers closely, realized war was coming. Long before Pearl Harbor there were appeals to doctors to join up, and twice the Navy had approached him with offers of a commission.

"There's no question about my being qualified," he explained to his wife. After all, wasn't he a member of the American Board of Radiology, as well as the AMA? Of course, had he been known as a Negro he might not have been elected to either, but this had not come out. "But if the Navy does accept me," he went on, "people can say what they like about us, but we will have given our children a real background!"

The doctor was deeply moved by the war and anxious to help if his country got in, so although he knew that candidates for all commissions were thoroughly investigated, and that he might well be exposed all around, he decided to chance it and went down to Boston for his physical. He came back greatly elated. The Navy had been most anxious to have him, as in the whole country there were only 2500 radiologists, and many of these were over-age.

Shortly after this the doctor received a visit from a neat young man who explained that he had been sent by the Bureau of Naval Intelligence to ask a few questions. He then consulted a paper. "You graduated from the University of Chicago in 1924?"

"Yes," said the doctor.

"We understand that, even though you are registered as white, you have colored blood in your veins."

"Who knows what blood any of us has in his veins?" said the doctor.

The neat young man, who had been asked to sit down, now got up. "Thank you very much, Doctor," he said. "That is all we want to know," and he left.

Thyra Johnston tried to be helpful. "Maybe they only wanted to be sure what you look like—that you aren't really black."

But it was useless, for a few days later the letter came from the Bureau of Navigation saying that it was "unable to approve your application because of your inability to meet physical requirements."

Meanwhile it was getting embarrassing with his friends and with other doctors, who knew how anxious he had been to get into uniform. What could he say?

If the Navy and the "White" Army would not have him, Thyra Johnston urged, then why not the "Colored" Army? Better to go frankly and openly with his own people than not to go at all. He took the matter up through colored channels, clear up to Judge William Hastie in the War Department, telling them the whole story, but finally a letter arrived in which his supposedly powerful Negro friends admitted that this too was hopeless. And that evening little Albert returned from Mt. Hermon with his praise for Charlie Duncan, the Negro who had offered to give up his place.

Now up to the moment that Albert had turned off the hot water in the tub to hear what his father had to say, he had been like any other New England boy with most of life before him, during which he could eat and sleep where he chose if he could afford it, ask any girl he liked for a date, plan any career which pleased him and follow it to the limit of his ability.

Of course he had told his father he was proud to be colored. And he *was* proud, only what exactly did being colored mean?

He hadn't changed, had he? So why not keep right on as before? Nobody was supposed to know, so why not skip it? Yet when he got back to school he found you couldn't skip it. Here he was, a senior now, and in the choir, the glee club, assistant editor of the Senior Yearbook, and captain of the ski team. But what would happen if everybody knew? Maybe not much. But you couldn't be sure. He quit having dates at the seminary as the other boys did. He didn't exactly decide not to, but every time he thought of calling a girl, then he thought, suppose she found out?

The previous year he had made the honor roll but now his marks began to slip. Why work hard to prepare for some job when you got out? Suppose they found out? What kind of jobs could Negroes hold? Maybe he was studying all the wrong things. Presently he had the medical department worried with a curious "nervous" rash, which wouldn't clear up.

But in the spring they had a seminar on American and foreign relations, and for this Albert really worked. He got from the library a lot of material on the American Negro and presented it so eloquently that they asked, without suspecting, "Why are *you* so interested in this?"

He became obsessed with the suspicion that perhaps there might be discrimination against Negroes even at Mt. Hermon. Charlie Duncan had been admitted, but was there a quota? If 20 or 30 Negro boys qualified, would all be let in? He was assured they would be and for a while he felt better. But, as he remembers it, "I got out of Mt. Hermon in an awful state."

Although his first choice of colleges had been Dartmouth, he also applied to Williams and went there for a personal interview where he was rejected because, they explained, his marks weren't high enough. It was true these had dropped badly yet they were still above college entrance requirements, so his father's reaction was, "They must have looked you up."

Which was true? Maybe they didn't have to look him up—perhaps the interview had spoiled it. Hadn't the French-

Canadian maid once called him a "little pickaninny"? And what of his first-year Mt. Hermon roommate who kept saying "I bet you've got *some* nigger in you"? Now that he knew he was colored, he began looking for Negroid speech inflections which occasionally would slip out of someone seemingly white, and then wondering if others did the same with him.

In the middle of this came a letter from Dartmouth accepting him, so that was over.

But in Dartmouth he seemed to be out of it, as he had never felt before in any other place or school. Most of the boys were looking ahead to the war and training for commissions. But of course this seemed out of the question for Albert.

He was, he remembers, in a terrible state of mind, and began to get queer notions, like going up on top of a high tower (it was, he felt, the only place he could study) and then being afraid he would jump off. At other times he felt he wanted to die. His marks dropped off, and at last his father took him out of college and sent him to a well-known Negro psychiatrist in Boston. But the psychiatrist could find nothing seriously wrong.

Then he decided to try the Navy. His father warned him he would never get by the front door, but he passed the exam as a hospital apprentice and went to Rhode Island for training. In all of his tests Albert's marks were so unusually high that they asked if he would like to take radio training, but he refused this, for suppose they sent him to some naval base in the South?

So with nothing to do all day but scrub decks and think he got more depressed and more jittery. And one night in December, he remembers, "the whole bottom seemed to fall out of my stomach, and I began shaking, not knowing what I was afraid of.

"I was sent to the psychiatric ward of the hospital, and for five days they would allow me no razors, knives or forks. Finally they brought me out for tests, and I helped them in every way I could, telling them everything except about that colored business. They asked me how I would like to leave the Navy, and I told them that I thought I would. Actually I was overjoyed.

"While waiting for the discharge papers to come through, I often would talk politics with the other patients, and I guess I would usually bring up the Negro question. I remember one day in the heat of an argument I came right out and told them I had Negro blood. In talking about the Negro I would say he should have social equality, and some of the patients said I would be strung up for such thoughts."

His mother, after he got home, was also worried about his point of view because, as she explains, "I just call that rabble-rousing."

His father was even more gloomy, as he had had high hopes for this son who now seemed not to care what he did or what happened to him. They finally persuaded the boy to take a job in an ink factory in Keene, but he soon left it.

There seemed to be only one thing he liked to do. For three years during his Mt. Hermon days he had not touched the piano at which he had been so skillful as a boy. Now he went back to it, and, for the first time, wrote something of his own, a sad little tune which somehow could find no ending.

But by now his father, who was very angry at the way things were drifting, decided something should be done. He even planned to have Albert committed for treatment in a veterans' hospital but when Albert's mother heard of this she was furious. She said the family should stick by the boy—not put him in the hands of others.

Yet, what could a family do for him? The melancholy moods continued. "I was scared of people, and I didn't know why," says Albert. "I wandered from this to that and there was constant friction with my father."

And then, just after Easter, Walt, an old friend of Albert's from school days in Gorham, called to say he was hitchhiking to Syracuse, New York, and invited Albert to go along. So why not?

If you are with an old friend for several days and have something on your mind, it's pretty hard not to tell him, so by the time they got to Syracuse Albert told Walt everything.

And the funny thing was that Walt not only didn't give a damn but wasn't even interested.

"All right, so you're part colored. But what difference does it make? Why are you so worked up about it?"

It was like putting down a huge load which he had carried for more than a year.

In Syracuse the boys decided to go on to Buffalo to see Niagara Falls and then on to Cleveland. In Cleveland Albert had an uncle who lived in the Negro section and was a bartender in a wealthy Cleveland club. They looked him up and he got them both jobs in defense factories. After work they would go to night clubs in Cleveland's Harlem. "We had a great time," says Albert. "Lots of them were good, some of them were low, but it was all interesting." And here for the first time he met a colored girl who fascinated him—it was just a flash, yet it was the first.

But presently they were restless, particularly Albert. He had other relatives out on the West Coast he wanted to see. He wasn't scared any more, only curious. So why didn't they start out and really see America? Walt thought it was a swell idea.

They arrived in Los Angeles half starved and almost in rags but Albert got $12 for his wrist watch and they bought a meal, and a pair of pants each and then set out to find Albert's relatives.

Foremost among these was Albert's uncle Fred and his wife. Albert knew that Uncle Fred was extremely light, and had married a woman somewhat darker than he. Also that they had a son, and lived near the Sugar Hill section of the Negro district, so called from Sugar Hill in Harlem where the well-to-do Negroes live.

"I got a big surprise," Albert remembers. "It was a large district with fine palm trees, well-trimmed and watered lawns, three-story houses as nice as any I had seen. When you ring the doorbell a colored maid usually answers. In this district live Negro doctors, lawyers, engineers and merchants, most of whom make their money not from the whites but from other Negroes.

"I first met my aunt, whom I had never seen. But when I asked for my uncle I found that much had happened. He had owned a business and had been fairly well-to-do. Also, he had been interested in various welfare organizations. But he found that his enemies were saying that he wasn't really interested in helping his race, that he was out only for himself, and had become a 'white man's Negro.'

"There may have been other things behind it, but this incident decided him. He divorced his wife, married a white girl, moved to another state, and was now 'passing' as white. My aunt, although terribly wounded by all this, had never betrayed his secret. No Negro ever does, although they bitterly resent it if a Negro really has 'gone over on the other side.'

"They will condone a Negro who 'passes' for white only if it is temporary and for the purpose of getting an education or holding a job. But they expect them to spend their social life with Negroes. 'It's all right to pass for a job, so long as you socialize with us.' they say.

"The number of crossbred people, many of whom now 'pass' for white, is greatly on the increase. The last census listed 12,800,000 registered Negroes in the United States, but some Negroes believe there are as many as 13,000,000 additional crossbred people not officially registered as Negroes, many of whom now 'pass' for white and some of whom do not even know they are colored.

"In our own family, we can count 50 who are regarded as white. There are many thousands of colored people, even in the South, who 'pass' as white. Some may be rather dark, yet they travel freely on southern Pullmans and buses because the companies are now fearful of making mistakes, since they have been sued by Greeks, Jews and other dark-skinned people.

"Many light-colored Negro men 'pass,' as my uncle did—you never see them again. I found that the one ambition of my 17-year-old cousin is to 'pass.' His mother, who couldn't do it herself, is very much against this. After all, she lost a husband who went 'on the other side.' This urge to 'pass' is very strong in light-colored boys.

"I also found that light-colored Negroes are often prejudiced against darker ones, and many will not associate with someone completely black. The majority of Negro political leaders are light. People try to say that this is because they are smarter, because of their mixed blood, but actually it is because it is easier for them to deal with the whites. In the arts and sciences, however, light-skinned Negroes certainly do not predominate, and sociologists find just as high a degree of intelligence among black as they do among the light-colored men.

"In general, when barriers and boundaries begin to break down, white people usually prefer light-skinned Negroes to dark ones. And prejudice always increases with the numbers of the minority. If there are only one or two Negro families in a town, usually there is little or no prejudice. It grows directly in proportion to their numbers. Also, the closer you get to marital relations, the stronger it becomes.

"During my trip across the country I think I learned the exact degree of prejudice in the average white American. They did not know I was colored, and the average man would say, 'Yes, the Negro deserves an opportunity. I know of many intelligent, hard-working Negroes. But we think they must keep their place.'

"But when they come to know Negroes, this prejudice usually fades. For instance, a friend tells me that while she was working in an office in Boston one of the clerks was a girl from South Carolina who threatened to quit if the firm hired a Negro girl. The girl was hired anyway, and two or three weeks later the two were going out to lunch together.

"Most white people are ashamed of prejudices and often try not to show them. For instance, if I bring a colored boy into a college dormitory room, everybody makes an extra effort to be polite. They will all get up, say 'I'm very glad to know you,' and ask him to sit down. Whereas if I bring in a strange white boy, they will scarcely look up. All Negroes who have had much contact with whites are just as accustomed to this 'over-politeness' as they are to open prejudice.

"My aunt in Los Angeles gave both Walt and me a warm

welcome. But when I told her that Walt was white, she was embarrassed. She had a very good social position with the Negroes of Los Angeles' Sugar Hill district and she explained to us that, if it were known that she had a white boy staying in her house, she would get a lot of criticism.

"She finally solved it by saying, 'We must present him as part colored and a cousin.' Walt had no objections to 'passing' in order to avoid race prejudice—in fact he was very much tickled by the whole idea.

"She bought us some proper clothes and then gave a big party for us—inviting all the sons and daughters of leading doctors and lawyers of the Sugar Hill section. All were good, upstanding, respectable people. They were of all degrees in color: one was as black as that telephone, others were as light as glass curtains, and still others are what Negroes call 'mariny,' which is a definite type in between—golden skin with crinkly hair.

"It was the first Negro party I had ever attended. Negroes are in general more friendly to strangers than are whites, but their social parties tend to be more formal. All the girls were primped up in long gowns, and everything was done and served in an impressive manner.

"The stock question at a Negro party, after you are asked where you come from, is 'How do people treat you there?' or 'There aren't many Negroes there, are there?' or 'Are you passing?'

"The rest of the talk was as intelligent as you would hear at any New England party, except that there was of course a lot of emphasis on the racial question. They discussed music and books and colleges—the usual stuff that people of our age talk, but always in terms of Black and White. This I wasn't used to.

"I was asked, 'What college do you go to?' (This is always a very important question.) And when I said Dartmouth, it immediately made me a big wheel. They were fascinated by the fact that I had only recently learned that I was colored, and that my father's practice was entirely confined to white people. And they were particularly astounded by the amount of life insurance Dad carried, because they said many companies either refuse altogether to insure Negroes or will let them carry only small amounts.

"Top Negro society is, as I have said, stiffer and more formal than anything I had been used to in New Hampshire, and after this and other parties my aunt often scolded me for being too exuberant. And I began running into taboos. I would mention having been to Ciro's, the Mocambo, or some other fashionable night club up on Hollywood's Sunset Strip. But then a silence would fall and I could see that they didn't like it. They would say coldly, 'We don't go there.'

"My viewpoint was, why should I stop doing things I had done all my life simply because I had been told I had Negro blood? But the Los Angeles Negroes had, for the most part, come originally from the South and had lived as Negroes all their lives. They avoided mingling with whites, because they felt they were not wanted, and therefore enjoyed themselves more freely in Negro places.

It was shortly after I arrived that I met Helene. She was going to the University of California at Berkeley, was a brilliant student, and very popular in Los Angeles. She was beautiful—a little darker than I was, and had a brilliant mind. She sparkled but had a serious side, too. She wanted to do everything she could to help the cause of the Negro, and all her studies at Berkeley were with this in mind.

"Her father was dead, and her mother had then been remarried to a prominent Negro doctor. I would frequently go over to her house for supper. She was as fascinated by my story as I was by her, and wanted to know what mingling with white people was like, and exactly what my father did. And what had been my relations with white girls? Had I ever kissed them? And I would ask her the same questions, because I knew as little about colored people as she did about whites.

"About this time my interest in music began to come back. My aunt rented a piano, and also I met my mother's cousin Leon. He had written 'When the Swallows Come Back to Capistrano,' and in collaboration with his brother Otis,

'When It's Sleepy Time Down South.' But it was mostly for Helene that I felt I wanted to compose something big and important—something that would make her proud of me.

"I enrolled in the University of Southern California under the GI Bill of Rights to study music seriously. In addition, I went out for skiing, and early in my first term was elected secretary of the ski club.

"At the club and at the university I suppose they assumed I was white, although I didn't tell them so. However, I saw no reason why I shouldn't take my colored friends along on our trips. I asked one of Helene's girl friends, and also my cousin. The girl wouldn't go, though she was broad-minded and did not object to my socializing with whites to this extent. When my aunt found out that I had taken her boy, she was furious. He was very light, as his father was, and would have no trouble 'passing.' My aunt felt I was a bad influence and said that I was only a white man's Negro.

"It seemed also that, at the University, some of the Negroes were saying I was snobbish and avoided speaking to them. This certainly was not true, and their critical sensitiveness annoyed me.

"So I decided to move out of my aunt's house, away from that whole atmosphere which seemed thick with taboos and suspicion, and stay in one of the University houses where I could lead the normal student's life which I always had in New Hampshire.

"My cousin Leon was for it.

"'You get everything you can,' he said, 'because you're going to need it. And if you have to pass to get it, well, do that."

"Helene's girl friend also understood, but she warned me, 'You're going to have trouble with Helene. She's been raised differently from you.'

"I was sure she was wrong, but when I told Helene what I planned to do, she listened quietly but all she said was, 'Well, go ahead if you want to.' And after that whenever I called it seemed she was busy. Her voice over the phone was friendly, but the old warmth was gone. It was as though I had crossed some kind of boundary. There never had been boundaries for me, and I felt that there should never be. But now when I started going out with white girls again that wasn't a success either. I found I had little in common with them, and also began wondering how they would react if they knew I was colored. The old fear came back—I was unsure of myself again.

"And about this time I went to the hospital for an operation. It was not a serious one, but I had to stay there ten days. My aunt knew of it, but neither called nor came to see me. Nor did Helene. Maybe they had cut me off. Maybe they considered me as 'on the other side,' and felt if they visited me it would betray me to my white friends. In either case the result was the same.

"The whole thing had failed, and as soon as I was out of the hospital I packed my trunk and went home. Walt had left some time before.

"Immediately after I arrived, there was more friction with my father when I said I wasn't ready to go back to school. He said I had no ambition. That wasn't quite true, for I was working hard on my music.

"But I didn't know yet just what I wanted to do about college, so I got a job soda-jerking at the Howard Johnson restaurant at the edge of Keene. In the evenings I would often go out with the girls of our old crowd. But this now bothered me, just as it had with the white girls back in California. Finally after I had gone with one girl for a few weeks, I decided to tell her. But she interrupted me to say that most of their bunch of girls had already heard or suspected it, and it didn't seem important to any of them."

That was nice to know, but clearly the dread secret was beginning to seep out—at least in Keene. Also Albert discovered that, even in tolerant New England, intolerance rises when there is any hint that marital relations may become involved. One girl told him she had "got in a little squabble with my boy friend," because she had been out with him. And there were the parents of another girl who said, "While of course Albert is one of the finest boys who have ever come to our house, still—"

Yet things were getting straighter for him now, and he decided to enroll in the University of New Hampshire. Its music department was particularly good, and he felt he had gone as far as he could on his own.

MEANWHILE as the secret became a little more widely whispered, he noticed that his younger brother and sister, Donald and Anne, also were having their problems. Little Paul was too young to be told, but Donald, when he learned the truth, at first didn't believe it, and then he didn't like it.

"But I have the features of a white person," he protested. Then he walked over to the mirror and for a long time stood looking at his blond curly hair, his brown eyes, his fair complexion, frowning.

And Donald still doesn't like it. When Anne mentions anything about their being colored, he will say, "Not so loud!"

As for Anne, who is a year younger, her parents are glad to say that she is "proud of it" and so she is. "The boy I go steady with," Anne explains, "told me it didn't make any difference. And my high school friends never say anything to embarrass me.

"Of course," Anne adds, "now and then there is a slip. If someone is passing around a pack of cigarettes and they accidentally miss someone, that person may say, before he thinks, 'What's the matter, am I colored?' Then there is a silence."

At 16 Anne is very pretty, with large brown eyes, an olive skin and soft brown curly hair. Both she and her brother Donald are popular in Keene high school. Donald plays hockey and is manager of the football team, and Anne was elected both cheer leader and vice-president of her class. But sometimes she is uncomfortable. It's all right in Keene, where everybody knows her. "But at each game," explains Anne, "I have to meet cheer leaders from other towns, and I don't know how they will react."

It isn't easy.

"Another thing," Anne adds, "it would be different if we were either black or white. But this in-between stuff!"

Recently she got into a discussion with some of the other

kids, and one of them asked her who she was going to marry. And she answered, someone like herself.

"What do you mean by that?"

"Just someone like myself," Anne insisted. Not very happily. Because it isn't easy.

AND WHAT of Dr. Johnston today? Well, that Navy incident has left its scar. "Before," he remembers, "I was always a good mixer." He still smiles and says hello on the street, but he has resigned from Rotary and quit going to Masonic Lodge. "I guess I've become morose," he said, sadly. And then, apparently apropos of nothing, he tells his story of the white piano. It concerns a woman who taught music and who, as a girl, always dreamed of owning a real concert grand, white and with gold legs. Then, after many years, it all came true. But by then, it was just another piano, and in spite of its gold legs it didn't sound anything like the white-and-gold piano in her dream.

Since the Navy incident, which undoubtedly must have reached the hospital, there has been no difference in the attitude there, but somehow he doesn't try to make friends any more. He is content to "sit down, make a living and that's all."

And why? Well, what else is there to do? Back in 1944 he was offered an association with the head radiologist of Wayne University, the largest medical school in Detroit. But he felt he would have to refuse. There are occasional race riots in Detroit, and the doctor feels that if he went he would have to 'pass' completely, with the always present danger that he suddenly might be out of everything.

Then there is the other side. There was serious talk of an offer from a large Negro college in the South. But should he make his family conform to social conditions of the Deep South? "And me too," says the doctor. "It would take me five years to learn how to live there."

When he travels, Dr. Johnston finds a good deal of prejudice. At medical conventions, southern doctors will tell him earnestly, "Johnston, you just don't know the problem. Negroes don't have the brains, or any sense of moral values like you and I have. You have to treat 'em like that."

"And," says Dr. Johnston, "I have to sit there silent and take it—feeling like a traitor." He would like to come out openly as a Negro. But had he done so, could he have achieved what he did? Only the trouble now is that, in spite of his own accomplishment and everything he has done for his family, "whatever I do, my race gets no credit." And, thinking of this, presently he says softly, "I have more or less an empty life. Sometimes it all seems as disappointing as that white piano with the gold legs."

How DO New Englanders feel about the Johnstons now that a number of people have learned the secret? Well, although the Johnstons didn't know it, there have been rumors for years. "Do you think it's true they are colored?" people would ask each other. Only in New Hampshire it didn't greatly matter what the answer was, for it was not considered very important.

And somehow New England felt it showed its tolerance by not emphasizing it one way or another. It wasn't polite to be too interested in it, or to mention it before the Johnstons. As one of the doctors who works at the hospital puts it, "Johnston has never told me, so why should I tell him?"

Why should not the children play with the others and have a normal social life in the high school? Why shouldn't the Johnstons live in one of the nicest houses on one of Keene's best residential streets? New Hampshire sees no reason.

Then there is Gorham, a much smaller town, where the Johnstons are more intimately known even than in Keene, and where, the Johnstons thought, their secret was even more carefully guarded. But was it?

Mrs. Ensign Barrett, wife of the druggist, remembers that the matter of race wasn't exactly "discussed." That is, it would never be brought up officially in any large gathering like the White Mountain Ladies Circle. But from the very first it was "generally mentioned." Something was different about the Johnstons, and Mrs. Barrett remembers talking it

over with the Libby girls as to what they might be—colored
or Indian or maybe Jamaica Negro. In the end they decided it
was better to "live and let live" because, as Mrs. Barrett said
at the time, "whatever Dr. Johnston is, he's a very nice man."
And that is the verdict of New England.

As for Albert, who is now at the University of New Hampshire, when he first came he was immediately asked to join a
Greek letter fraternity. But he thanked them and said no.
Suppose he joined, and this colored thing came out, and then
some of them didn't want him?

But the thing which influenced him most was meeting Bill
Ballard in connection with a seminar on domestic and inter-
national problems. This one had touched on the Negro question and Bill Ballard, one of the few Negroes at the University and a fine, level-headed boy like Charlie Duncan, had
stood up and given the Negro point of view.

Albert Johnston had said nothing then, but afterward he
had come to Bill Ballard to say that he had particularly enjoyed it because he also was colored. Bill had looked at him
sharply, said he never would have dreamed it but that he was
glad he had told him, and of course he would tell no one if
Albert didn't want him to.

But then they had a long talk on this last point. And Albert finally said, "Well, after all, why not tell everybody?
Why carry a lie around all your life? And if you really want
to help the Negro, isn't the first step to stand up and say,
'Sure, I'm one, this is the way it is, this is how it feels to be
colored.' And then if you amount to anything in life, if you
can make something beautiful, isn't the Negro race entitled
to credit for it? And aren't you cheating your own people if
you deny them?"

Bill warned him that of course it wasn't going to solve the
race problem. Color lines would still be here for many decades. "But," said Bill, a little sadly, "it might help blur
them a little around the edges; that would do something for
all of us. Boundaries wouldn't be quite so sharp."

Just as clearly as Albert Johnston remembers that time in

their house in Keene when his father, standing in the bathroom door, told him, "Well, you're colored," he also remembers that college seminar. Of course, some of his close friends had been told it as a secret. Probably most of his other friends had heard or guessed it. Maybe a good many other people who did not know or like him very well suspected it.

But a good many people suspecting something is far different from everybody knowing it as a fact forever, and this is why Albert Johnston remembers even the room the seminar was held in—a medium-size college lounge with about 20 students sitting a little listlessly on the upholstered chairs.

After Bill Ballard had finished his part of the discussion of the Negro problem and it was time for him to rise, Albert Johnston remembers thinking that, even now, he didn't have to go through with it. Because if he did, it could never be undone. All his life he would sit, pencil in hand, before those printed blanks which read "Race: White or Colored—" and if he went through with this now there could be only one answer for him.

He remembers that the students listened casually until he came to the place where he said he felt that perhaps he could contribute something special to this discussion because he was himself a Negro. And how at this point there was a rustle as that crowd leaned forward to look at him and then to glance at each other. He remembers how very still it then got, and remained through the rest of his little talk.

AND what difference has it made? At the University of New Hampshire, very little that he can see. His friends are still his friends, he makes new ones as fast as the other boys do, and now it almost seems like a lot of pother about nothing.

Only he feels better himself. There aren't any more secrets, nothing to be afraid of. And he can go ahead writing his concerto which is based on that tune he was going to lay at Helene's feet, a concerto which the music department says shows a real grasp of harmonics and deep feeling. No longer a heartbroken little tune which can find no ending, but a slow, sad, sturdy song for all his people.

Our Hearts were Young and Gay

A condensation from the book by
CORNELIA OTIS SKINNER
AND EMILY KIMBROUGH

EMILY and I had been planning a summer in Europe for over a year. Pinching and scraping, and going without sodas, we had salvaged from our allowances and our small-time vacation jobs the sum of $80, which was the cost of a minimum passage on a liner of the cabin class. Our respective families had augmented our finances by letters of credit generous enough to permit us to live for three months abroad if not in the lap of luxury, at least on the knees of comfort.

We were to meet in Montreal at whatever hotel it is that isn't the Ritz, and sail from there in early June of the year of our Lord I shan't say exactly which, for Emily and I have now reached the time in life when not only do we lie about our ages but forget what we've said they are. Emily was to come to Montreal from her home in Buffalo and I from New York.

I tried to bid my parents a worldly, indifferent good-bye but it was hard to get away with. Mother, despite my 19 years and a lamentable determination to look like Theda Bara, the "vamp" of the movies in that era, still persisted in calling me "Baby." She kept reminding me to put my purse in my pillow, never to speak to any strange men, always to spread paper on "the seat," and to wire if I arrived safely. This was my first flight from the home nest; Mother cried a little and Father looked as if he never expected to meet me again. This despite the fact that they too were sailing for England, although on a different ship. They had no idea of cramping our style but they thought it just as well to be in the same hemisphere as we.

Montreal was my first experience of registering alone at a hotel, and far from feeling emancipated and like Theda Bara, I felt frightened and forlorn. I was too shy to venture forth alone in a strange town, and was afraid of not being on hand when Emily arrived. I wrote letters, studied bits of Baedeker, and every 15 minutes made certain my passport and letter of credit hadn't been stolen.

This last activity involved opening up a humiliating little contraption that Mother had harnessed about my person. It was an incredible object known as a "safety-pocket," a large chamois purse that dangled at the knees in the manner of a Scot's sporran and was attached to an adjustable belt around the waist. It was supposed to be worn inconspicuously under skirt and slip. I daresay in Mother's youthful and voluminously clad day it could be thus concealed, and nobody was the wiser. But in my more skimpy day, everybody was not only the wiser but the more bewildered. The bag was heavily stuffed with British bank notes, my passport and letter of credit. When I walked it would swing, catching between my knees and making me go into a gait of an animated ice-hook. When I sat still it had an unfortunate way of coming to rest along my outer thigh, giving me the outline of someone concealing a squash.

At long last Emily arrived, and the sounds of our greeting made ring whatever the welkin is. At bedtime that night in the hotel room which we shared, the moment was at hand when Emily would see me attired only in that safety-pocket, and I thought it wise to prepare her. "Emily," I began, "I must tell you . . . I have to . . . to wear something—"

She cut me short. "Stop!" she cried. "I've been wondering for days how to tell *you*." With a dramatic gesture she swished up her skirt and there, dangling between her legs like a gourd from a vine, was the twin of my ghastly safety-pocket. "Mother made me wear one too," she groaned.

This heartened me a good deal. Emily's luggage and clothes were very smart, whereas I always felt a little unsure of the "slinky" numbers I affected, and Mother didn't care what she packed my things in so long as the receptacle was clean. With my canvas trunk, straw "telescope" and various other oddments, I felt like a refugee at Ellis Island. Then, too, Emily had read Henry and William James while I still had a secret letch for Ethel M. Dell. Most impressive of all, she had been engaged and had broken it off. At 19 I hadn't thought of being engaged. That is, I had but nobody else had. The discovery that she too wore a safety-pocket brought her nearer my level.

N EXT MORNING we went aboard the *Montcalm*; in due time the gangplank was hoisted clear, the foghorn let forth its shattering but beautiful bark, and slowly, the steamer headed for England. Our trip of independence had begun.

At lunch we found the table assigned us was off to one side near the swing-doors where stewards in order to get past had to graze our heads with their trays. It held about ten people in addition to a grim officer who said nothing. As a matter of fact, all ten of us said nothing. Eventually the rather nice-looking man on Emily's right asked if he might trouble her for the salt and she burbled her reassurance that it was anything but trouble. Then to the left of me an English lad uttered in my general direction that the weather was jolly decent and I agreed rather strenuously, yes wasn't it, and he said yes it was and that stretch of ice was broken.

After lunch we went on deck and watched the scenery slip past. Gradually I became aware that it was no longer slipping. It was staying perfectly motionless. The engines were still pounding, harder than ever. Looking down I saw that water was passing the ship, only it was going the wrong way. Also it was suddenly very muddy. People began to gather along the rail studying alternately the stationary shoreline and the churning brown water. The words "gone aground" sounded out ominously. The English lad came up beside me and announced cheerfully, "Well, we've caught bottom. All right for a time, but when the tide goes down she'll settle onto rocks. Probably means a few large holes in the hull. She may even capsize. Cheer-o!"—and he hurried off to spread gladness among others.

One side of the deck was now perceptibly lower than the other. Seamen were appearing in doorways and disappearing down hatches and ladders. Officers with "for-King-and-

Country" expressions were hastening to the bridge. Life-
boats were swung out on the davits. Apprehensive passengers
began making muttering sounds like the crowd extras in
Julius Caesar. The tide was rapidly going down and we waited
for the happy moment when the steel plates of the hull would
start caving in.

Then it occurred to me that my parents were by now on
the high seas and, remembering that the little daily ship's
newspaper carries all the latest maritime reports, I was
afraid they might read news of the *Montcalm* being aground
and come to melodramatic conclusions. So I went to the wireless room and dispatched a message: "Don't worry. Everything will be all right." My father later told me he received
this odd communication while walking about the deck in a
state of anything but worry. Mother read it and said it boded
no good. They never did hear about the *Montcalm* and during
the remainder of their voyage they were in a state of bewildered uneasiness.

Later a government boat came alongside and some official
boarded our derelict to book passages on whatever other
ships might be sailing. Emily and I drew berths on the *Empress of France*.

When the tide came in, the *Montcalm* lifted off the rocks
and slowly, at an angle like an invalid with a droop to one
side, a bevy of little tugs fussing around her, began stag-
gering downstream. We hopefully asked an assistant purser
when we would get to Quebec, and he answered unfeelingly,
"That's just the question," which seemed to us just what
we'd asked him.

At Quebec next day all passengers left the ship the moment
the gangplank was down. I must say they left in the traditional manner of rats rather than human beings.

They treated us royally on the *Empress of France*. No sooner
had the ship got under way than a diminutive cabin boy
brought us the captain's compliments and an invitation to
come to his quarters for tea. We devoured everything with
delight, all the time saying we really couldn't and the captain who knew better insisting that we could. Happy, happy

girlhood! Hip-free and not yet calory-conscious, we'd have downed a suckling pig if he'd had it handy.

One of the many bits of parting advice we had received was to identify ourselves with some nice women on shipboard as soon as possible. So next day we looked about for nice elderly, unattached women but without much enthusiasm and without any results. As a matter of fact, we never met up with any women at all. Instead we went around with a varied assortment of males which included two very nice young doctors freshly hatched from medical school—Paul White and Joseph Aub, who are now distinguished Boston physicians.

The day before we were to land, I awoke to the realization that my throat was scrapy and my nose stopped up. By midafternoon my throat felt like something dangling from a hook in a butcher's shop. I felt rapidly worse, and Emily went forth to summon the ship's physician but ran into Joe Aub first, and yanked him down to the cabin. He looked me over, listened to my lungs, and looked extremely grave.

"My dear girl," he said, "you're coming down with a hell of a case of measles."

"But I thought I was past the age for such things," I croaked.

"Adults can have measles," he said. "And when they do it's pretty serious."

Paul White came down, verified Joe's diagnosis, and then the two tackled the problem of what to do. The boat was due at Southampton next morning and Emily and I were to disembark there, but if it became known I had measles I'd never be permitted to land. The rash wouldn't come out for perhaps 24 hours, and Paul and Joe would devise some way to smuggle me into England.

My parents were to meet us at Southampton, and once I had safely run the gamut of the health inspector I could go direct to a hotel where Mother would take care of me. Then we could wireless the ship to fumigate the cabin so its next occupants wouldn't be exposed. Paul and Joe managed to get medicine from the ship's infirmary, and I spent the night in a stupor, roused now and then by Emily who would shine a dazzling flashlight in my face, study its condition, and say in the tone of someone trying to pep up a losing team: "You hold that rash back!"

To camouflage my rash-red face, which had swollen into the shape of a harvest moon, I put on slathers of foundation cream and half the contents of a box of face powder. The effect was that of a girl who had been ducking for apples in a bucket of paperhanger's paste.

With some curious notion that it would distract from the rest of my visage, I painted my mouth, which was normally no dainty little rosebud, to look twice its normal size, and topped off my startling appearance with a bright red hat and a flowing white veil which, I pointed out, would make me less conspicuous. I guess I'd gotten a little delirious by then.

The ship was now coming up to the dock and in half an hour we'd be ashore. I was left propped against some cushions in a dark corner of a deserted card room, while Emily went on deck to locate my parents. They were in the thick of the crowd staring up at the ship. Mother was waving furiously at passengers who bore not the remotest resemblance to us. Eventually, she located Emily, and pointed her out to Father, who had seen her for some time and had been waving intermittently in a vague but happy manner. Mother, cupping her mouth and standing on tiptoe as if that would make her voice carry higher, called out: "Where's Cornelia?" Emily merely smiled, waved and pretended she hadn't heard.

At last the gangplank was lowered and Emily, shooting out of the ship like a bat out of Carlsbad Caverns, rushed up to Mother and Father and said in the tense voice of a conspirator, "Don't say a word to anybody, because if it becomes known, we are lost: Cornelia has the measles!"

Whereat Father, in that voice which for fifty years thrilled the topmost occupant of the highest seat in the gallery, whooped "MEASLES?" and would have whooped it again except that Mother deftly put a hand over his mouth. Then Mother started up the gangplank. An officer told her she

wasn't allowed on board and some able-bodied seamen held
out restraining arms. What happened to them was what happened to anyone on whom Mother shed her charm. She just
smiled at them and in her beautiful voice murmured a lot of
charming jargon about her child and a friend . . . at Bryn
Mawr together . . . just outside Philadelphia . . . they had
lived there too but not recently . . . and they were all going
in a motor somewhere, but that was a surprise for the dear
children . . . so brave, too, although she hadn't approved of
their being alone in the first place. And somehow, with
Father following, she got up the gangplank and onto the
boat. People just gave way, dazed.

Mother was dazed herself when she saw me. Father stared
at me a moment, then collapsed onto a gilt chair and laughed
till the tears ran down his cheeks.

Somehow the three of them got me past the inspectors and
off the ship, then through the lobby up to a quiet room in
Southampton's leading hostelry—where, once they got me to
bed, I went completely and noisily delirious.

The *Empress* stayed in port three days before going on to
Hamburg. We had one bad moment when the ship's doctor,
who possibly had had his suspicions aroused, sent up his
card saying he'd heard I'd been suffering from a slight cold
and could he see me. I was certain they'd found out about me,
and began to think that maybe even now I'd be whisked off
to a quarantine camp. But I was reckoning without Mother.
She put on her prettiest hat and with a radiant smile tripped
down to greet the doctor. A half hour later Emily and Father
came upon them having tea in the lobby. The doctor was
asking if he might show her about Southampton, that is,
if her husband would trust her to an old dog like him . . .
ha-ha! . . . an old sea-dog . . . ha-ha-ha!

In ten days I was sufficiently recovered for us all to depart
for London.

O NCE ARRIVED in London Emily and I parted company with
Mother and Father, and set forth for the more Bohemian
atmosphere of "lodgings." We had arranged to take rooms

on the topmost floor of an ancient manse situated somewhere back of the British Museum.

The landlady had gone off for a vacation up the Thames and we were left to the tender mercies of a cockney slavey. She'd clatter in at seven to fix the one fire we had all day, at 7:30 she'd charge back with a pitcher of hot water, which in London's damp, chilly weather doesn't stay hot very long; at eight she'd bring us breakfast. When we petitioned ever so meekly permission to receive these blessings a trifle later in the day she said, "Carn't, Miss. Mrs. 'Iggins horders."

The bathroom was down two flights of stairs; this resulted in some interesting encounters with the other tenants —all elderly gentlemen in bathrobes, carrying towels, shaving mugs and copies of *The Daily Mail*.

The water for the tub was heated by one of those little gas-jet arrangements which flicker beneath a small copper boiler. After a while if you're lucky, a forlorn trickle of hot water dribbles forth. The slavey called this contraption a "geezer" (geyser) and warned us if the flame went out while we were running the water we should immediately drop tuppence into the slot—otherwise "everythink might blow hup."

One morning as I was disporting myself like a dolphin in a couple of inches of tepid water, the gas gave a little hiccough and went out. Recalling the slavey's warning about the thing blowing up unless, like Mammon, you kept it stoked with coins, I yelled for Emily to bring me tuppence. She had no change, but always active if not logical in an emergency, she dashed downstairs. The house was deserted, so she sped on into a passing bus. She rode one  block, got change for two and six, and jumped off, murmuring to the bewildered conductor, "You see, my friend is up

there stark naked with the geezer." By the time she returned
I was quite blue with cold, but old faithful had not yet
erupted.

One day Mother, who had read that the Royal Family was
to leave for the country at eleven, scuttled us off to Bucking-
ham Palace to watch their departure. We stood along with
a handful of casual passers-by until the gates opened and the
Family appeared, crowded into one car like any other family
starting for the station.

The few men around us took off their hats, the nannies
pointed out the car to their children, and Emily and I just
looked. But not Mother. Not for nothing had she assisted, on
the stage, the entrance of kings and queens. She fluttered to
the ground in a deep curtsey, spreading as wide as possible
the skirt of her tailored suit. We looked down at her in
amazement. We weren't the only ones amazed—Queen Mary
nearly fell out of the car.

Mother and Father received a constant stream of callers
and whenever we thought them sufficiently well-known we'd
horn in if possible. One afternoon Gilbert Miller, the famous
theatrical producer, was to come for tea. The prospect of
meeting him made me twittery. I was hoping to launch forth
upon a stage career and Mr. Miller might offer me a job if I
made an impression on him.

A decided impression was made on Mr. Miller, but not
by me. My thunder was stolen by Emily, who in her excitement over this distinguished occasion ate the pink baby-
ribbon which was tied around the sandwiches. It was hard
to chew and even harder to swallow but she had to gulp it
down, for to pull it out hand over hand would have been
even more spectacular. Gilbert Miller never took his eyes
off her. As for topping that impression, I hadn't a chance.

H. G. Wells invited us all to spend Sunday at his country
place. When we arrived Mr. Wells bustled us into the dining
room, hurtled himself into a chair beside Emily, and said:
"Now, young lady, tell me all about what you do. What do
you read? What part of America do you come from? Marvel-

lous place, America. Ever been to Hollywood? The coming intellectual and artistic center of the world." He didn't give her time to answer all his questions but she did manage to talk to him. The rest of us ate and listened avidly.

Luncheon finished, Emily rose and turned with a willowy swoop and a brilliant smile for our host, intending to sweep on away from the table. Instead, there was a crash and a sort of whizzing sound. In that willowy swoop she had in some way hooked her toe in a loop of the electric table-bell-cord and snapped it. The released wire had whipped itself in coils about her leg from ankle to knee, like an Elizabethan cross-garter, and held her immovable.

Mr. Wells got down on his hands and knees, lifted the tablecloth, crawled under and got her unwound.

Emily, I was beginning to find out, is the sort of person who attracts incident as blue serge attracts lint.

SHORTLY after that we once more took leave of the family and departed for France, crossing the Channel to Dieppe. We were now really setting forth on our own. The prospect at once entranced and awed us.

The moment the gangplank was down at Dieppe, a bunch of brigand porters rushed on deck in the manner of a buccaneer boarding party, seized all luggage and hustled us off to the customs. It is a miracle how anyone finds his baggage amid the pandemonium of a Gallic landing, but there was our collection safe and intact. An inspector with a bushy moustache, soiled uniform and a medal or two asked us if we had anything "à déclarer." We assured him we had nothing dutiable. He opened Emily's valise and was instantly hit on the chest when a large tin of English cigarettes fell out. He examined it solemnly, then with a wink said, "Since there is nothing, one sees nothing!" and replaced it carefully in the suitcase. He didn't bother to open our other pieces, possibly because he was afraid of discovering other evidences of our perjury. I let ten francs flutter from my purse, which he pocketed with dignity, and told us to "passer." That we had "bribed an official" made us feel very adult indeed.

One of the brigand porters grabbed our things and asked if these Mesdemoiselles were taking the Paris train or staying in Dieppe and if so at which hotel were these Mesdemoiselles going to descend. I told him we were to stay overnight in Dieppe and then go on to Rouen and Paris. He said entendu, to meet him outside, he would get us to a hotel in style. His solicitude increased our sense of self-importance and we walked with terrific poise out of the Customs House. After a time he appeared with a small cart into which he dumped our trunks and larger suitcases; the remaining pieces he fastened onto himself by means of a stout leather strap. I never saw a human being so burdened. If he'd been a donkey we'd have notified the S.P.C.A. As he loaded himself he explained that the hotel was nearby and one could march there facilely at foot. So Emily and I, who had imagined ourselves whipping through the city in a handsome equipage, found ourselves stumbling and lurching over the cobblestones on our high heels behind a glorified wheelbarrow.

At the hotel we dived into our purses and between us made up a truly handsome pourboire which we handed to the porter. Emily was unprepared for that sudden stream of injured invective which invariably follows the tipping of a French porter. He claimed that it was not enough, that these Mesdemoiselles had not acted nicely with him, that for them he had given himself many boredoms (ennuis) and that he had a wife and five little ones, also an ancient mother. Emily, before I could stop her, doled him out five francs, an English penny and an American dime. This mollified him somewhat but all the time we were making arrangements for a room, he hung about muttering, "Espèce de concombre, espèce de consombre?" It's surprising how terrifying it can be to be called a "kind of a cucumber" by a Dieppe porter.

MOTHER was a joiner. She would join any organization of which her friends were presidents or committee members, provided that the dues weren't excessive. One of her enthusiasms was known as "The Ladies' Rest Tour Association," which published a monthly pamphlet listing comfortable, inexpensive and respectable lodgings for ladies traveling alone through Europe. From this invaluable pamphlet Mother had selected a boarding house in Rouen for Emily and me.

Upon our arrival in the town where Joan of Arc had been burned at the stake, we spent a day of strenuous sightseeing and then looked up the address Mother had sent us. We rang the bell and after a time the door was opened a crack by a frowsy maid who didn't seem to want to let us in. But we smiled and said "bon soir" and blandly asked to see "la Madame," meaning "landlady." The maid looked slightly astonished and walked off, returning in a second with an awfully dressy landlady, who looked even more astonished.  We told her we'd like a room for the night, which obviously increased her amazement, so, to establish our respectability, I told her that her house had been recommended to us as just the place for "deux jeunes filles." She murmured a faint "Ah?" and, beckoning us to follow, led us down a hall lined on either side with smallish rooms, rather elaborately decorated. Some of the doors were open, and we caught glimpses of the other guests who seemed quite surprised to see us They were all young women in striking evening dresses.

Madame led us up several flights of stairs and alloted us a modest room quite removed from the more elaborate ones below. She explained we'd be more "tranquille" there. Then she asked how we'd happened to come to her place. We told her we'd read all about it in a book published by an American society. She opened and closed her mouth several times but nothing came forth, then, with a wan, Camille-like wave of the hand, backed out of the room.

We washed, went out and found a quiet near-by restaurant where we dined. When we returned to our snug abode the frowsy maid, still looking astonished, admitted us and we went down the long hall, tiptoeing because the doors were all closed now, and we didn't want to disturb anybody.

The following morning, bright and eager as daisies, we rose, packed and asked for the bill. Madame named a sum which was most reasonable, and as we paid it we told her we'd most assuredly recommend her establishment to all our friends. Her eyes glazed over a bit at that, and faintly she asked us if we'd have the kindness to give her the name of the American "société" which had informed us about her: she would like, she said, to write to them.

THE TRAIN for Paris bustled along fussily and at alarming speed. Every hundred yards its whistle let out a high nervous shriek like the whoop of an elderly spinster who has suddenly been pinched.

The farther we journeyed toward Paris, the faster the train went, like a horse smelling its oats. Ours was the end car and the engineer rounded all corners as if he were playing "crack the whip." Emily decided she wouldn't look out the window because she'd just as soon not know when we left the rails.

At the Gare St. Lazare the inevitable band of maniacal porters seized our pieces of luggage and hurtled us across the station to an open taxi, which rattled and progressed in the manner of a fleeing kangaroo. We could see the ends of the driver's moustache working furiously the entire way to the hotel, as he bellowed greetings or anathema to other drivers. His only concession to street crossings was to sound his horn, and putting on greater speed, rush at them as if leading a cavalry charge.

At last we came to a stop before the France et Choiseul, a hotel at which Mother and I had put up the preceding winter. With a tip and a gracious smile to the driver and a regal nod for the hotel porters, we walked into the lobby as if we had either coronets or books on our heads. We were met by Josef, the concierge. Our bearing impressed him, for he gave us a deep, respectful bow. Then suddenly he recognized me and broke into a roar of delight.

"Ah, c'est la petite Mlle. Skinner!" he informed us and everyone within the radius of a block or two. "Quel plaisir! 'Ow is Momma?" This was humiliating. "Maman" at least would have been "Frenchy," but "Momma" made me suddenly feel that I had bands on my teeth.

Josef said he would give us a nice room, and still talking about "Momma," led the way to that emblem of France, the automatic ascenseur, into which we all squeezed at once and by some fluke ascended to our floor without its getting stuck.

We decided not to unpack until later, for Paris was waiting out there, and it was only a strong sense of decorum which kept us from skipping as we went out of the hotel onto the rue St. Honoré and LIFE!

A fiacre was standing outside, and the cocher, an amiable soul with a face like an apoplectic walrus, called out that he was about to turn in for the day, but that it was such a lovely evening, he'd drive us to the Etoile and back for half fare. We hopped in with alacrity. It was late twilight, the time of day the French call "la crépuscule," one of the loveliest words in the world.

As we drew near the Arc de Triomphe we were able to discern in the dim light its stark sculpture groups with the thundering figure of La France, arms outstretched, mouth wide open as if crying out, "Aux armes, citoyens!" The driver pulled up his old beast and asked us if we wouldn't like to get out for a few minutes. We walked up the steps and stood under the great span of the largest triumphal arch in the world, where, in the flickering light of an eternal flame, lay the tomb of the Unknown Soldier. "Look," I said, and I pointed down the Champs Élysées. "This street is the history of France. That's the Louvre at the other end."

We could just make it out, in the soft gloom, the winter residence of the Kings of France; half way between was the Place of anything but Concorde, where fell so many of those effete but gallant powdered heads of French royalty. And here, at our end of it, the Arc de Triomphe, where, under such names as Austerlitz, Iena and Marengo, we two stood, young and hopeful in the young and hopeful 1920's. Then the soft

pink street lights began to flicker on. Not all at once, but
starting far off at the Louvre, then coming on toward us,
chapter by chapter, from François Ier to the Unknown Soldier,
the common denominator of the course of history.

Slowly we returned down the steps and our eyes were wet.
The old driver was waiting beside his dozing nag. He, too,
had been looking at things and had been having his own
meditations. His shiny leather hat was in his hand. He observed us shrewdly for a moment and in his husky voice said,
"I thank you, Mesdemoiselles, in the name of France." Then
with a gesture of ferocity he clapped his hat on, muttering
a stream of complaints about how he and his horse had been
kept waiting in the night air. Then he drove us home.

WHEN MOTHER and Father arrived at the France et Choiseul, we departed to stay at a pension patronized solely by
French people. We found the hotel too full of Americans and
we had come abroad, we said, not to see Americans but to see
Life.

It is hard to believe how little we knew about that all-ab-
sorbing subject. In comparison with the modern generation,
ours was an innocence which bordered on arrested development. It was not that our mothers were Victorian prudes.
They were both wise and brilliant women, but they had never
felt it necessary to dispel our vague notions about certain
fundamentals.

One day Emily had been out to tea with an American couple who lived on the Left Bank. Among their enthusiasms was
an earnest group from a pseudo-Russian ballet—short-haired
girls named Mash or Tania, and long-haired lads named Igor
or Dmitri, most of them hailing from Chicago. Emily met
two of the young men. "They were so different from the men
I know," she told us, "although they were very pleasant."

Father, who had been reading, at this point looked up over
his glasses. Emily, encouraged by his interest, continued, "It
was odd—they both had rouge on and eye shadow." Father
made a choking sound. "But then I learned that they were
from the theatre. I imagine they must have just come from a

matinee and hadn't bothered to take off their make-up. *You know*," and Emily turned on Father her most social smile. "You've probably done the same thing lots of times yourself."

Father rose in wrath. "Emily Kimbrough," he thundered, "my makeup belongs to my profession and my profession is *inside* the theatre. Maude!" he roared at Mother "Tell her!"

Mother took a deep, sad breath. Then she said, "Come, girls," and led us into the next room. She sat Emily down beside her and gently patted her hand.

"Darling," she said, with a catch in her voice, "Mr. Skinner was upset because what you said showed a certain lack of understanding, and so I want to explain a few things to you."

Here she paused in search of the proper words, while Emily and I sat there looking the way we did when we'd been sent for by the principal. Mother went on, "Darling, you know who Oscar Wilde was?"

Emily nodded, too bewildered to speak.

"You know, I suppose, why he was sent to prison?"

"Of course," said Emily with loud eagerness. "Debt."

Mother patted her hand again a long time. Finally she spoke. "Well, not exactly, dear. You see, there are unfortunate people in this world who do not conform in their behavior to that of others. It isn't their fault, but still society can't condone it. So you see, it makes it very unpleasant. And now that I've explained it all, I'm sure you'll understand."

And we went out of the room, feeling that even if we had not quite grasped the essentials, this had all been extremely momentous.

We had another glimpse of Life when we moved to the pension. That same day our doctor friends, Joe Aub and Paul White, wired us that they were arriving in Paris next day and would we dine with them. We tried to react to this intoxicating invitation in a blasé manner, but in no time we had shed sophistication like an old shoe that hurts, and were twittering away about our clothes, our hair, and our "line."

At the pension, the proprietress allotted us a large room with an enormous canopied bed. When we protested that we could not possibly share a bed, she provided a cot.

Tomorrow was to be a day of days and we must get a good night's rest. Nothing, Emily said, was a greater aid to beauty than a long slumber. With sweet unselfishness she insisted that I sleep in the large canopied affair, and she took the cot. Toward morning I began to feel curiously uncomfortable. Something was definitely wrong. It was my face. Slowly I sat up in bed and apprehensively raised my eyes to a reflection in the ornate mirror which, I realized with horror, was my own. My upper lip was swollen forth in a fabulous sort of disk —like those of the Ubangi people in *The National Geographic*. The swelling took up so much of my skin, my eyes were pulled down like a bloodhound's.

"Emily!" I commanded in ringing tones which Duse, Bernhardt and Modjeska never equalled. "LOOK at me!" Emily started to speak, but the sight of me paralyzed her. At last she was able to croak in an awed whisper, "What did it?"

"BEDBUGS!" I declaimed, and fell back on the pillows.

If I had burst forth in the most lurid blasphemy, Emily could not have been more shocked. The very word, she told me later, was one which a nice person never even uttered. But the awful word galvanized her into action. "We're going to the American Drug Store," she said, and leapt out of bed. "They'll tell us what to do." We dressed with alacrity. Clad, and with my hair fixed, I was even more horrifying to behold. Whenever Emily looked at me, she went into a paroxysm which started in a wild laugh and ended in a sort of hysterical sob. I put on a hat with a wide brim and again got out the same white veil which had shrouded me through the measles. It seemed to be my idea of protective coloring, although it did not cause me to pass unnoticed.

We leapt into a taxi, telling the driver to go as fast as possible. To issue such an order was, we knew, risking our lives, but we were desperate. We had just two hours before the "men" would arrive. The driver, after a shuddering glance at me, covered the distance in record time. We threw him his fare and shot into the haven of the American Drug Store.

And there, just inside the door, stood Miss Mary Orr of Brooklyn Heights. She was an elderly spinster, a friend of Mother's. She was very aristocratic and rich, which awed us, and we were anxious to make a genteel impression on her, for she sometimes gave us rides in her Rolls Royce. At sight of her I retired into the recesses of my white veil, and Emily stood blocking me from view as best she could.

"Hello, girls," Miss Orr said cheerily. "What's brought you out so early?"

Emily rose to the crisis. "Miss Orr," she said, "we are in terrible trouble. It's really Cornelia. She's the one in trouble physically . . ."

"What do you mean?" Miss Orr asked sharply; "Cornelia's in trouble physically?"

"Well, she was—she was attacked last night."

Miss Orr grabbed Emily's arm. "Where?" she asked hoarsely.

"In bed. We just moved into the pension yesterday and we didn't know about it." She meant the bed.

Miss Orr groaned. "Oh, these French!" She was very pale.

"We don't want to tell Mr. Skinner"—Miss Orr nodded her head violently in agreement, but seemed incapable of speech—"but we thought we could get something at the Drug Store." I thought Miss Orr was going to faint, but Emily kept right on. "Isn't there something that will keep them from coming back?"

"*Them?*"

"Yes," Emily insisted. "Or should we burn the bed?"

"What *are* you talking about?" Miss Orr demanded.

"*Bedbugs*," I announced, and wondered what on earth she *thought* Emily had been talking about.

"Young man!" this scion of old New York roared out to the clerk. "Make up a gallon of Lysol solution. These ladies have bed bugs. And give me a chair. I've had a bad fright."

She appeared to be quite put out with both of us. Then, to my further chagrin, she drove us to the France et Choiseul. When Mother saw me she cried out in anguish, and Father gasped, "My God, she's turned into an anteater!" They said they'd better come along and do something right away.

At the pension Father took off his coat and set to work, and Mother applied lotion to my face which by a miracle deflated my lip to normal. When Paul and Joe arrived and we swept down to meet them, they enquired politely about my parents. We did not mention the fact that at the moment Mother and Father were on their hands and knees upstairs with brushes and a jug of Lysol.

ONE DAY as we were lunching at a sidewalk café, a young man we had met through a prominent French actor whom Father knew approached us and asked if we would do his cinema company the great honor of acting out for them a little movie scene. We were quite stunned, but managed to say we should be glad to assist. He sighed with gratitude and told us to stay just where we were, the mise-en-scène was perfect. Then he piled about us a mound of very smart luggage, all quite new and bearing labels from almost every corner of the globe. He trained the camera on us. Movies were silent in those days, but we spoke lines for him in luscious throaty voices. He told us we had given a beautiful performance and if we cared to see the film it would be shown in two weeks at such and such a cinema house.

The two weeks seemed endless. When the night of our world première came around, we persuaded Mother and Father to go with us, telling them we had a little surprise for them. After the feature picture and news reels, to our suffocating delight there we were on the screen as large as life, sitting at a café table, completely surrounded with enormous pieces of luggage, both of us grinning like apes. Father emitted a loud "WHAT?" and Mother began making little cooing sounds. We saw ourselves going through all those dramatic bits of spontaneous dialogue, but the audience heard not a word of it. Instead, there appeared on the screen a caption

Verdun, and to eke out his small pension he made bead necklaces and choke collars which Emily and I helped sell to
Americans for him.

For one week out of every year he was sent home with a
nurse to spend a vacation with his family. One day he told us
that his leave had just been granted, and then, with much
embarrassment, asked us if we would do him and his wife the
honor of coming out to their house for lunch.

We were deeply touched to be asked and the following Sunday took a train to the little suburban town. Our friend's
house was tiny but immaculate. The mistress of the house
came out of a delicious-smelling kitchen to greet us. She was
lovely to look at and she seemed touchingly young. We had
thought of her husband as an old man, his body was so
twisted, the lines of suffering on his face so deep. She must
have guessed our thoughts, for as she led us into the small
parlor, she pointed to a picture on the wall.

"That was my husband in 1916," she said, and she turned
abruptly into the kitchen. It was one of those awful wedding
pictures, the bride sitting rigid in a chair and the bridegroom
standing with a hand clamped firmly on her shoulder. He
looked like a small boy, round-eyed, proud and rather scared.
The banal little portrait made our throats contract.

When we joined the young woman in the kitchen, she was
composed and smiling. Her husband was in the salle à manger
on a high movable bed, and he was a very different man from
the sad cripple of the Invalides. His eyes were bright and he
was full of gay talk. We suddenly realized that for this week
he was a man of property, a citizen of a community, not just a
number in a bleak government hospital.

His wife slipped in with glasses and a bottle of wine and we
drank to our mutual "bonne fortune." Toward the end of the
delicious lunch, we heard a roar of machinery and a voice
which roared even louder. "C'est mon père," Madam explained simply. Her father proved to be a colossus. He strode
into the room, came up to us, bowed over our hands and said
he had come to pay his respects to the friends of his son-in-
law. He touched the shoulder of the blessé as gently as a

woman. The old man said he had time only for a glass of wine to drink our health. He wished, he said on behalf of his daughter, his son-in-law, and his country, to thank us and America . . . was it true there were buildings there of fifty stories? . . . a most unnatural height . . . for our kindness and good will. Was it also true that wine was forbidden there? But that also was unnatural, and detrimental to the health. He then offered a tribute to the two countries and a prayer that their mutual "sympathie" might deepen through the years to come.

The speech was impressive; Emily whispered to me, "He must be the mayor or something." He rose to leave, full of regret, but a new roadbuilding enterprise needed his attention, he said, even on Sunday. We said good-bye with a good deal of ceremony. In a minute, we heard the same deafening chugging and rattling of a machine that we had heard when he arrived, and a voice shouting above it, "Vive l'Amérique! Vive la France!" Through the window we had a final glimpse of the distinguished old gentleman. A smock now covered his best Sunday suit—and he was driving the local steamroller.

Summer was drawing to a close, and so was our trip. The thought was a dismal one.

The day before our departure, we blew ourselves to a superb lunch at Prunier's, after which we went on a pilgrimage to say good-bye to some of the places we had loved best—the rose window in the transept of Notre Dame, the little garden of St. Julien le Pauvre, the lights at dusk coming on up the Champs Élysées.

We didn't weep, but we were awfully quiet. It was the end of something and we both knew it. We would come back again but it would never be the same. Our hearts were young and gay, and we were leaving a part of them forever in Paris.

OUR
UNKNOWN EX-PRESIDENT

A condensation from the book by

EUGENE LYONS

Elected at perhaps the unluckiest moment in modern times, Herbert Hoover after enduring defeat and obloquy has emerged again as a truly great public servant.

JUST BEFORE America entered the war, the personal stock of our only living ex-President was at an all-time low. With war fever mounting, he was staunchly noninterventionist. With the Roosevelt administration reaping credit for war-boom prosperity, he continued to battle the New Deal philosophy. Worst of all, in defiance of official opinion, he demanded that we feed starving children in France, Greece and other Hitler-held countries.

He seemed on the "wrong" side of every issue, the center of the bitterest prejudices of the moment.

Today, in the 74th year of his crowded life, in the 15th year since he went directly from the White House to the doghouse, Herbert Hoover again enjoys immense popular esteem and an influence in public affairs second to no other private citizen. Not since his first year as President have his views weighed so heavily. His "fan mail," which averaged a dozen or so letters a day from 1933 to 1946, now runs between 500 and 1000 a day—an almost mathematical measure of his renewed popularity.

The tone of the press has suddenly turned deferential. Even those who dislike Hoover's conservative ideas are impressed by his moral stature. In asserting that he is wrong they no longer imply that he is wicked. Except in the Communist propaganda, slander has given way to respectful disagreement.

In October 1935, on the eve of a presidential year, a *Collier's* article quoted leading Republicans as saying, "Lord, if only Hoover would get out and leave us alone." Today, on the eve of another such year, Republicans seek his guidance; indeed, there was hardly a day during the last session of Congress when members of both parties did not solicit his advice.

Hoover heads a bipartisan 12-man commission to study ways of simplifying and improving the structure of the federal government. Speaker Martin of the House, who appointed him, declared that this may be the greatest job in Hoover's career. In the light of the gigantic enterprises Hoover has generaled, this is saying a great deal.

A new appreciation of its former occupant prevails in the White House. In his second month in office President Truman invited Hoover to call. The two men have often consulted since. At the last Gridiron Club dinner, Hoover's neighbor on the dais reached over and inscribed his speech manuscript: "With keen appreciation—to a great American." It was signed Harry S. Truman.

The spiral of the ex-President's new popularity was touched off when Truman asked him to make a world survey of food stocks and relief measures in the spring of 1946. Accompanied by his own experts, Hoover girdled the globe and then, without a breathing spell, made a swing through Latin America. The gallantry of such an undertaking by an aging man somehow bridged three decades. It helped restore Hoover to his role as the most effective instrument of America's idealistic conscience and charitable impulses—in *Newsweek's* phrase, "the symbol of hope and sympathy" for a distressed world.

This year a Republican Congress and a Democratic President canceled out a political vendetta of which no one was too proud by restoring the original name of the Hoover Dam. The ex-President is indifferent to such things; but to his friends the action, and the approval it evoked in the country, meant a lot.

Though Hoover has retreated from none of his opinions, there has been a distinct mellowing of his personality. His recent speeches have had more sparkle and less solemnity. More of the affectionate, often droll, always sympathetic Hoover is getting through to the general public.

Anyone who attains the Presidency of the United States might reasonably be presumed to possess great political talents. Yet the one thing on which Hoover's friends and enemies seem to agree is that he is "no politician." There is no implication that he is deficient in grasp of political trends. Where he falls short is in dexterity—in maneuvering people, playing on crowd emotions, selling himself to the masses.

Hoover, one of his close associates told me, has always

seemed "out of character" in the political arena. Another declared that "the ways of the politician were never quite clear, and on the whole distasteful, to the Chief." Having conceded that he lacks color and appeal for the great electorate, they usually add, in fond irritation, that he would never do anything to remedy those lacks.

On the eve of the Hoover campaign in 1928, some Republican stalwarts met to outline a program for "humanizing" their candidate. But Hoover would never lend himself to public-relations stunts, insisted he did not want a synthetic picture projected on the public mind.

Americans as a whole think of him as austere, monumental and rather cold. Few have any inkling of the warm, whimsical Hoover known to his intimates, the very human and deeply humane Quaker behind the solemn façade. Even those who share his conservative philosophy accept the myth of an impersonal, almost machinelike engineer-statesman.

When traced to their source, his shortcomings as a politician are seen to derive from elements in his character of which the public is utterly unaware. The most striking of these is shyness—an almost physical shrinking from strangers and crowds. He is at his best when talking informally, in a friendly setting. His voice is then rich, his features light up. Once started he can be fluent and epigrammatic, drawing easily on a remarkable memory.

But on the platform or in front of a mike, he seems to freeze up. His voice is somehow drained of color and his face of expression. Only the intense earnestness remains, rarely relieved by those sly asides which enliven his intimate conversation.

Those who meet Hoover for the first time run the risk of mistaking his diffidence for hardness. There is no easy glibness or phony intimacy about him. He is likely to wait, with lowered eyes, for the other fellow to start the conversational ball rolling. When people called on President Hoover in the White House there were often long and embarrassing pauses while he waited for them to state their errands. I have been told of instances when men and women came to seek Hoover's help—he is if anything too accessible—and departed crest-fallen, sure they had failed, only to discover later in amazement that he had acted quickly and generously on their problems.

Hoover has no gift at all for that backslapping, glad-handing, first-name familiarity one expects from the politician. And matters are not improved by his one intolerance, which is intellectual: an intolerance for beating around the bush, fuzzy thinking and vague facts.

Private Lives Shielded

FEW OCCUPANTS of the White House have curtained their private lives from public scrutiny as stubbornly as the Hoovers. Mrs. Hoover, who died in 1944, was a gracious, handsome, highly intelligent woman. The Hoover sons, Herbert, Jr., and Allan, are attractive, capable men who have become independently successful. The Hoover grandchildren who swarmed over the President were as cute as any youngsters born to the White House. Yet the private life of a Scottie named Fala received more press, screen and radio attention than the private lives of the whole Hoover clan combined.

Herbert, Jr., was attending Harvard Business School while his father was President. One summer he decided to get himself a job. He did, with the Baltimore Electric Company—under the assumed name of Watson. The secret leaked out, as secrets will, but the incident is typical of the family's attitude. When Herbert, Jr., was offered a post obviously too big for him, he turned it down indignantly. "My father's name is not for sale," he explained to a friend in describing the offer.

Had Hoover had a better eye for personal glorification, his heroic efforts to stem the tides of disaster in the early depression years would have provided a four-ring circus for an avid press. He might easily have dramatized his almost unprecedented burdens of office, his inhumanly long hours. But reporters had to dig hard for news which another President would have blown up for them with the help of battalions of public-relations officials.

The incessant comings and goings at the White House of

industrialists, labor leaders, financiers, for emergency conferences were smothered. Hoover insisted that his exertions
be played down, because he was anxious not to stampede an
alarmed public into panic. But this reticence helped along the
fantastic charge that he "did nothing" and remained "indifferent" to mass distress when the world economy was
collapsing.

Another quality that limits Hoover as a political craftsman
is his sensitiveness. He "was always the thinnest-skinned
executive in Washington," according to Charles Michelson,
former Democratic Party press chief. Under the kind of opposition Hoover faced after 1930, Michelson wrote, "a stronger
President would have carried his fight to the people." But
Hoover's "instinct recoiled from conflict." Where F. D. R.
relished a slugging-match in the klieg lights, Hoover suffered abuse in silence.

Hoover will defend his views and policies to the limit. But
slurs on his motives and private character he is likely to treat
with hurt contempt. You can ignore attacks "if you're right
with God," according to Quaker precept. It is not a precept
exactly suited to politics. In any case, his Christian humility
under hailstorms of brickbats has saddened and exasperated
his friends.

Political Naïveté

NAÏVETÉ is a strange word to apply to a man who amassed a
fortune before he was 40; who has dealt as an equal with all
the great of his lifespan; who knows the peoples of the world
more intimately than any other American in public life. But
it is a word that cannot be by-passed in appraising Herbert
Hoover.

Despite sad experiences, he continued to deal with politicians on the level of disinterested patriotism. Then he stared
in pained disbelief when leaders broke solemn pledges; when
Congressmen failed to keep confidences involving the public
welfare; when Senators made agreements only to break them
at a convenient moment.

His basic trouble, declares a one-time member of his cabinet, is that he won high office at one bound, without passing through the rough-and-tumble of precinct politics with its free and easy opportunism.

Hence his failure to use the potent levers of patronage. There is the story—typical of dozens—of two midwestern Senators who came to urge the appointment of a party hack to a vacant federal judgeship in their state. What were his qualifications, Hoover asked. Chiefly that his influence was badly needed in the next election, they admitted. "Well, put that in writing," the President said with a straight face, "and I'll give it due consideration."

The fact that he has a great aversion to ghost writers seemed to some stalwarts of his party as old-fashioned as his collars. He has discarded the collars but not his allergy to literary ghosts. Be it ever so unglamorous, there's no speech like your own, Hoover insists.

He scrawls his first draft in pencil, edits it laboriously, then has it copied. It looks like a futurist design gone haywire before he is through. This is set up in type by a printer accustomed to deciphering the puzzle, and Hoover will revise a dozen or so successive sets of proof before he is satisfied.

Quaker Influence

THE FACT is that Hoover never went into politics at all. He went into public service. That is why the usual political yardsticks fail to give his true measure. The first and only office for which he ever ran was the Presidency.

From the apex of financial fortune he could look back on austere years and strenuous struggles. The public has somehow forgotten how humble were his beginnings. But wealth for him was never an end. It was simply the means to an end: the independence that would allow him to serve his fellow men.

He sometimes confided this personal program to close friends, and they have recorded that there was no bravado about it. It was not a dream of self-abnegation but of self-fulfillment. Hoover talked of doing something for humanity in the way that other rising young men talk of achieving yachts and estates.

Men rarely outgrow their childhoods. Hoover's deepest faults and steepest virtues alike are related to his Quaker background. He was born on August 10, 1874, in a one-story cottage not far from his father's blacksmith shop in the Friends' settlement of West Branch, Iowa. Among the birthplaces of Presidents, only Lincoln's log cabin was a shade more humble.

The Hoovers dressed in Quaker gray, used the plain speech, filled with "thees" and "thys." Their days and years centered around the meetinghouse. To them life was real and earnest, and "doing good" its main purpose. In the Quaker view man is born good, though the world may corrupt him. It enjoins service to others, not as a sacrifice or duty but as a God-given privilege.

Herbert Clark was only six when his father died; but before his mother passed away he was nearly ten, so that her sweetness and humility remained with him forever. In the four years of her widowhood Huldah Hoover supported her three children by taking in sewing, but her real vocation was preaching. Quakers throughout Iowa came to know her soft, unstudied eloquence. Though Herbert remembered few of her words, their general purport, which was love and charity, colored his mind and instincts indelibly.

When he was 11, the orphaned Hoover went to Oregon to live with an uncle, Dr. John Minthorn. There he spent six years among the pioneers of the Northwest. It was there that a visiting mining engineer fired the boy's interest in geology and gave the decisive bent to his life.

First Jobs

IN THE SUMMER of 1891 he entered the newly opened Stanford University at Palo Alto, Calif., a member of its very first class. He paid his way by working as secretary to a professor, as agent of a laundry service, at other chores. He became a campus leader and made friendships that endure to this day. Above all, it was there that he met Lou Henry, the tall, good-looking, studious girl who was to share his life.

His first job after graduation was as a common laborer in a

mine in Nevada City, at $2.50 a day. The experience stood him in good stead in judging mines and miners.

Over in San Francisco a leading engineer, Louis Janin, reigned in the profession. Hoover went to him "cold." There was no job but he got one anyhow, for Janin was a connoisseur of ability. Two years later Janin was asked by a London firm to recommend a director for its properties in Western Australia, where a gold rush was under way. The request was explicit: an engineer with "the strength of a man of 25 and the experience of a man of 75."

The 23-year-old Hoover could scarcely believe his employer had picked him. But he signed up, at $7500 a year, and was off on an adventure that put him among the most celebrated and successful practical engineers of his generation.

Marriage waited another two years, until Lou Henry had gotten her engineering degree. A long trek of exploration in the heart of China was their honeymoon. Together they weathered a thousand trials and dangers, including the siege of Tientsin in the Boxer riots. The hundreds of Chinese and foreign lives they saved at the risk of their own made a saga of courage among old China hands.

Political propaganda later put an accent of irony into the phrase, but Hoover was in simple truth the Great Engineer. He climbed rapidly in his profession until his enterprises stretched around the globe.

Meanwhile the seed planted by his mother flourished in his heart. He looked on his amazing success as only a prelude to the vocation of service. When the time was ripe, he stepped into it like one returning home.

Then Came War

THE SHOT at Sarajevo in 1914 stranded some 200,000 Americans, tourists and permanent residents, in Europe. The banks ceased to honor American checks. Ships were scarce. Frontiers were closed. It was a tangled situation touched by panic. Then Ambassador Walter Hines Page in London asked Hoover to take hold of the whole mess.

This Hoover did, quietly, without ballyhoo, and so expertly that only a few realized they were witnessing a miracle of efficiency. Somehow he found the staff, the transportation. With ten others whom he drew into the gamble, he induced an American bank in London to cash any kind of paper for stranded Americans—on the personal pledge of himself and his associates to make good the losses. Before the exodus was completed, $1,500,000 had been cashed. And his faith was vindicated: only $400 was lost in the gigantic transaction. By the time Congress appropriated a million dollars for repatriation, the job was virtually finished.

Hoover was winding up his European enterprises preparatory to going home when Ambassador Page invited him to organize relief for seven million Belgians facing almost certain starvation. It was not an easy decision. Though well off, he was far from the goal he had set for himself as the measure of independence. With his associates he controlled a substantial part of the world's lead and zinc. At the start of a mechanized world war, these metals were suddenly worth their weight in gold.

There was never any doubt that he would answer the challenge of human misery. The real question was whether to retain business interests or to renounce private ambitions entirely. For three days he wrestled with the decision. Quaker-fashion, he and Mrs. Hoover prayed for guidance. On the fourth morning, when he came down for breakfast, he seemed unusually serene, according to Will Irwin, who was present as a house guest.

"Well, let fortune go to hell," Hoover remarked, as casually as if he were canceling a week-end vacation. Recalling the moment, Irwin later wrote: "I felt then, I know now, that I had witnessed a significant moment in history."

His decision was destined to affect the lives of hundreds of millions of human beings. From that moment the story of Hoover became the stuff of world history. Never had a great business career been so abruptly renounced and a greater career of social service launched. "You can take the business," he announced simply to his associates. He was through with mining and money-making.

Accepts No Remuneration

SINCE THEN, Hoover has not kept a dollar in remuneration from any source for his own use. From the first hour of the Belgian job to the last of his recent mission to Europe, he has paid his expenses out of his own pocket. His salary as Secretary of Commerce he distributed in full to raise the incomes of aides who needed it or to pay for expert personnel not provided by Congress. He sent a check for $300,000—his entire income as President—to the Treasury Department on the day he left the White House. Money from writing or speaking went to private and public charities.

The Belgian relief effort was an entirely new kind of undertaking for Hoover, but it succeeded supremely under almost impossible conditions. Vast sums and mountains of goods were dispensed, at an overhead cost of seven eighths of one percent; normally charity projects are lucky if they keep overhead under 20 percent. It was the greatest relief undertaking in human history; greater ones came later, also under Hoover's management.

Hoover became Food Administrator for President Wilson during the war; "to hooverize" became a new verb in the dictionary. If it is true that food won that war, then he must rank with Pershing among the architects of victory. After the Armistice he became Director General of Relief and virtual economic dictator of all Europe; for three years he fed and clothed ten million children in Central and Eastern Europe. Then famine-stricken Soviet Russia absorbed his attention.

All in all, in the decade 1914–1924, Hoover raised and distributed over five billion dollars—34,000,000 tons of supplies —under war and chaotic postwar conditions. Every dollar, every pound was accounted for, without a single scandal, without taint of profiteering or waste.

Russian Relief

THE LEGEND that he used food as a political weapon is dear to the hearts of Communists. But I have before me the resolution of the Council of People's Commissars, signed at the

Kremlin on July 10, 1923. It thanks the Americans, and specifically Herbert Hoover, through "whose entirely unselfish efforts . . . millions of people of all ages were saved from death."

So far as he could do so without giving offense, Hoover evaded all honors. But grateful peoples in a dozen countries named streets and squares for him and raised statues to him. Messages of thanks signed by the great and the humble poured in on him—bearing a total of nearly four million signatures.

To THE FRIENDS of Hoover—there are hundreds of them, scholars, journalists, businessmen, diplomats—he was "the Chief" long before he became President. He has never built a personal political machine; very few of his intimates are politicians. But they form a kind of loose fraternity. Because of their intense loyalty to Hoover, they are loyal to one another.

I became increasingly aware, in talking to a great many of these friends, that I was dealing with initiates of a cult—a cult that rested solely on affection. Once a year as many of these initiates as can manage it get together at a dinner. There are usually several hundred of them. It is a purely sentimental occasion, a family gathering, and no one knows just how it started. A "silver" loving cup made of tin, presented to the guest who has come the longest distance, has been won by men who arrived from Europe and China, Africa and Australia.

Probably no one in our times, unless it be Franklin D. Roosevelt, has been under such terrific personal attack. But no attack has ever come from people close to Hoover. He has many enemies but no ex-friends.

In fighting his battles, however, his friends get little encouragement from Hoover. He has always been remarkably restrained, for instance, in discussing Franklin D. Roosevelt. His associates have no such inhibitions. They are unanimous in the opinion that no other American President ever was so shabbily treated by his successor.

Their indictment begins with the day of Roosevelt's inauguration. Traditionally the departing President continues
to be guarded by Secret Service men as long as he deems it desirable. That tradition was broken on March 4, 1933. Anti-
Hoover feelings were then inflamed. Some crackpot act was
quite conceivable. But Hoover's secretaries were informed
that on orders from higher up all his federal guards had been
withdrawn.

Their indictment ends, of course, with the notorious refusal of the Government to use Hoover's services during the
war. Secretary of War Stimson, Secretary of State Hull,
Bernard Baruch and others pleaded with the White House to
put Hoover's talents to work. If only as a token of national
unity, some of them argued, the only living ex-President
should be given a share in the national effort. Pleas and arguments were of no avail. Hoover had opposed armed American
participation in the war up to Pearl Harbor. He had proposed
alternative policies which he believed would lead to a more
stable and prosperous world. But on the night of Pearl Harbor he announced that "the debate was closed" and pledged
his wholehearted devotion to the cause of victory.

The tasks of the war and later the problems of rehabilita-
tion were too important, he maintained, to squander national
energies in post-mortems and recriminations. In line with
this conviction he has consistently refused to be interviewed
on the rights and wrongs of the Government's actions leading
up to the entry into the war. When I referred to a statement
attributed to him in a recent article widely quoted in the
press, he declared firmly that no quotations on this subject
purporting to come from him had his sanction.

The Hoovers would never tolerate personal attacks on the
Roosevelts in their home. One night some years ago a guest
was heatedly assailing the character of F. D. R. Mrs. Hoover
turned to her neighbor—on whose authority I have the story
—and whispered, "Please, *please* talk loud and fast about
something else, anything else!" He did and his stentorian
voice drowned out the Roosevelt-hater.

Tracing the Vilification

No PRESIDENT, not even Washington or Lincoln, escaped vilification in his lifetime. But Hoover received vastly more than his normal quota. Usually the defeated party in a presidential election subsides until the next contest. Not so after Hoover's election. The Democratic National Committee proceeded to pour more than $3,000,000 into a continuous attack on the Hoover administration—at the time the largest partisan expenditure between campaigns in American history.

The major portion went into high-powered assault on the President. Every new disaster—drought, flood, or financial crash—was processed into ammunition against the administration. Hoover's every slip of the tongue blossomed into thousands of mocking cartoons.

The partisan drive, moreover, was expanded by a prodigious private campaign that was to continue long after Hoover left the White House. Arthur Train, lawyer and author, described the published anti-Hoover stuff as "a veritable library of scurrilous books . . . conceived either in partisan animosity, in the mere lust for profit, or in a surreptitious hope of blackmail."

He was referring especially to five books, of which the most reckless was *The Strange Career of Mr. Hoover Under Two Flags* by one John Hamill, a naturalized Englishman. It was an unprincipled stew of falsehoods, which Hamill himself finally repudiated. The other books derived mostly from "the same polluted source," as Train put it.

Yet these books have furnished the raw stuff on which anti-Hoover propaganda has fed ever since. People who cannot cite a single specific proof still echo the vague impression that there was something "fishy" about Hoover's mining operations; that he accepted British citizenship; or some other farfetched invention.

If there was one thing beyond doubt, it was Hoover's preeminence as an engineer. He went to the top of a profession in which a reputation for probity was as important as technical ability. He became what one associate called "a great doctor of sick companies." His technical writings set standards for the industry.

During those years he warned the public against speculating in mines. "Idiots" was his word for gullible investors, contempt his feeling for promoters who practiced what he called "the science of extracting the greatest possible sum of money from some other human being."

The principal fable launched by the attackers, however, was that Hoover had been a promoter and speculator rather than an engineer. Surely it was not for his prowess in promotion that his colleagues—in a close-knit professional community familiar with every item in his career—elected him president of the American Institute of Mining and Metallurgical Engineers, and of the American Engineering Council; or bestowed endless other honors for his services.

Hoover was a junior partner in Bewick, Moreing and Company when one of its members secretly speculated with funds entrusted to him, piling up losses of $900,000. In 1902 when he was exposed and sent to prison, the 28-year-old Hoover was in charge in the London office.

Though there was no legal compulsion on the firm, Hoover, without waiting to consult his associates, announced that they would make good every dollar out of their own pockets. This is precisely what they did. For Hoover it was a financial calamity, wiping out his savings. But in the hands of the smear artists even that episode was twisted into a fable of frenzied finance.

The "two-flags" part of the fabrication was worked overtime. Assignments abroad are in the nature of the mining engineer's calling. In addition to Australia, Hoover's duties took him to China, South Africa, Russia, Latin America, wherever metals were stored in God's earth.

Always it was as an American, introducing American machinery and methods, that he worked. Throughout the English-speaking world he was referred to as "Hail Columbia" Hoover, his initials being H.C. It is a remarkable fact, considering his world-wide interests, that he spent only two full years, 1898 and 1907, wholly outside the American borders.

Others whose business takes them abroad may live for a dozen years away from home without having their Americanism questioned.

But it suited Hoover's detractors to spread the two-flags legend, alleging that he had become a British citizen. They offered "documentary evidence"—his name on a local English voters' list. Hoover owned a house in England and all taxpayers were automatically put on such lists. Had he tried to vote he would, of course, have been disqualified as a foreigner. It is of such flimsy stuff that smears are manufactured!

The other half of the accusation against Hoover, especially after he left the White House, was to the effect that he "did nothing" to combat the depression. Under examination such charges boil down to disagreement with his basic economic and political philosophy. It is not that he "did nothing" but that he did not do the things which advocates of totally different philosophies demanded.

Hoover was then, and remains today, an inflexible believer in free economy, individualism, maximum local self-help; a principled opponent of "big government," inflationary spending, excessive government controls. To impugn his humanity because he adopted policies in line with his deepest convictions makes little sense.

Social-Betterment Program

WHAT MATTERS, in appraising Hoover's character, is that he worked with superhuman zeal to stem disaster and relieve suffering. Year after year, as Secretary of Commerce, he had warned against the dangers of overproduction and speculation. On January 15, 1925, when it was heresy to doubt the millennium of American prosperity, he pointed to "the unemployment and bankruptcy which comes with the inevitable slump." Now that his fears were coming true, he spared neither himself nor his staff to stave off panic and to safeguard the American way of life and government.

He set up the Reconstruction Finance Corporation, the Home Loan Banks, the National Credit Association, the

Railroad Credit Association and a score of other enterprises novel and even revolutionary in their day. He forced through a hostile economy-minded Congress public works and relief projects of a scope without precedent at that time. He pleaded with the Democratic Congress, in vain, for $120,000 to continue the President's Organization on Unemployment Relief. During his four-year term, more peace-time public construction was undertaken than in the 36 years preceding, including the Panama Canal.

He had assumed the Presidency with an ambitious plan of social betterment in mind. The White House Conferences on Child Health and Protection, on Home Building and Housing, the President's Research Committee on Social Trends, his specific proposals for reform in every department of American life are indications of a program that was thwarted by events.

It was a tragic Presidency, and never so tragic as in its last four months, between the November election and the March inauguration of Roosevelt. To grasp the picture it must be recalled that the depression had been arrested and recovery started by the middle of 1932. "The change for the better in the last half of 1932 is beyond dispute," the Democratic New York *Times* wrote editorially on June 16, 1934. "That this evident revival of confidence was suddenly reversed in February 1933 is equally true." The Kansas City *Star* (January 26, 1936) declared that "there was an abrupt and important revival" in the summer of 1932 but that in November, after the election, "began a deterioration." The Brookings Institution in 1937 reached the same conclusion.

The new confidence was obliterated by the result of the election. Business was paralyzed, bank withdrawals skyrocketed; stock prices, which had risen from a low of 34 in July to 56 in September, tobogganed again. The panic which Hoover had warded off for three years was "around the corner."

This time he was powerless to stop it. It has been truly said that there is nothing as dead as a defeated administration. Only the President-elect had the prestige to reassure the public. No doubt he had his own good reasons, but the fact is that Roosevelt adamantly rejected Hoover's pleas for co-operation in that direction. "The baby is not on my door-step," he was reported as saying.

The decline touched off by Hoover's defeat reached the panic point with the bank closings at the moment his successor took over. Whatever may be said about the preceding years, surely the final debacle had more to do with the incoming than the outgoing administration. But full blame for that, too, was loaded on Hoover by the busy mythmakers.

I asked Hoover this question: "In the perspective of time, if you knew then what you know now, would you have changed any of your major policies as President?"

"No," he answered promptly. "I am convinced of the essential correctness of my administration's policies. We definitely had the depression licked, but the election of the New Deal reversed the trend and perpetuated the depression. Remember that mass unemployment and relief remained higher than at any time during my term—until a war came along to solve the situation.

"As to relief policies, I believed then and believe even more so now, after the spectacle of the New Deal years, that we were right in keeping it on a local basis and out of politics. Centralization of relief brought with it bureaucracy, waste and political trading on human misery. The cost of administering relief went up threefold as soon as it was federalized. Armies of relief officials were created with a vested interest in prolonging the emergency. The instincts of charity and mutual help, all the vast spiritual leverages, which can be brought into play only on a local basis, were never used again."

Perhaps the most striking example of how Hoover was made the scapegoat of every new trouble is provided by the famous Bonus March of July 1932. In the folklore of our time it is firmly fixed that Hoover's federal "cossacks" shot down and killed veterans. That statement can still be found in Communist assaults on Hoover. But there is not a shadow of truth in it.

Two veterans had been killed and several wounded in clashes between the local police force and rioters *before* U. S. troops came to the scene; it was that, in fact, which led to the calling of the troops. But—and I quote from a letter to me by General Patrick J. Hurley, then Secretary of War—

"Not one single shot was fired nor was any person seriously injured after the arrival of United States troops. Law and order were restored in Washington."

The Unknown President

FATE HAS BEEN generous to our 31st President in allowing him to live long enough to see his own reinstatement in the public's good graces. Despite this, he remains the "unknown ex-President," so many facets of his personality are still hidden from the public.

It is not generally known, for example, that Hoover's passion for research and knowledge is as deep as his passion for fishing, which is saying a good deal. His *Treatise on Mining*, published in 1909, ranks high in the literature of that field. While working huge properties in China, he found time to write a dissertation on Chinese mathematics.

For five years he and Mrs. Hoover worked on a translation of the famous *De Re Metallica* by Agricola, dating back to 1550. Where generations of Latin scholars had failed to render this classic into English, because of their lack of technical equipment, the Hoovers succeeded.

The magnificent Hoover Library, pride of Leland Stanford, is also an expression of his penchant for exact knowledge. In the midst of multitudinous labors during World War I, Hoover began to gather vital war documents which otherwise would have been lost to posterity. This collection he has kept up ever since. Priceless records of the Russian Revolution and civil wars—three carloads were transported with Lenin's help—are at Palo Alto, along with such invaluable finds as the archives of the Kaiser's General Staff; documentary materials on the recent underground resistance movements; valuable archive materials of the suppressed Baltic republics.

There are people who practice sin in secret—but Hoover has reversed the process. He is one of the rare few who practice virtue in secret. He goes to extraordinary lengths to hide his benevolences, especially from those who benefit.

"For 20 years," Will Irwin wrote in 1928, "I have in California or New York observed men and women of our common acquaintance sliding smoothly through a crisis like a long illness or unemployment. Then, years later perhaps, I will learn that the solvent was—Hoover."

He will wangle a job, a loan or some other help for distressed individuals. Only years later, if ever, do they discover who was behind it.

The hallmark of Hoover's personality, however, is his limitless concern for children. Every one of his associates sooner or later remarked on this. Two of them confided that they had seen the Chief weeping. The incidents were more than 20 years apart, but they both involved Hoover's extreme sensibility to the sufferings of children.

The first incident was after the first World War, when a campaign for child famine relief was under way. Some 30 urchins called on Hoover, each clutching pennies in hot, not overly clean palms: their contribution to the fund. Hoover began to talk to them, but suddenly tears came to his eyes and he walked away to hide them.

The second incident was in his New York suite, during the second World War. My informant was present when a visitor was describing in detail the ordeal of little children in Nazified countries. Hoover suddenly walked to the window and turned his back on the room. The others looked away in embarrassment when his shoulders began to shake with sobbing.

There has been incomparably more work than play in Hoover's life, from childhood up. His favorite recreations have been of the meditative brand, particularly fishing and camping with a few loved friends.

No doubt there is an atavistic edge of sinfulness for his Quaker conscience when he plays a hot game of gin-rummy, for microscopic stakes, with Hugh Gibson or some other crony. At last reports Gibson was in the hole to the chief for nearly two bucks.

Personality Sidelights

HIS CAPACITY for work, and his bodily stamina, are legendary. During critical periods in the White House, most of his staff literally collapsed under the Hoover regimen—a typical day began at six a.m. and ended around midnight.

In a letter home by Frank E. Mason, one of Hoover's companions on the 1946 world jaunt, I found this passage: "Several members of the crew were indisposed and even our medico, Dr. Rey, spent the day in bed. Through it all, the Chief goes imperturbably on, writing his talks with a pencil, and handing them to Hugo Meier to be copied. He has stood up under the terrific pace in a miraculous manner."

Hoover's memory is close to phenomenal. He is an omnivorous reader—everything from economic and sociological works to mysteries. He can devour a large volume in one sitting and retain what he has read well enough to pass a test on it. In Shanghai during the 1946 visit, top American military officers one night spread out maps and explained the complex Chinese military picture. Drawing on his experience of nearly half a century before, Hoover was able to contribute exhaustive details about local topography in remote regions. The officers were awe-struck by that feat of memory.

Most revealing of his personality, however, are the stories his intimates tell that express his inborn humility, his flight from the limelight. One of his keenest annoyances as President was the constant presence of guards, reporters and cameramen when he went to Quaker meeting. One Sunday he escaped surveillance.

At breakfast Mrs. Hoover announced to their guests, Mr. and Mrs. Rickard, that she had heard of a tiny meetinghouse somewhere near Baltimore. Like conspirators the Hoovers and the Rickards stole out of the White House and drove to this little prayer room. There were only a dozen or so worshipers. No one paid any attention to the new arrivals, as is the Quaker way. After long silent meditation, the

Washington group headed for home. The President confided that it was one of his truly happy days.

HERBERT HOOVER's life has been long and variegated beyond most human experiences. It has run the gamut from Lincoln-esque poverty to riches, from common manual labor to the Presidency, from global business to global benevolence. But in the variety there is a discernible pattern. Strands from one period continually show up in the design of other periods.

When he was visiting Oslo in 1938, a farmer journeyed a long distance especially to see him. He brought with him a boy's jacket. He had kept the child's garment for nearly 20 years, he explained to the American visitor, as a memento of Hoover relief and had come to thank him personally.

Hoover's arrival in Brussels in 1946 brought cheering thousands into the streets, among them many who owed their survival 30-odd years ago to his work. In Belgrade, a member of Tito's cabinet, Foreign Minister Simich, declared at a public reception, "If it were not for Hoover relief in Serbia 30 years ago, I wouldn't be here tonight."

In Warsaw a woman physician in the course of a conference blurted out that she owed her life to Hoover: she had been one of the millions of East European children fed by his organization. Then she turned to the Communist officials at the conference table. "Own up," she said, "that but for Mr. Hoover's food you, too, wouldn't be here." They solemnly acknowledged the fact.

Some weeks later, in Shanghai, two socially prominent Chinese women asked separately to pay their respects to the former American President. Amazingly, each told the same story: she had been taken in by the Hoovers during the Boxer riots in 1900 when the lives of less fortunate children were being snuffed out.

Yes, there is a pattern in the diversity of the Hoover career and its distinctive design is mercy. Neither the ravages of time nor the malice of political propaganda has sufficed to blur it. The soft-voiced woman preacher of the Friends' settlement in West Branch, Iowa, though she died early, did not live in vain.

We Shook the Family Tree

A condensation from the book by

HILDEGARDE DOLSON

Illustrations by Robert Day

THE Dolson household in Franklin, Pa., was a hilarious one. Hildegarde, the eldest of four live-wire children, contributed her share to adventures and escapades that kept the family tree aquiver.

In *We Shook the Family Tree* she tells the whole funny family story with engaging irreverence, a barbed pen and an amusing feeling for the less important but more lighthearted things in life.

PERHAPS the surest way to tell when a female goes over the boundary from childhood into meaningful adolescence is to watch how long it takes her to get to bed at night. My own crossover—which could be summed up in our family as "What on earth is Hildegarde *doing* in the bathroom?"—must have occurred when I was a freshman in high school. Until then, I fell into bed dog-tired each night, after the briefest possible bout with toothbrush and washcloth. But once I'd become aware of the Body Beautiful, as advertised in women's magazines, my absorption was complete.

I particularly had my eyes on a miraculous substance called Beauty Clay. In the advertisements the story of its discovery was a masterpiece in lyrical prose. Seems this girl was traveling in an obscure European country when she ran out of make-up. Through some intuitive process she had the presence of mind to go to a nearby hamlet, pick up a handful of mud and plaster it on her face. Then she lay dozing in the sun. When she came to and washed the claylike mud off her face, she was transformed. Judging by the Before-and-After pictures, the treatment had benefited even her nose, eyes and hair.

After pondering all this, I could well understand why a jar of the imported Beauty Clay cost $4.98. In fact, it was dirt cheap at the price, and my only problem was how to lay my hands on $4.98.

With such important things as Beauty Clay on my mind, it was understandable that my school marks should suffer. Each month, the high school honor roll, consisting of the names of the ten highest students in each class, was published in the Franklin *News-Herald*. And each month, my own name was prominently absent. Appeals to my better nature, my pride and the honor of the Dolsons did no good. Finally my father said that if I got on the honor roll he'd give me five dollars. It took me only a flash to realize this sum was approximately equal to the price of the Beauty Clay. Miraculously the next month I got 89 in algebra and climbed to the bottom rung of the honor roll. What is more important, I got the five bucks.

To my chagrin Riesenman's drug-store had no Beauty Clay in stock, but I left an order and went home to wait. With admirable restraint, I waited five days. After that I made daily inquiries on my way home from school. Finally came the wonderful afternoon when Mr. Riesenman said, "Here you are, Hildegarde."

It took a week more before I could achieve the needed privacy for my quick-change act. Mother was taking Jimmy and Sally downtown to get new shoes, Bobby was going skiing and my father, as usual, would be at the office. As soon as I got home to the empty house I made a beeline for the Beauty Clay. According to the directions, I then washed off all make-up, which in my own case was a faint dash of powder on my nose, and wrapped myself in a sheet "to protect that pretty frock" or, more accurately, my blue serge middy blouse. Then I took a small wooden spatula the manufacturer had thoughtfully provided and dug into the jar.

The Beauty Clay was a rather peculiar shade of grayish-green, and I spread this all over my face and neck—"even to the hairline where telltale wrinkles hide." The directions also urged me not to talk or smile during the treatment and indeed, as the thick green clay dried firmly in place, it was the last thing I wanted to do. My face and neck felt as if they'd been cast in cement; obviously, something was happening.

After 15 minutes of this, the door-bell rang. At first I decided to ignore it, but in my eagerness to see who it was I ran to my window, opened it and leaned out. It was only the man who brought us country butter each week, I was glad to note. When he looked up and saw me, he let out a hoarse, awful sound and ran down the steep hill at incredible speed.

It wasn't until I'd remembered the clay and went to look in a mirror that I understood. Swathed in a sheet and with every visible millimeter of skin a sickly gray-green, I scared even myself.

According to the clock, the Beauty Clay had been on the required 20 minutes now, but it occurred to me that if 20 minutes was enough to make me beautiful, 30 minutes or even 40 minutes would make me twice as beautiful.

By the time my face was so rigid that even my eyeballs felt yanked from their sockets, I knew I must be done, on both sides. As I started back to the bathroom, I heard Bobby's voice downstairs yelling, "Mom!" With the haste born of horror I ran back and just managed to bolt myself inside the bathroom as Bobby leaped up the stairs. Then I turned on the faucet and set to work. The directions had particularly warned: "Use only gentle splashes to remove the mask—no rubbing or washcloth." It took several minutes of gentle splashing to make me realize this was getting me nowhere fast. Indeed, it was like splashing playfully at the Rock of Gibraltar. I decided that maybe it wouldn't hurt if I rubbed the beauty mask just a little, with a nailbrush. This hurt only the nailbrush.

By this time I was getting worried. Mother would be home very soon and I needed a face—even any old face. Suddenly it occurred to me that a silver knife would be a big help, although I wasn't sure just how. In desperation, I ran down to the sideboard, tripping over my sheet as I went, and got the knife. Unfortunately, just as I was coming back through the dusky upstairs hall, Bobby walked out of his room and met me, face to face.

I had often imagined how my family would look at me after the Beauty Clay had taken effect. Now it had taken effect—or even permanent possession of me—and Bobby was certainly reacting, but not quite as I'd pictured it.

"Wh-what?" he finally managed to croak, pointing at my face.

I tried to explain, but the sounds that came out alarmed

him even more. Frantically I dashed into the bathroom and began hitting the handle of the knife against my rocky visage. To my heavenly relief, it began to crack. Taking advantage of the fissures in my surface, I dug the blade of the knife in, and by scraping, gouging, digging, and praying, I got part of my face clear. As soon as I could talk, I turned on Bobby, who stood at the door watching, completely bemused. "If you tell anybody about this, I'll kill you," I said fiercely.

Bobby nodded mutely. Whether it was the intensity of my threat or a latent chivalry aroused by seeing a lady tortured before his very eyes that moved him, I still don't know. "But what is it?" he asked in a hushed voice.

"Beauty Clay," I said. "I sent away for it."

Suddenly I remembered why I'd gone through this ordeal, and I now looked into the mirror expecting to see results that would wipe out all memory of suffering. The reflection that met my eye was certainly changed all right, varying as it did between an angry scarlet, where the skin had been rubbed off, to the greenish splotches still clinging. I gazed at myself wearily, all hope abandoned. Instead of the Body Beautiful I looked like the Body Boiled.

"You look awfully red," Bobby said. I did indeed. To add to my troubles, we could now hear the family assembling downstairs, and Mother's voice came up, "Hildegarde, will you come set the table right away, dear?"

As I moved numbly toward the stairs, Bobby whispered, "Why don't you say you were frostbitten and rubbed yourself with snow?"

I looked at him with limp gratitude.

When Mother saw my scarlet, splotched face, she exclaimed in concern, "Why, Hildegarde, are you feverish?" She made a move as if to feel my forehead, but I backed away. I was burning up, but not with fever.

"I'm all right," I said, applying myself to setting the table. With my face half in the china cupboard, I mumbled that I'd been frostbitten and had rubbed myself with snow.

"Oh, Cliff," Mother called, "little Hildegarde was frostbitten."

My father immediately came out of the kitchen. "How could she be frostbitten?" he asked reasonably. "It's 34 above zero."

Bobby had followed me out to the kitchen to see how the frostbite went over. My father stared at him. "Bobby, did you and your friends knock Hildegarde down and rub her face with snow?" he asked.

"Me?" Bobby squeaked. He gave me a dirty look, as if to say, "You'd better talk fast."

I denied hotly that Bobby had done any such thing. In fact, I proceeded to build him up as my sole rescuer, a great big St. Bernard of a brother who had come bounding through the snowdrifts to bring me life and hope.

My father and mother remained unconvinced. Against this new setup of Brother Loves Sister they were suspicious, but they let the subject drop.

And in a way I *had* been frost-bitten, to the quick. I was sore and unbeautiful, and mulcted of five dollars.

There seems to be a popular theory that little girls who have brothers learn very early to adopt an easy, bantering manner toward members of the opposite sex. In my own case, this theory held water like a sieve. When it came to social presence, I had none.

At Miss Steele's dancing school, when the boys chose partners, I was invariably among the leftovers for whom Miss Steele had to rush up reinforcements by the napes of their necks. On the days when there weren't enough boys to go around, somehow I was always one of the girls who danced with a girl. As a wallflower, I was rapidly going to seed.

I was now a sophomore in high school and much more concerned over the fact that Mother wouldn't let me wear high heels than that I was undoubtedly about to flunk geometry. Even more acute was the throbbing fear that I wouldn't be asked to the Junior Prom. I had a grim conviction that now was the test of whether I was to face the future as a withered old maid or a prom-trotter.

Unfortunately, a freshman in short pants named Freddie Perkins settled the matter five days before the prom, by edging up to me at the end of study hall and requesting my company. Somehow it had never occurred to me that it was possible to be asked to a prom by the wrong man—especially a man in short pants—and the stark horror in my face must have frightened even Freddie, because he backed away several paces and stood waiting for my answer. He had non-descript hair parted in the middle above goggle-rim glasses, and the whole effect was profoundly depressing.

I began concocting an elaborate excuse about going to Meadville to visit an aunt, when a nasty thought struck me. "Does your mother know you were going to ask me?

"Of course," Freddie said, obviously surprised that I could think him capable of such folly on his own hook. "She *told* me to."

The thought of what would happen when Mrs. Perkins cross-questioned Freddie and phoned my mother stopped me short. I muttered something which Freddie took to mean consent and went glumly down to gym class.

While we were struggling into our middies in the locker room, Ellie May Matthews, a sharp-nosed girl I disliked with abandon, said maybe I could get my kid brother to take me to the prom. With that, I yanked up my bloomers and prepared to defend my honor. "I'm going with somebody else," I said haughtily. Looking her straight in the eye, I unblushingly added that as a matter of fact I'd had two invitations, but Mother had made me turn down the best one.

"Then who are you going with?" she persisted. It was one of those moments when I'd gladly have traded my present setup for a desert island and a geometry teacher. "Freddie Perkins," I said.

The ensuing silence was hideous, with the thought of Freddie's pants hanging unmentionably in the air. Even Ellie May was too taken aback to speak. "The family made me," I added hopelessly. My friend Betty Evans did her loyal best for a lost cause by saying that Freddie was awfully bright. "He's on the honor roll every month." As we filed onto the gym floor, she said delicately that maybe the Perkinses would buy Freddie a new suit.

For five days I silently implored Heaven to get Freddie out of short pants, and argued with Mother about my own costume for the prom. She was lengthening my pink organdy dress by adding a ruffle around the knees, and she listened unmoved to my wild-eyed descriptions of what the other girls were wearing. "I don't know what their mothers can be thinking of," she'd say firmly, making it clear that my chances of getting a pleated red crepe and high-heeled satin slippers dyed to match were as remote as judgment day. She was equally adamant about dangly earrings from Woolworth's, but she finally promised that if it were a nice warm night I could wear her Spanish shawl, at present decorating the piano.

Cheered by a mental image of myself tossing a shawl about with Castilian grace and a rose in my hair, I concentrated on coaxing for a boyish bob. Always before I'd had my hair cut by the same barber who did my brothers'. The one ladies' hairdresser in town was a man named Mister Leo, who often vanished for a week at a time on what I now realize must have been binges of the first magnitude. Mother disapproved of him sharply, but, on the afternoon of the prom, worn down by my bulldog tenacity, she finally consented.

I think I must have caught Mister Leo in an off moment just after a binge, because he whacked off my hair in what struck even me as a somewhat impetuous manner. Mother let out an involuntary shriek when I trotted home proudly to display my coiffure, and at dinner Bobby referred to me crudely as "Ratface," until Father threatened to send him from the table.

After dinner Mother got to work on me with a curling iron, and the Spanish shawl was dragged from the piano for my further adornment. Sally, whose bedtime had been postponed to allow her to watch this gilding process, was big-eyed with envy. "Will you stay up past ten o'clock?" she kept asking. I said, "Pooh," ten o'clock was early, and intimated that if there were a creak on the stairs toward morning it would be Hildegarde Coming Home.

Mother, who was now brandishing the iron on my shortest

back wisps, said amiably that 12 o'clock was late enough for
a little girl of 15. However, she agreed that as long as I was
with Freddie she wouldn't worry. In a way, I could see what
she meant.

By 8:15 I was dressed to the teeth. As I stood before the
downstairs hall mirror, trying the Spanish shawl at every
possible angle, the sound of the doorbell froze me in my
tracks. Would Freddie have new pants or wouldn't he?

I opened the door, took one look at Freddie's legs and experienced a primitive urge to push him off the porch. The
fact that he was not only in short pants but carrying an umbrella filled me with sullen rage. "It's going to rain," he said.
"You'd better wear your rubbers."

Rather impulsively I shut the door in his face, knowing
that if Mother saw Freddie's rain outfit I'd never get out of
the house without my rubbers. Grabbing up the shawl, I
dashed into the living room to say good-bye. "Can't Freddie
come in, dear?" Mother asked.

"No, he says we're late. Some other kids are waiting at the
corner." Then I turned and bolted to my doom.

Freddie watched patiently while I hitched the Spanish
shawl up over one shoulder and anchored it at the left hip
with my elbow. "What's that?" he asked.

"It's an evening wrap," I said fiercely.

In silence we started out. About halfway down the first
block, Freddie asked me what I got in Latin last month. He
also checked up on my marks in English, history and geometry, and then mentioned smugly
that he'd had all A's. About that
time it began to rain, and he hoisted
the umbrella with the righteous air
of a man who's always right. "It's
a good thing I brought this," he
said. It was at this point that I remarked pleasantly I'd rather die of
pneumonia than be seen carrying an
umbrella.

We walked the rest of the way

in damp silence. In those days, a boy who wore a yellow slicker with everybody's nickname written on the back was *smooth*. A boy who got all A's and carried an umbrella was *dumb*. The fact that Freddie also wore short pants put him in some horrible category beyond description.

I felt this even more despairingly as we walked into the high school gym past laughing groups of couples, all of whom I suspected darkly of laughing at Freddie's pants and my Spanish shawl. The gym was a brilliant glare, with Japanese lanterns strung along the walls for exotic atmosphere, and the five-piece orchestra a dazzling spectacle on a platform at one end of the room. Somebody handed Freddie a dance program with a dangling little pencil attached, and my heart went down into my damp white shoes as I looked at it. Ten dances to fill out. All around me were boys in white flannels and dark-blue serge coats, but I was doomed to dance all evening with a pair of short pants.

In panic, I fled to the girls' dressing room. It was crowded with the same girls I sat with in classes, but now that they were all dressed up and laughing shrilly together I felt stiff with loneliness. While I stood miserably in one corner, trying to decide where to put my shawl, Betty Evans came in. She admired my new boyish bob with heartening coos and then turned all around so that I could get the full effect of her lavender crepe with lace panels. When we went back to the gym, I hung on her arm trustingly, because she'd been to three dances in the last year and it reassured me to be seen with such a sophisticate.

Our escorts were nowhere in sight, but that didn't abash Betty in the least. She hailed one of the boys, a senior I viewed with awe because he played halfback on the football team. "Ooooooo, Stevie," she called gaily. "What I don't know about you."

Stevie promptly came over. "Yeah, what?"

"Oh, I couldn't tell for anything. You'd die if you knew."

This went on for several minutes, until Stevie insisted he'd get the second dance with Betty and make her tell. "Don't you dare," she squealed after him. I'd been listening in alarmed fascination, and as soon as Stevie had gone off to look for Betty's escort, I asked, "What *did* you hear about him?"

"Nothing," she said. "It's just a line. Boys always like you better if you hand them a line." I stared at her in shocked admiration as her partner came to claim the first dance. Suddenly I felt nakedly young, with no line to guide me.

The next two hours still come back to me in nightmares. Freddie had exchanged dances with five members of the freshman debating team and with Mr. Higgins, the Latin teacher. To say that neither Freddie, his fellow debaters nor Mr. Higgins were good dancers is to wallow in understatement. Freddie went on the principle that a dogged walk from one end of the dance floor to the other was good enough for any girl. Plowing back and forth with him until my legs ached, I tried desperately to look as if I'd never seen him before and was coolly amused at the mistake which had brought us together.

It was while we were plodding through the next to last dance that I heard somebody say, "Hi, Fred, mind if I cut in?" To my utter astonishment, ten seconds later I was gliding down the floor with a tall, handsome boy in a gray suit. "I'm Fred's cousin," the boy said. He mentioned something about stopping overnight on his way home from Allegheny College. "Aunt Helen sent me over here to see Fred," he added. We smiled at each other, and in a daze of emotions, I stumbled all over his feet. I apologized frenziedly, seized with the awful fear that he'd give me back to Freddie. "That was my fault," he said. "I was trying a new step they do down at school, called the Charleston. See, it's kick to the side and then forward."

From then on I drifted along in a rosy haze, kicking to the side and forward. I think he had brown eyes and brown hair, but the important thing was that he was *smooth*, and he actually went to college. We exchanged names—his was Donald—and he told me he was coming back later in the summer to visit. "Now that I have a good reason," he said tenderly, squeezing my hand. At this, I was so overcome that I kicked in the wrong direction and landed a mean one on his shin. Even that didn't seem to discourage my dream prince. "Do you date Freddie very often?" he asked.

I shook my head violently and proceeded to make it very clear that Freddie had little part in my gay, prom-trotting existence. "The family made me come with him tonight and I was furious." Then, remembering that Freddie was his cousin, I added hastily that he was a very nice boy. "But I'd really rather date older men," I concluded brightly. My conscience gave a startled lurch as I said it, but it seemed to have a devastating effect on Donald, because he immediately invited me up for a football game the next fall. Somehow I managed to accept without swooning. We both forgot Freddie completely after that, until he turned up at the tag end of "Home Sweet Home." "Hel-*lo*, where've you been?" I said roguishly.

In the dressing room I was surprised and gratified when at least ten girls greeted me fondly and told me I looked awfully cute. I was even more overcome when the most popular girl in the senior class came up to say that she simply adored my dress. She herself wore a short red taffeta evening wrap, and I was almost blinded by her glory.

"Who were you dancing the last two dances with?" she asked. All the girls crowded around to listen, and suddenly I knew why they'd admired my dress. Instead of resenting it, my lungs nearly burst with pride. "Oh, that's a college man I know," I said. "He's invited me up for a football game next fall."

In the midst of a rustling, respectful silence, I flung the piano shawl grandly over my last year's organdy. "He has a marvelous line," I said. Then I swept out the door.

Probably the only man I have ever left an indelible impression on is my high school physics teacher, who went through hell trying to reduce Archimedes' principle to something I could grasp.

"Now, look, Miss Dolson," he would say, breathing rather hard. "Here we have a jar half full of water, and I will now drop in a block of wood. What happens?"

As far as I could see, nothing happened, but I knew this couldn't be the right answer. To me, it was just a block of wood in water. It grieved me to see Mr. Lowrie suffer, but there was nothing I could do about it, unless Clark Frame, the brightest student in our physics class, managed to slip me the written answer. However, toward the end of the second term, I learned to say glibly, "A floating body displaces its own weight in water," and Mr. Lowrie decided to pass me. After all, I had been with him nine months, and a man can stand just so much.

Thanks to this, and the law that what goes in as a freshman must come out in four years, I was being graduated with the Class of '26, from the Franklin High School. My grasp on *The Deerslayer*, *Julius Caesar* and the dangling participle being considerably firmer than my grasp of physics, I had even been chosen to deliver a speech at commencement.

My entire family and at least ten of my relatives were in the auditorium. It was a very warm evening in June, and all of us seniors, sitting in rows on the platform, found our heavy black robes rather excessive, as speaker after speaker droned on. Finally my name was announced, and I stepped confidently to the center of the stage.

"Ladies, gentlemen and teachers," I began. "We of the Senior Class are now going out into the great world, to stand or fall on our own merits." (This must have been news to all those parents, including my own, who expected to provide food, shelter and clothing for some time to come.)

I drew a deep breath, preparatory to plunging into the body of my speech. In the next second, I knew, with icy shock, that I'd plunged into vacuum. All memory of the speech was gone.

With 500 faces looking up at me in polite expectancy, I shifted my feet and waited. Suddenly the very last sentence of the speech floated into my head, and I grabbed at it thankfully. "Let us all hitch our wagon to a star," I said ringingly, "and continue ever upward—higher and higher and higher." Then, having consumed approximately 55 seconds for my entire oration, I sat down.

The audience, which had come to value brevity almost as much as a good breeze, applauded me roundly. Afterward, all my relatives congratulated me on my nice little speech. I was now presumably ready for college.

Several years before, I had picked the college of my choice —Allegheny—in Meadville, 25 miles from home. My parents had long ago agreed to this choice, but I knew that going to college cost a lot of money, and I wanted to help out. My idea of helping was to crack down on my brothers and Sally whenever they asked my parents for something that cost more than a dime. "We can't afford that until after I've gone to college," I'd announce firmly. This rapidly became the most unpopular slogan in our household. Bobby, Sally and Jimmy mimicked me with fierce displeasure, and whenever they squandered a nickel, they'd say, "Yah, yah, now Hildegarde won't get to college." When September came and Father piled my luggage into the Ford and drove me off, it must have been a relief.

I can't remember just when I first conceived the idea of going to New York "to become a writer," but it must have been shortly after a college beau introduced me to Mencken and Nathan (embalmed between book covers). I became so enamored of Nathan especially, I vowed that when I went to New York I would sit on the doorstep of his hotel till I saw him in person.

Secretly I already thought of myself as a writer, although why I should use the word "secretly" I don't know, since I proclaimed my calling loudly to all comers. After all, didn't I lie in the tub at Hulings Hall and make up poetry for the *Allegheny Literary Monthly?*

At the start of my senior year I suddenly came to the conclusion that I must leave school at once. In my world young ladies didn't become seniors and then say, "To hell with this. Who wants a diploma anyway?" The very idea appalled me, but I knew with a curious grim certainty that I'd come to a dead end, and that there was nowhere to go but out.

My parents received the announcement with tact and loyalty. I was their oldest child and I was doing something they didn't like or understand, but if it was necessary for my peace of mind, then they'd back me up all the way.

Somewhere I had read in an Allegheny catalogue that if a student paid his tuition and board and then became ill and had to leave school, his money would be refunded. I thought this over carefully and decided to talk to the president of the college. When I was finally ushered into his office, I wasted no time in palaver. "I have to leave school because I'm mentally ill," I said breathlessly, "so may I please have my money back?"

The president backed toward a chair and sat down hard. "Er—uh—what makes you think you're mentally ill?" he asked.

Whatever I told him must only have confused him more. I can't remember how we finally settled my mental status, but in the end we shook hands cordially, and I left with the happy assurance that my money would be refunded. Two weeks before, it had been my father's money, and now it was mine. I'm not sure just what logic I used to arrive at this alchemy, but I needed cash to go to New York, and that was logic enough.

THE DAY I arrived in New York, in October of 1929, the stock market crashed with a bang, though certainly I myself hadn't the remotest notion, as I stepped off the train, that this was the start of the depression. I was 21, I had a shiny new patent-leather suitcase and my ex-tuition money was firmly pinned to my underwear, where it crackled ostentatiously at every step.

Mother had told me to take a cab to the McAlpin Hotel where my cousin, Betty Dunn, would meet me. Betty, who was just 18, had come from Meadville to New York to study dancing and was staying with our Aunt Lou and Uncle George Porter in Brooklyn. I was to stay there too, until Aunt Lou found us suitable rooms.

Finally I saw a taxi with one man sitting in the back and rushed over to it. In Franklin, where there were only three taxis, it was customary to share rides, and I yanked open the door and shoved my suitcase into the back. The man looked astonished, and the driver said, "Listen, girlie, this is already taken." "But there's plenty of room," I said, bewildered. The driver shrugged and turned to look back at his passenger, a middle-aged man wearing a derby and holding a brief case in solid dignity. "It's—er—it's all right, driver," he said. "If the young lady is going uptown."

"Is the McAlpin uptown?" I asked. They assured me it was, and we rode off in silence. After several blocks the man asked if this were my first visit to New York. I nodded, hurt that he had guessed. From then on I tried not to stare out the window to gape at the sights, but when we stopped for a red light, I forgot and pointed eagerly to a skyscraper in the distance. "Oh, is that the Flatiron?" The man said it was the Metropolitan Life Insurance Building. Warming to his new job as guide he pointed out several other spires. As we drove up before the McAlpin and I dug into my purse, he said, "Oh, no, this ride is on me." A bellhop grabbed my bag, and suddenly I was standing on the sidewalk waving to the man as the cab drove off. "Why, New Yorkers are *sweet*," I thought.

Just inside the lobby, I saw my cousin Betty's cute round face. I was impressed by her worldliness in tipping the bellhop, and her casual way of saying, "Let's go across the street to Schrafft's." At home she had seemed to me simply a kid cousin with exceptionally pretty legs, but now that she had been in New York several months, I looked up to her as a cosmopolitan who had instant access to places like Schrafft's. While we ate a second breakfast, we talked about our plans for living together. Betty said Aunt Lou wanted us to stay in Brooklyn with her for at least two weeks while she investigated rooms suitable for her nieces.

"But don't we want to live on Broadway?" I asked. I had long ago decided that in New York all the important people must live on Broadway. Betty seemed charmed with the idea.

"Let's go and find our room right now," I said.

We bought a paper and a half-hour later we were entering a dingy brick building at the corner of Broadway and 56th

Street. It had been our first choice in Rooms for Rent, listed tersely as "Clean double room, $12 week, ring Little's bell."

We rode up to the fourth floor in a tiny elevator that heaved and wheezed. A dark-haired woman in a red-and-white house dress who said she was Mrs. Little showed us the room. It contained a double bed, a bureau, a brown plush-upholstered chair, two cane-bottomed chairs, an upright piano and a washstand. While Betty exclaimed over the piano, I ran to the window and leaned out. Below was the roaring traffic of Broadway; across the street and level with our window was a huge electric sign for Chrysler cars. Betty came and leaned beside me, and we beamed first on Broadway and then on each other. We had found our nest.

We paid the first week's rent and then set off for Brooklyn, to surprise my aunt and uncle with news of our find.

They were surprised, all right.

Aunt Lou kept saying weakly, "But it must be an office building." When Uncle George came home, he said, "On *Broadway!* Good Lord! Are you girls out of your minds?"

At dinner, just as the uproar had died down, I happened to mention something about "the man who took me to the McAlpin."

"She means the cab driver," Betty said hurriedly.

I said I did not mean the cab driver, I meant the nice man who paid my fare.

Uncle George's face took on a purplish tinge. "I suppose you never heard of girls disappearing into white slavery," he said ominously.

"But he was old," I said. "He was at least 40."

My uncle nearly dropped the carving knife. "Oh Lord," he muttered.

Aunt Lou said she was sure that now Hildegarde understood that New York wasn't like Franklin she'd be careful, and why didn't we talk about something else. Nevertheless, when we were ready to leave that night, Aunt Lou said maybe our uncle should escort us home and look over our new living quarters. Betty and I looked at each other and then both protested ringingly that Uncle George was tired from stock crashing and everything, and he mustn't take that long trip. Finally he let us go off alone, after we'd assured Aunt Lou that Mrs. Little lived in the rooms next to ours. "Like a motherly chaperon," I said. I was learning rather fast.

By night our new home seemed even more dazzling. The huge Chrysler sign blinked on and off, casting its brilliance into our room so that even in bed we were as radiantly lit as if we'd set up a cot at Times Square. For a long time we lay discussing our plans for becoming famous, Betty as a dancer and I as a writer. "And sometimes on the side you could write a musical comedy and I could play the lead," Betty said. I agreed happily. Eventually we went to sleep, with the screeching honks of Broadway for background lullabies and the Chrysler sign blazing in on our angelic young faces.

For the first few days whenever Betty took me over to Fifth or Park Avenue, I'd favor these streets with a few polite comments and then hurry back to my richly tawdry love, Broadway. I spent hours walking there, looking down the side streets at the theater marquees, stopping to hear the spiel of the World's Strong Man clothed in a leopard skin at the corner of 49th Street or gazing at the displays in the little Broadway dress shops.

My father had urged me to get some new clothes, and Mother had said Best's was a nice store to go to; but after seeing the creations in the Broadway shops, I knew what I wanted. Right below our window, on the street floor, was a dress shop that specialized in "afternoon frocks," and I asked Betty if she'd go in with me while I bought a dress. All my life I'd longed for black, and only Mother's conviction that bright colors were nicer for young girls had kept me from swathing myself in widow's weeds. Now was my chance. Soon I was standing before the dressing-room mirror in a black crepe dress that wound starkly up to my chin and had a Grecian front panel that dipped down well below my shinbones. The rest of the dress came to my knees, in the normal length, but tight as a vise. "It looks awfully—er—black," Betty said. The salesgirl said that was "so drahmatic," and besides this was the forerunner of a new Paris style. That settled it. I was intoxicated with the idea that I, fresh from Franklin, Pa., would be setting the style in New York. And all for $16.95.

When I appeared in The Dress and passers-by on the streets of New York turned around to stare—a few froze in their tracks, openmouthed—I simply took it as a tribute to my new-found chic.

Betty took singing lessons from a Mrs. Bellamann, whose husband was "a sort of writer." "I don't think he makes much money," Betty said. "He does music reviews for some little magazine, and tries to write books."

At Mrs. Bellamann's suggestion I showed him some of my work, including a story I'd written at school in which the Devil and God discussed a frigid wife and a purehearted mistress. After Mr. Bellamann had read it, he looked at my young, dumb face and seemed puzzled. "The story shows a very sophisticated viewpoint," he said. "Er—uh—it's difficult to understand how you've learned so much about life."

He said I should try the story on *Cosmopolitan Magazine*. Immediately I composed in my mind the wire I would send my family, telling them that this, my first piece to be sent to a magazine, had sold. I went off feeling very benign toward this mild, kind man whom fame had passed by. Years later, when I read a best seller called *Kings Row*, by an author named Henry Bellamann, you could have knocked me over with a typewriter.

THE REJECTION from *Cosmopolitan* was the first in a long, distinguished line of these formula slips saying The Editors Regret. My conception of my talents was undergoing quite a mauling and to bolster my dwindling capital I enrolled at a typing school. At the end of four weeks I was duly recommended along with four other girls for a job in the complaint department of Remington Rand, at $18 a week.

For three days I sat in a room with at least 50 other girls checking figures, and boredom seeped out of me in languid trickles. I would have changed places with a doughnut machine and counted myself lucky. On the afternoon of the third day, a revolutionary thought hit me.

"Where do you go to resign?" I asked the girl at the next desk.

She pointed to a door. "There."

I had planned simply to say, "I resign," and then go away, but it wasn't that easy. The man in the private office insisted nicely that I sit down and talk things over. It seemed rude to tell him that I wanted to leave because I was bored. Finally, I muttered I'd just discovered I was going blind.

His horrified, sympathetic reaction was more than I'd bargained for. I got out of there fast, but not too fast to collect my three days' pay.

A few days later I was working on a story when Betty came in and said that Arthur, the pianist at the tap school, had been going over some new tunes at rest period that day. "They're his own tunes," she said, "and he needs somebody to do the lyrics. So I told him you could write them. You could, couldn't you?"

"Oh sure," I said. When you're 21, and you've never written a song lyric, and your morning mail consists solely of The Editors Regret, it's a simple matter to say, "Oh, sure."

Arthur asked Betty how she'd like to work in a chorus lineup for one week for $30. "And Hildegarde can write the lyrics for the chorus's opening song," he said. "I'll pay five dollars for them." Both Betty and I were beaming. Arthur said a friend of his ran a theater on 42nd Street and needed some extra girls for the chorus. "It's a burlesque house," Arthur added casually.

To Betty and me, coming as we did from a long line of Presbyterians, burlesque was simply an interesting new word. On our way home Betty said she thought burlesque was a kind of vaudeville. "Won't our families be pleased?" I said happily.

Betty was to enter the show on a Monday night, and that noon she rehearsed for the first time at the theater. "Did you see the rest of the cast?" I asked when Betty came home. She said the only principals at rehearsal were two men comedians and a minstrel singer, but several people had mentioned a girl named Peggy, who was evidently the star. "She'll be there tonight, of course," Betty said. "She must sing and dance."

Arthur had given me two tickets for the first performance, and I invited an ex-Allegheny beau to accompany me. As we arrived at the theater, my escort asked in a rather strangled voice, "Are you sure this is it?"

"It's the right name," I said.

"But, Hildegarde," he said with considerable agitation, "this is a burlesque house."

"Oh, then that's all right. Arthur said it was burlesque."

My friend's voice became hoarser. "You mean you knew all the time?"

"Why, of course, silly." I found it very gratifying that he should be so overcome at the heights Betty and I had achieved. "It's sort of like vaudeville," I added.

As we were ushered to our seats I wondered aloud why there were so many more men than women in the audience, but my escort made no reply. I think now that his vocal cords were paralyzed with shock.

Suddenly the curtain rose and the chorus danced on stage, wearing short, ruffled blue gingham dresses. Betty was in the front row. "Oh, doesn't she look darling?" I cooed. Three seconds later the girls were singing my lyrics, the sweetest noise that had ever smote my ears.

After the chorus came the minstrel singer with several whiny songs, then the comedians Betty had mentioned. The jokes seemed to be concerned exclusively with a dog's fondness for trees. Burlesque was awfully dull, I thought. I hoped the star named Peggy would be better.

At last the comedians disappeared. There was a roll of drums and a blinding spotlight center stage. Into the spotlight came one of the prettiest girls I've ever seen, very blonde, very young, dressed in a long-sleeved sequined dinner dress and a feather cap.

"That must be Peggy," I whispered proudly. At last things were looking up.

Instead of launching into a song, as I'd expected, the girl

began an odd, weaving motion with her hips, while the audience cheered. Suddenly, still weaving, she reached to the side of her dress, yanked at something and the dress slid to the floor revealing Peggy in a black satin slip, plus the feathered cap.

"Mercy!" I whispered. "What on earth is she doing?"

"She's taking off her clothes," my escort muttered.

It seemed an awfully odd thing to do.

As Peggy removed even more garments and wriggled even more frenziedly, I sat round-eyed with astonishment. I wasn't shocked, just surprised. As Peggy came down to a fig leaf, I decided it might be better to omit a few details in writing to my parents about our Broadway debut. As Betty said later that night. "You and I know the whole thing is perfectly respectable, but it might sound a little peculiar in a letter."

I'm not sure whether it was Arthur, Heaven or our own impenetrable naïveté that guided us through the week of burlesque with very much the same effect as a schoolgirls' conducted tour of Radio City.

Betty and the other members of the chorus had three tiny dressing rooms, and between numbers, while the girls put on their stage make-up, we sat around and talked about clothes and our families, and tried on each other's hats.

But it was Peggy, the strip-tease queen, who attracted me most. Peggy was 17 and had started in the chorus a year before. Now she'd been the star for three months, with the star's dressing room all to herself, and I think she was lonely. She particularly liked Betty and she often called us into her dressing room, usually on the pretext that she wanted us to see a new costume. She told us her mother made all her costumes. "See, they gotta have very special fasteners so I can get out of them easy on stage." Betty and I agreed that her mother sewed beautifully, and it struck neither of us as odd that motherly fingers should sew in place the fasteners that aided a strip-tease.

Peggy lived with her parents in Flushing, and she told us she had already made the down payments on a new house and a five-passenger Buick sedan. "Papa drives in every night to take me home," she said. "He chaperoons me all the time."

"Gosh," Betty said sympathetically. "Our parents aren't nearly that strict. Hildegarde and I can do anything we want."

The strip-tease queen looked at us two Presbyterians enviously. "It must be swell not to be chaperooned," she said.

We were impressed to learn that Peggy was making $100 a week. "It's respectable, steady work, not like night clubs," she explained. "In night clubs you hafta mix, and take a drink almost every night."

Seen in this light, Peggy's choice of burlesque as a career seemed to us the height of conservatism.

Once when she called us into her dressing room, she held out a box of candy. "Look," she said excitedly. "Five pounds of assorted chocolates." She showed us the card that had come with them. It said, "You're beautiful," and was signed simply, "A college boy." Peggy kept turning the card around fondly. "I wish he'd have come backstage," she said. "I never been out with a college boy."

She asked me if I had ever dated one, and my affirmative answer seemed to raise my stock tremendously. "Gee," she said. "Gee, if I was allowed out like you kids . . ."

I have never seen Peggy since, but I have often wondered how she made out and if her papa ever let her go out with a college boy.

DURING the year that followed our one enchanted week, my own career came to a standstill. I did manage to find a number of jobs, ranging from temporary Christmas helper at McCreery's to cashier and assistant hostess at the men's Allerton House, but when Betty decided to go home to Pennsylvania for the summer, I was glad to go along.

By late summer I was terribly homesick for New York. The depression had now reached out its octopus arms even to Franklin, and my parents were understandably dubious about my chances of getting a job, but I insisted it would be a cinch. Hadn't I found jobs before? Finally I was allowed to embark with Betty, on a low-rate excursion ticket, with the understanding that if I didn't get a job in two weeks (when the ticket expired) I would use the return half to go home. To buoy my hopes I had a new Empress Eugénie hat, that hurtled down one side of my head as if I were riding to hounds, and a pair of lounging pajamas Mother had made out of an old black velvet evening dress, with the pants a yard wide.

Betty and I had written Mrs. Little to reserve our old room, and when we arrived there, I removed the Empress Eugénie hat, put on my lounging pajamas and leaned blissfully out the window, a cosmopolitan returned to her Broadway habitat in fitting raiment. I had also written a beau that I'd be back in town that day, and when the community phone rang, far down the corridor, I leaped up to answer it. In my haste, I became so tangled in my floppy pajama pants that I tripped and was thrown against the door headfirst.

But even if a woman is mortally stricken, she'll manage to get to her feet to answer a ringing phone. Unfortunately, it turned out to be for someone else.

By the time my own call came, an hour later, the results of my fall were remarkably apparent. My forehead was swelled out like a goose egg and below it was a black eye of amazing scope and hue.

The next morning my forehead was so swollen I couldn't bear to have the Empress Eugénie model tilted down pressing on it, so I wore the hat pushed up and on the back of my head, like a Broadway bookie's derby. The whole effect was incredibly raffish. As I started out on the round of employment agencies, Betty said, "Now remember, it isn't looks they care about. It's brains." If such brains as I possess had been visible they still couldn't compete with the black eye.

In the next two weeks, I must have tramped over almost every block in New York. The depression was on full blast, there were a thousand applicants for every job and, as my black eye faded, so did my hopes. I rushed to every address given me by an agency or discovered in the fast shrinking help-wanted columns, and came home each night with no job. On the 14th day I knew there was no reprieve.

Betty and I went down the corridor to say good-bye to

Mrs. Little. She seemed genuinely sorry to have our twosome broken up. "You certainly picked a terrible time to look for a job," she told me. "And then getting that black eye."

While I packed, Betty sat on the bed and tried to reassure me. "You'll come back in a month or so," she kept saying, in a would-be cheerful voice. But both of us knew there wasn't a chance.

Presently there was a knock and Betty went to the door. Mrs. Little stood there beaming beside a small, dirty-faced man in khaki overalls.

"This is Dave," Mrs. Little said happily. "He lives here and works in a picture-frame factory."

The man in overalls looked at me silently. "Why don't you tell her?" Mrs. Little poked him with her elbow. "Tell her you've got a job for her."

She turned to me. "It's only $15 a week," she said. "Dave's boss needs an office girl. Would you take the job?"

"Yes," I said. My knees shook so hard I had to sit down.

A few minutes later everything was settled. Dave gave me the address of the factory and told me to report at 8:30 the next morning. As soon as he and Mrs. Little left, Betty and I began to pull clothes out of my suitcase with a drunken gaiety. "I'd better tear up my return ticket right now," I said, "before that man changes his mind."

I tore it into bits and we made a ceremony of throwing the pieces out the window, to fall like confetti on Broadway.

Never having been in a factory, I had a clear, movie-tinged notion of what the place would look like: shining, modern efficiency, floor after floor of gleaming machines, and down one tiled corridor a door marked Private, behind which I, the well-groomed secretary, would sit in a sunny outer office at a mahogany desk with two telephones.

In order to keep up my end of the picture, I pressed my best black dress and attached freshly laundered white collars and cuffs. When I started off for the factory at eight the next morning, I was groomed within an inch of my eyebrows, with dainty white frothing at my wrists.

I found the address on a dirty, dark side street piled with boxes all along the sidewalk and decided I'd taken down the wrong address. Obviously it couldn't be the factory. Puzzled, and hoping to get directions, I went inside the rickety wooden building and up a flight of creaky old stairs. At the top, I found myself in a narrow loft about the size of an ordinary living room, crammed with men in overalls working at hideously screeching machines. The smell of banana oil was so heavy I held my nose with my white-gloved fingers. I went over to the nearest man, tapped him politely on the arm and said, "Please, do you know where I might find the Royal Frame Factory?"

"What?" he yelled.

This time I shouted my request. He stared. "This is it."

I rocked on my feet. I leaned against something for support, and it swayed behind me. I staggered and turned to see that two workers had grabbed a high stack of unpainted picture frames just in time to save them from toppling over. But nobody saved the things that were toppling in my head. I was suffering from the shock of reality.

Somebody shouted in my ear, "Oh, hello, so you found it all right." It was Dave. "I'll show you your desk," he yelled. "The boss will be back in an hour."

The desk was jammed into a corner beside one of the screeching machines. It was covered with a sprawl of grimy papers, two unwashed milk bottles and an overlay of gritty dust that kept whizzing from the planing machine beside it. Dave pushed the papers and milk bottles to one side, then pulled up the top of the desk and a typewriter came into view. "Make yourself at home," he said.

For a while I just sat there miserably, thinking, for the first and only time in my life, that it would be simple to jump out a window. Finally I found a blank, rather grimy piece of paper and began to type furiously.

I must have typed the alphabet a thousand times before Dave came back with a tall, thin-faced man in a rather bright-blue business suit and ordinary felt hat. "Meet the boss," Dave said. "Mr. Harding."

The man shook hands with me, took off his hat and suit coat, tossed them on a pile of lumber, pulled a packing box up beside the desk and sat down. His clipped way of talking was as economical as his motions. He showed me how to type a bill of lading. It seemed simple enough. After a few minutes he said, "Call me if you want to ask questions," and walked away.

Now that I had something to do, the sickish smell of banana oil didn't bother me as much, but the noise was still awful. Every time the phone on the desk rang, I would clench the receiver to my ear, put a finger in the other ear and try desperately to hear through the din. Then I'd have to run for Mr. Harding. "I can't hear a word," I would scream.

At noon there was suddenly a deafening quietness. Every machine had been turned off; the workers got out parcels of food wrapped in greasy brown paper and started to eat. Three girls whom I now saw for the first time came out from behind a pile of corrugated paper boxes and sat down with the men. They looked Spanish or Italian. I was enormously relieved to see some women, because it meant there must be a ladies' room.

Presently Harding came to get his hat and coat. "Like to have lunch with me at a good spaghetti place?" he asked. He was so businesslike about it that I said "Yes" without a second's hesitation.

The spaghetti drove the bananaoil vapors out of my head, and Harding was easy to talk to. He was the kind of man who is passionately in love with a business, and I think it was essential to his vanity that even the new office girl should view the Royal Frame Factory with respect. Perhaps he'd sensed my feelings, because he said, "This is only the beginning, this hole we're in now. We're moving to a bigger place next week."

Harding told me that a big corporation owned the factory, a corporation which also owned the inexpensive photograph studios in department stores all over the country. "See, they'll sell these dollar or two-dollar frames to the people who get their pictures taken for a dollar," he said. "It's a perfect set-up, the kind that will beat the depression."

By the end of lunch I'd worked up enough courage to tell my boss he'd have to answer his own telephone. It seemed to amuse him. "So you can't stand a little noise," he said, grinning. "I'll bet you got a college sheepskin, and you can't even answer the phone. Why doesn't a girl like you run home to mama?"

I told him about wanting to stay in New York to learn to be a writer.

He nodded. "O.K., kid. At least you're stubborn. I thought at first you were a stuck-up college snip."

That first afternoon I set out to tidy up my four square feet of the factory. I was just in the process of dumping what I thought were silly old scraps of wood into the wastebasket, when Harding came along. "Holy Christmas!" he said. "These are my only samples of frame moldings."

By the end of the third day, I could hear enough to answer the telephone. Compared to that problem, the rest of the work seemed simple. On my fourth day, Maria, the prettiest of the three Spanish girls, came to my desk to use the phone. When she'd finished, she smiled brilliantly, said, "*Gracias*, 'ildegarde," and ran away fast. After that everybody called me Hildegarde. In spite of my debut in the frothy white cuffs, they had forgiven me my sheltered past.

At the end of two weeks we moved to the new factory. It was another loft, but about six times as big as the old one and in a less rickety building. To my newly adjusted eyes, it looked fine. My desk was moved over on a Saturday morning, and since I had Saturday afternoons off, I left Harding and the workers setting up the machines and work tables. They promised to put my desk near a window. When I came back on Monday morning, I stepped off the freight elevator which went up to our new fourth-floor loft and blinked in amazement. I was standing in an honest-to-goodness office.

The men had marked off a good-sized corner of the loft and built beaverboard walls, with a door leading into the factory.

There was my desk with a rose sitting in a paper cup (I recognized Maria's feminine touch). It was all so wonderful I just stood there gaping. Harding walked in and grinned. "The boys fixed it up Sunday. They wanted to surprise you."

In letters to my parents, the factory acquired a size and gloss that partly reassured them. Harding had raised my salary to $16, and this made a fine, prosperous piece of news to send home. Allowing six dollars a week for rent, and eight dollars for food, subway fare and even more important essentials such as silk stockings and lipstick, I had two dollars a week for riotous living, or having a wisdom tooth pulled. It still gives me envious twinges to read about captains of industry who started on a five-dollar wage, out of which they claim to have saved two dollars a week for a rainy day or an aged mother. I would like to bet these Horatio Alger characters that the room I slept in was smaller than any of theirs, unless, of course, they curled up in a packing case.

A few weeks after I'd gone to the factory, Betty took a job with a vaudeville unit, to go on the road, and I was living alone, wedged like a folding ironing board into the smallest quarters at Mrs. Little's, with no view of Broadway or, indeed, of anything. Instead of a window, there was a small ventilating shaft that opened onto a pitch-black courtyard. Lying in bed, I could reach out and touch everything in the room. There was no radiator, so, as soon as I came home after work I crawled into bed to keep warm.

When my mother came to New York for a visit and I proudly showed her my room, she murmured, "Oh, darling!" Then she hurried out to the hallway, ostensibly to make a telephone call, and came back red-eyed but cheerful. Both she and my father would have liked to have me at home, but they never denied me the right to choose. It must be awfully tough for parents not to run interference when their children, grown up, are learning once more to walk by themselves.

Orders for frames were coming into the factory so fast that Harding now had 40 workers to supervise, and he spent all his time with them. Little by little I was learning to handle all the office work, but when Harding said it was high time I learned to keep the books, I knew we were both in for a bad period. Since he was usually too busy to go out, he had a sandwich brought in for lunch, and my first lessons took place while he ate his cheese-on-rye in the office. Between bites, he'd point to an open ledger and say, "Now look, you draw a thousand dollars out of the bank so that's a debit." This logic mystified me utterly. To me, a thousand dollars drawn out of a bank was a credit any girl might well be proud of. In a way, my incredible dumbness rather gratified Harding, because it confirmed his scornful belief that colleges never taught anything worth knowing.

I still remember with awe that I made the Royal Frame Company's monthly accounts balance, although to this day I can't tell the difference between a debit and a credit. Any woman, when faced by the bared teeth of necessity, invents fearful and wonderful systems for achieving her goal. "Let's see," I'd say to myself. "If Harding subtracted this thing from that thing last month, I guess I may as well subtract too. And if depreciation of machinery is added in the credit column, then maybe the thing on the next page is a debit." The first time the two sets of figures came out even, I stared unbelievingly, as if I'd just brought off the miracle of the 20th century. Waving the ledger, I rushed through the office door into the factory yelling, "Harding! Look!"

My boss came on the run. "Fire?" he panted. "Where?" In a place filled with inflammable paint and flimsy wood frames, that was a constant worry.

The news that I'd struck a trial balance came as rather an anti-climax.

Every Tuesday morning I went to the bank for our payroll. The teller would sort out the proper amounts of bills and silver, usually over a thousand dollars, and, cramming all this into my purse, I'd start for the side streets that led to the factory. This last stage of the journey made me a little nervous. In the months since I'd come to work, there had been five holdups in that same neighborhood. When a girl from the building next door was hit over the head with a blackjack, while carrying a payroll, I complained mildly to

Harding that I ought to have an escort. He said he couldn't spare one of the boys. However, he agreed magnanimously that if any gunman held me up I didn't have to argue with him. "Just drop the money and run like hell," he said.

It was just after my 23rd birthday that I decided to send a piece to *The New Yorker* magazine. As a connoisseur of rejection slips, I thought it was high time to add one of theirs to my collection.

Four weeks later I decided the manuscript had been lost. At the end of six weeks, I'd forgotten it completely. On a Saturday morning I picked up some mail as I wended my sleepy way out to the subway. "Why, *The New Yorker* used one of its own envelopes to send the piece back in," I said to myself. "Aren't they nice?" As every young writer knows, it gets awfully boring always to receive envelopes back in your own handwriting. I must have sat in the subway at least five minutes before it occurred to me that the unopened letter felt awfully thin. *What had become of my manuscript?*

Five seconds later I was holding a slip of blue paper at which I stared stupidly. "Payable to—Fifty dollars . . ."

The world blurred before my eyes, and I groped for the note that came with this blue mirage. ". . . which we've titled *Bus Journey*—and we hope you'll send us lots more. Sincerely, K. S. White."

My first impulse was to leap off the subway, rush back to my room and put every manuscript I owned into envelopes to send this divine being called K. S. White. After this feverish flush had subsided, I looked vainly around the subway car for somebody to tell the news to, but even in my delirium I was too shy to open a conversation with a stranger. I held the check almost under the nose of the woman sitting next to me, hoping she'd say, "Excuse me, but is that really a check from *The New Yorker?*" but she only looked out the window.

I ran all the way from the subway to the nearest Western Union office, where I wired the family my news. When I got to the factory, each of the 40 workers took turns handling and admiring my check, although I was a little nonplussed

that none of them had ever heard of *The New Yorker*. Maria said, "But maybe some day you sell story to *True Confessions*, yes?" She was eager to have me get into the big time.

For two weeks, I carried the check around with me by day and slept with my purse parked on my bed. This dreamy attitude about something that could so easily be converted into cold cash made Harding nervous. "Listen, kid," he said, "never hold onto a check. Take it to the bank pronto and make sure it won't bounce."

Somewhere I had read about a writer who framed his first check. When I explained this delicate sentiment to Harding, he was horrified. "Cheat yourself out of 50 bucks?" he asked. "Are you crazy?"

I am a blend of Dutch, Scotch and Irish, and at least one of these elements sided with Harding and finally got me to the bank. The second I'd shoved the pale-blue paper through the teller's window, I felt an awful sense of loss.

The teller counted out ten new five-dollar bills and then tore off the upper half of my square, perforated-across-the-middle check and gave it back to me. "That's yours," he said.

"Mine?" I squeaked. "You mean I may *keep* it?"

"Sure," he said. "Frame it, for all we care."

"I will," I said simply.

THE AUTOBIOGRAPHY
OF

Benjamin Franklin

Condensed from
"Benjamin Franklin's Autobiographical Writings"

With a foreword by Carl Van Doren

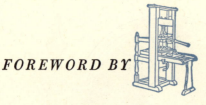

FOREWORD BY   *CARL VAN DOREN*

WHEN Benjamin Franklin died at Philadelphia in April 1790 he was the most famous private citizen in the world. The news of his death reached Paris, and Mirabeau declared to the National Assembly: "Antiquity would have raised altars to this mighty genius, who, compassing in his mind the heavens and the earth, was able to restrain alike thunderbolts and tyrants." In England before the American Revolution, Chatham had told a hostile House of Lords that Franklin ranked with Newton as a scientist and was "an honor not to the English nation only but to human nature."

Franklin's scientific experiments had made him a hero to his age. Before him, lightning had been for men an incalculable threat, the deadly evidence of an inexplicable divine wrath. Franklin, first working out the basic principles of electrical science, had proved that lightning was only electricity acting in accordance with knowable laws. He had proved this with an instrument as familiar as a boy's kite. To the world at large this was more than science. It was magic.

If he seemed somehow a wizard, he was also a wit. It was Franklin who first said that nothing is certain "except death and taxes," as it was he who first said: " 'Tis hard for an empty bag to stand upright." Besides hundreds of such sayings in the character of Poor Richard, there were Franklin's lively hoaxes. Long before Mark Twain, he had parodied all tall tales by telling how in America the whales chased the cod up Niagara Falls.

Yet while Franklin was known as a wizard and a wit, he was even better known as a self-made man. Not that he made a vast virtue of this, as some self-made men do. Poor Richard had said: "Learn of the skillful; he that teaches himself hath a fool for a teacher," and "Experience keeps a dear school, but fools will learn in no other." Franklin left school at ten, and signed his indentures of apprenticeship at 12. He retired from business at 42, and devoted another 42 years wholly to the service of the public, as scientist, philanthropist and statesman.

Besides the lightning rod he invented the Franklin stove, drafts for fireplaces, bifocal glasses, the convertible ladder-chair found in most American kitchens, the long arm used in grocery stores for taking objects down from high shelves—refusing to patent any of these inventions and so make the fortune he might have made. He was a valuable pioneer in the scientific study of the Gulf Stream, of the prediction of weather, of the common cold, of the conduction of heat by different substances, and of the increase of human population. He printed, and almost certainly drew, the first American cartoon, founded the Dead Letter Office, and organized the United States postal service. He helped draft the Declaration of Independence and the Constitution, and helped make the treaties of alliance with France and of peace with England. He foresaw the possibilities of war from the air as soon as he saw a balloon capable of lifting men. "What good is a balloon?" somebody asked in Paris. Franklin replied: "What good is a new born baby?" Far from neglecting the pleasant graces, Franklin took pains to develop a masterly prose style, gave much attention to fine printing, wrote memorably about music, and encouraged poets and painters whenever he could.

Franklin was too busy making public history to take time out to write his private life, and his autobiography was never completed. Even so, he was the earliest self-made man who ever recounted the plain story of his beginnings. Tranquilly remembering his busy, lusty youth, he told the story in the language of an everyday world and more or less fixed the mode for all modern realistic autobiographies.

His *Autobiography* was intended by him to be a kind of philosophical legacy to young men. He died without knowing whether it would ever be printed; yet now the *Autobiography* has been published in almost every language that has a printing press. It is without question the most famous of all autobiographies.

The Autobiography of
BENJAMIN FRANKLIN

DEAR SON: I have ever had pleasure in obtaining any little anecdotes of my ancestors. Imagining it may be equally agreeable to you to know the circumstances of my life, I sit down to write them for you. Having emerged from the poverty and obscurity in which I was born and bred, to a state of affluence and some degree of reputation in the world, my posterity may like to know the means I made use of as they may find some of them suitable to their own situations.

Were it offered to my choice, I should have no objection to a repetition of the same life from its beginnings, only asking the advantages authors have in a second edition to correct some faults of the first. But though this were denied, I should still accept the offer.

Hereby, too, I shall indulge the inclination so natural in old men to be talking of themselves and their own past actions; and I shall indulge it without being tiresome to others, since this may be read or not as any one pleases. And (I may as well confess it, since my denial of it will be believed by nobody) perhaps I shall a good deal gratify my own vanity. Indeed, I scarce ever heard or saw the introductory words, "Without vanity I may say," etc., but some vain thing immediately followed. Most people dislike vanity in others, whatever share they have of it themselves; but I give it fair quarter wherever I meet with it, being persuaded that it is often productive of good; therefore, in many cases, it would not be altogether absurd if a man were to thank God for his vanity among the other comforts of life.

Josiah, my father, married young, and carried his wife with three children into New England, about 1682. By her he had four children more born there, and by a second wife ten more, in all seventeen. I was the youngest son, and was born in Boston.

My elder brothers were all put apprentices to different trades. I was put to the grammar-school at eight years of age, then to a school for writing and arithmetic, where I acquired fair writing pretty soon, but failed in the arithmetic. At ten years old I was taken home to assist my father in his business, which was that of a tallow-chandler and sope-boiler. Accordingly, I was employed in cutting wick for the candles, filling the dipping mold and the molds for cast candles, attending the shop, going on errands, etc.

I disliked the trade, and had a strong inclination for the sea, but my father declared against it; however, living near the water, I was much in and about it, learnt early to swim well, and to manage boats. I was generally a leader among the boys, and sometimes led them into scrapes, of which I will

This bookish inclination at length determined my father to make me a printer, though he had already one son (James) of that profession. I liked it much better than that of my father, but still had a hankering for the sea. I was to serve as an apprentice till I was twenty-one, only I was to be allowed journeyman's wages during the last year. In a little time I became a useful hand to my brother. I now had access to better books. An acquaintance with the apprentices of booksellers enabled me sometimes to borrow a small one, which I was careful to return soon and clean. Often I sat up in my room reading the greatest part of the night, lest it should be missed or wanted.

I now took a fancy to poetry, and made some little pieces; my brother, thinking it might turn to account, put me on composing occasional ballads. One was called *The Lighthouse Tragedy*, and contained an account of the drowning of Captain Worthilake, with his two daughters: the other was a sailor's song, on the taking of *Teach* (or Blackbeard) the pirate. They were wretched stuff, in the Grub-street-ballad style; and when they were printed he sent me about the town to sell them. The first sold wonderfully, the event being recent, having made a great noise. This flattered my vanity; but my father discouraged me by ridiculing my performances, and telling me verse-makers were generally beggars. So I escaped being a poet, most probably a very bad one; but as prose writing has been of great use to me in the course of my life, I shall tell you how I acquired what little ability I have in that way.

There was another bookish lad in the town, John Collins by name, with whom I was intimately acquainted. We sometimes disputed, and very fond we were of argument, which disputatious turn is apt to become a very bad habit, making people often extremely disagreeable in company. I had caught it by reading my father's books of dispute about religion. Persons of good sense, I have observed, seldom fall into it, except lawyers, university men, and men of all sorts that have been bred at Edinborough.

A question was once started between Collins and me, of the propriety of educating the female sex, and their abilities for study. He was of opinion that it was improper, and that they were naturally unequal to it. I took the contrary side, perhaps a little for dispute's sake. He was naturally more eloquent, had a ready plenty of words; and sometimes, as I thought, bore me down more by his fluency than by the strength of his reasons. As we parted without settling the point, I sat down to put my arguments in writing, which I copied fair and sent to him. He answered, and I replied. Three or four letters of a side had passed, when my father happened to find my papers and read them. Without entering into the discussion, he took occasion to talk to me about the manner of my writing; observed that, though I had the advantage of my antagonist in correct spelling (which I ow'd to the printing-house), I fell far short in elegance of expression, in method and in perspicuity, of which he convinced me by several instances. I saw the justice of his remarks, and thence grew more attentive to the manner in writing, and determined to endeavor at improvement.

About this time I met with an odd volume of the *Spectator*. I read it over and over, and was much delighted with it. I thought the writing excellent, and wished, if possible, to imitate it. With this view I took some of the papers, and, making short hints of the sentiment in each sentence, laid them by a few days, and then, without looking at the book, try'd to compleat the papers again, by expressing each hinted sentiment at length. Then I compared my *Spectator* with the original, discovered some of my faults, and corrected them. My time for these exercises and for reading was at night, or on Sundays, when I contrived to be in the printing-house alone, evading as much as I could the common attendance on public worship which my father used to exact of me, and which indeed I still thought a duty, though I could not, as it seemed to me, afford time to practise it.

WHEN about 16 years of age I happened to meet with a book, written by one Tryon, recommending a vegetable diet. I determined to go into it. My brother, being yet unmarried, did not keep house, but boarded himself and his apprentices in another family. My refusing to eat flesh occasioned an inconvenience, and I was frequently chid for my singularity. I made myself acquainted with Tryon's manner of preparing some of his dishes, and then proposed to my brother, that if he would give me, weekly, half the money he paid for my board, I would board myself. He instantly agreed to it, and I presently found that I could save half what he paid me.

But I had another advantage in it. My brother and the rest going from the printing-house to their meals, I remained there alone, and, despatching presently my light repast, which often was no more than a bisket or a slice of bread, a handful of raisins or a tart from the pastry-cook's, and a glass of water, had the rest of the time till their return for study, in which I made the greater progress, from that greater clearness of head which usually attend temperance in eating and drinking.

While I was intent on improving my language, I met with a specimen of a dispute in the Socratic method. I was charmed with it, adopted it, dropt my abrupt contradiction and positive argumentation, and put on the humble inquirer and doubter. From this, I retained the habit of expressing myself in terms of modest diffidence; never using, when I advanced anything that may possibly be disputed, the words *certainly*, *undoubtedly*, or any others that give the air of positiveness to an opinion; but rather say, I conceive or apprehend a thing to be so and so; it appears to me; or *I imagine it to be so;* or *it is so, if I am not mistaken.* This habit, I believe, has been of great advantage to me when I have had occasion to inculcate my opinions, and persuade men into measures that I have been engag'd in promoting. I wish well-meaning, sensible men would not lessen their power of doing good by a positive, assuming manner, that seldom fails to disgust, tends to create opposition, and to defeat every one of those purposes for which speech was given to us.

My brother had, in 1720 or 1721, begun to print a newspaper. It was the second that appeared in America, and was called the New England Courant. I remember his being dissuaded by some of his friends from the undertaking, one newspaper being, in their judgment, enough for America. After having worked in composing the types and printing off the sheets, I was employed to carry the papers to the customers.

He had some ingenious men among his friends, who amus'd themselves by writing little pieces for this paper. Hearing their accounts of the approbation their papers were received with, I was excited to try my hand among them; but, being still a boy, and suspecting that my brother would object to printing anything of mine, I contrived to disguise my hand, and, writing an anonymous paper, I put it in at night under the door of the printing-house. It was found in the morning, and communicated to his writing friends when they call'd in as usual. They read it, commented on it in my hearing, and I had the exquisite pleasure of finding it met with their approbation.

Encouraged by this, I wrote and convey'd in the same way to the press several more papers which were equally approv'd. When I finally discovered my secret, I began to be considered a little more by my brother's acquaintance, and in a manner that did not quite please him, as he thought, probably with reason, that it tended to make me too vain. And, perhaps, this might be one occasion of the differences that we began to have about this time. Our disputes were often brought before our father, and I fancy I was either generally in the right, or else a better pleader, because the judgment was generally in my favor. But my brother was passionate, and had often beaten me, which I took extreamly amiss; and, thinking my apprenticeship very tedious, I was continually wishing for some opportunity of shortening it, which at length offered in a manner unexpected.

One of the pieces in our newspaper on some political point, which I have now forgotten, gave offense to the Assembly. My brother was taken up, censur'd, and imprison'd for a month. During his confinement, I had the management of the paper; and I made bold to give our rulers some rubs in it, which my brother took very kindly, while others began to consider me in an unfavorable light, as a young genius that had a turn for libelling and satyr. My brother's discharge was accompany'd with an order that "*James Franklin should no longer print the paper called the New England Courant.*"

There was a consultation among his friends, what he should do. Some proposed to evade the order by changing the name of the paper; but my brother finally concluded to let it be printed under the name of Benjamin Franklin; and to avoid the censure of the Assembly, that might fall on him as still printing it by his apprentice, the contrivance was that my old indenture should be return'd to me, with a full discharge on the back of it, to be shown on occasion; but to secure to him the benefit of my service, I was to sign new indentures for the remainder of the term, which were to be kept private. A very flimsy scheme it was; however, it was immediately executed, and the paper went on accordingly, under my name for several months.

At length, a fresh difference arising between my brother and me, I took upon me to assert my freedom, presuming that he would not venture to produce the new indentures. It was not fair in me to take advantage; but the unfairness of it weighed little with me, when under the impressions of re-sentment for the blows his passion too often urged him to bestow upon me.

When he found I would leave him, he took care to prevent my getting employ-ment in any other printing-house, by going round and speaking to every master. I then  thought of going to New York, as the nearest place where there was a printer; but my father now siding with my brother, I was sensible that, if I attempted to go openly, means would be used to prevent me. My friend Collins, therefore, undertook to manage a little for me. He agreed with the captain of a New York sloop for my passage, under the notion of my being a young acquaintance of his, that had got a naughty girl with child, whose friends would compel me to marry her, and therefore I could not appear or come away publicly. So I sold some of my books to raise a little money, was taken on board privately, and as we had a fair wind, in three days I found myself in New York, near 300 miles from home, a boy of but 17, without the least recommendation to, or knowledge of any person in the place, and with very little money in my pocket.

My inclinations for the sea were by this time worne out, or I might now have gratify'd them. But, having a trade, and supposing myself a pretty good workman, I offer'd my service to the printer in the place, old Mr. William Bradford. He could give me no employment, having help enough already; but says he, "My son at Philadelphia has lately lost his principal hand by death; if you go thither, I believe he may employ you." Philadelphia was a hundred miles further; I set out, however, in a boat for Amboy, leaving my chest and things to follow me round by sea.

In crossing the bay, we met with a squall that tore our rotten sails to pieces, and drove us upon Long Island. In our way, a drunken Dutchman, who was a passenger too, fell overboard; when he was sinking, I reached through the water to his shock pate, and drew him up, so that we got him in again. His ducking sobered him a little, and he went to sleep.

When we drew near the island, we found a great surff on the stony beach. So we dropt anchor. Night coming on, we had no remedy but to wait till the wind should abate; and, in the mean time, the boatman and I crowded into the scuttle with the Dutchman, and the spray beating over the head of our boat, leak'd thro' to us, so that we were soon almost as wet as he. In this manner we lay all night, with very little rest; but, the wind abating the next day, we made a shift to reach Amboy before night, having been thirty hours on the water, without victuals, or any drink but a bottle of filthy rum.

In the evening I found myself very feverish, and went in to bed; but, having read somewhere that cold water drank plentifully was good for a fever, I follow'd the prescription, sweat plentifully most of the night, my fever left me, and in the morning, crossing the ferry, I proceeded on my journey on foot, having fifty miles to Burlington, where I was told I should find boats that would carry me the rest of the way to Philadelphia.

It rained very hard all the day; I was thoroughly soak'd, and by noon a good deal tired; so I stopt at a poor inn, where I staid all night, beginning now to wish that I had never left home. I cut so miserable a figure, too, that I was suspected to be some runaway servant, and in danger of being taken up on that suspicion. However, I proceeded the next day, and at Burlington a boat came by, which I found was going towards Philadelphia, with several people in her. They took me in, and, as there was no wind, we row'd all the way. We arrived there about eight or nine o'clock on the Sunday morning, and landed at the Market-street wharf.

I was in my working dress. I was dirty from my journey; my pockets were stuff'd out with shirts and stockings, and I knew no soul nor where to look for lodging, I was fatigued with travelling, rowing and want of rest, I was very hungry; and my whole stock of cash consisted of a Dutch dollar, and about a shilling in copper. The latter I gave the people of the boat for my passage, who at first refus'd it, on account my rowing; but I insisted on their taking it. A man being sometimes more generous when he has but a little money than when he has plenty, perhaps thro' fear of being thought to have but little.

Then I walked up the street, gazing about till near the market-house I met a boy with bread. Inquiring where he got it, I went immediately to the baker's he directed me to, and ask'd for bisket, intending such as we had in Boston; but they, it seems, were not made in Philadelphia. Then I asked for a three-penny loaf, and was told they had none such. So not knowing the greater cheapness nor the names of his bread, I bad him give me three-penny worth of any sort. He gave me, accordingly, three great puffy rolls. I was surpriz'd at the quantity, but took it, and having no room in my pockets, walk'd off with a roll under each arm, and eating the other. Thus I went up Market-street, passing by the door of Mr. Read, my future wife's father; when she, standing at the door, saw me, and thought I made, as I certainly did, a most awkward, ridiculous appearance.

Walking down again toward the river, I met a young Quaker man, whose countenance I lik'd, and, accosting him, requested he would tell me where a stranger could get lodging. He brought me to the Crooked Billet in Water-street. Here I got a dinner; and, while I was eating it, several sly questions were asked me, as it seemed to be suspected from my youth and appearance, that I might be some runaway.

Next morning I made myself as tidy as I could, and went to Andrew Bradford the printer's. I found in the shop the old man his father, whom I had seen at New York, and who. travelling on horseback, had got to Philadelphia before me, He introduc'd me to his son, who received me civilly, gave me a breakfast, but told me he did not at present want a hand, but there was another printer in town, lately set up, one Keimer, who, perhaps might employ me; if not, I should be welcome to lodge at his house, and he would give me a little work now and then till fuller business should offer.

Keimer's printing-house, I found, consisted of an old shatter'd press, and one small worn-out font. I endeavored to put his press (of which he understood nothing) into order fit to be work'd with; and return'd to Bradford's, who gave me a little job to do. A few days after, Keimer had a pamphlet to reprint, on which he set me to work.

These two printers I found poorly qualified for their business. Bradford had not been bred to it, and was very illiterate; and Keimer, tho' something of a scholar, was a mere compositor, knowing nothing of presswork, and had, as I afterward found, a good deal of the knave in his composition. He could not lodge me; but he got me a lodging at Mr. Read's, before mentioned; and, my chest and clothes being come by this time, I made rather a more respectable appearance in the eyes of Miss Read than I had done when she first happen'd to see me eating my roll in the street.

I BEGAN now to have some acquaintance among the young people of the town, that were lovers of reading, with whom I spent my evenings very pleasantly; and gaining money by my industry and frugality, I lived very agreeably, forgetting Boston as much as I could, and not desiring that any there should know where I resided. At length, an incident happened that sent me back again much sooner than I had intended. I had a brother-in-law, Robert Holmes, master of a sloop that traded between Boston and Delaware. He being at Newcastle, forty miles below Philadelphia, heard there of me, and wrote me a letter mentioning the concern of my friends in Boston at my abrupt departure. I thank'd him for his advice and stated my reasons for quitting Boston in such a light as to convince him I was not so wrong as he had apprehended.

Sir William Keith, governor of the province, was then at Newcastle, and Captain Holmes, happening to be in company with him when my letter came to hand, spoke to him of me, and show'd him the letter. The governor read it, and seem'd surprised when he was told my age. He said I appear'd a young man of promising parts, and therefore should be encouraged; the printers at Philadelphia were wretched ones; and, if I would set up there, he made no doubt I should succeed; for his part, he  would do me every service in his power. This my brother-in-law afterwards told me in Boston, but I knew as yet nothing of it; when, one day Keimer and I being at work near the window, we saw the governor and another gentleman, finely dressed, come directly across the street to our house, and heard them at the door.

Keimer ran down immediately, thinking it a visit to him;

but the governor inquir'd for me, came up, and with a condescension and politeness I had been quite unus'd to, made me many compliments, desired to be acquainted with me, blam'd me kindly for not having made myself known to him when I first came to the place, and would have me away with him to the tavern, where he was going to taste, as he said, some excellent Madeira. I was not a little surprised, and Keimer star'd like a pig poisoned. I went, however, with the governor, and over the Madeira he propos'd my setting up my business. On my doubting whether my father would assist me in it, Sir William said he would give me a letter to him, in which he would state the advantages, and he did not doubt of prevailing with him.

About the end of April, 1724, a little vessel offer'd for Boston. I took leave of Keimer as going to see my friends. The governor gave me an ample letter, saying many flattering things of me to my father, and strongly recommending the project of my setting up at Philadelphia as a thing that must make my fortune. We struck on a shoal in going down the bay, and sprung a leak; we had a blustering time at sea, and were oblig'd to pump almost continually, at which I took my turn. We arriv'd safe, however, at Boston in about a fortnight. I had been absent seven months, and my unexpected appearance surpriz'd the family; all were, however, very glad to see me, except my brother. I went to see him at his printing-house. I was better dress'd than ever while in his service, having a genteel new suit, a watch, and my pockets lin'd with near five pounds sterling in silver. He receiv'd me not very frankly, look'd me all over, and turn'd to his work again.

My father received the governor's letter with some apparent surprise, but said little of it to me for some days, when Capt. Holmes returning he show'd it to him, ask'd him if he knew Keith, and what kind of man he was; adding his opinion that he must be of small discretion to think of setting a boy up in business who wanted yet three years of being at man's estate. Holmes said what he could in favor of the project, but my father was clear in the impropriety of it, and at last gave a flat denial to it.

My friend and companion Collins, who was a clerk in the postoffice, pleas'd with the account I gave him of my new country, determined to go thither also; and set out before me by land to Rhode Island.

My father, tho' he did not approve Sir William's proposition, was yet pleas'd that I had been able to obtain so advantageous a character from a person of such note, and that I had been so industrious and careful as to equip myself so handsomely in so short a time; therefore, seeing no prospect of an accommodation between my brother and me, he gave his consent to my returning again to Philadelphia, advis'd me to behave respectfully, endeavor to obtain the general esteem, and avoid lampooning and libeling, to which he thought I had too much inclination. I embark'd again for New York, now with his blessing.

The sloop putting in at Newport, Rhode Island, I visited my brother John, who had been settled there some years. He received me very affectionately, for he always lov'd me. A friend of his, one Vernon, having some money due to him in Pensilvania, about thirty-five pounds currency, desired I would receive it for him, and keep it till I had his directions what to remit it in. Accordingly, he gave me an order. This afterwards occasion'd me a good deal of uneasiness.

At NEW YORK I found my friend Collins, who had arriv'd there some time before me. While I liv'd in Boston, most of my hours of leisure were spent with him, and he continu'd a sober as well as an industrious lad. But, during my absence, he had acquir'd a habit of sotting with brandy; and I found that he had been drunk every day since his arrival at New York. He had gam'd, too, and lost his money, so that I was oblig'd to discharge his lodgings, and defray his expenses to and at Philadelphia, which prov'd extremely inconvenient to me.

We proceeded to Philadelphia. I received on the way Vernon's money, without which we could hardly have finish'd our journey. Collins wished to be employed in some counting-house; but, whether they discover'd his dramming by his breath, or by his behaviour, he met with no success in any application, and continu'd lodging and boarding at the same house with me, and at my expense. Knowing I had that money of Vernon's, he was continually borrowing of me, still promising repayment as soon as he should be in business. At length he had got so much of it that I was distressed to think what I should do in case of being call'd on to remit it.

Soon after that, a West India captain, who had a commission to procure a tutor for the sons of a gentleman at Barbadoes, happened to meet Collins, agreed to carry him thither. He left me then, promising to remit the first money he should receive in order to discharge the debt; but I never heard of him after.

The breaking into this money of Vernon's was one of the first great errata of my life; and show'd that my father was not much out in his judgment when he suppos'd me too young to manage business of importance. But Sir William, on reading his letter, said he was too prudent. Discretion did not always accompany years, nor was youth always without it. "And since he will not set you up," says he, "I will do it myself. Give me an inventory of the things necessary to be had from England, and I will send for them. You shall repay me when you are able; I am resolv'd to have a good printer here, and I am sure you must succeed." This was spoken with such an appearance of cordiality, that I had not the least doubt of his meaning what he said. I afterwards heard it as his known character to be liberal of promises which he never meant to keep. Yet, at that time, I believ'd him one of the best men in the world.

I presented him an inventory of a little print'g-house, amounting to about one hundred pounds sterling. He lik'd it, but ask'd me if my being on the spot in England to chuse the types, might not be of some advantage. I agreed. "Then," says he, "get yourself ready to go with Annis"; which was the annual ship. But it would be some months before Annis sail'd, so I continu'd working with Keimer.

I believe I have omitted mentioning that, in my first voyage from Boston, being becalm'd off Block Island, our people set about catching cod, and hauled up a great many. Hitherto I had stuck to my resolution of not eating animal food, and on this occasion I considered the taking every fish as a kind of unprovoked murder, since none of them could do us any injury. All this seemed very reasonable. But I had formerly been a great lover of fish, and, when this came hot out of the frying-pan, it smelt admirably well. I balanc'd some time between principle and inclination, till I recollected that, when the fish were opened, I saw smaller fish taken out of their stomachs; then thought I, "If you eat one another, I don't see why we mayn't eat you." So I din'd upon cod very heartily, and continued to eat with other people, returning only now and then occasionally to a vegetable diet. So convenient a thing it is to be a *reasonable creature*, since it enables one to find or make a reason for every thing one has a mind to do.

Keimer and I liv'd on a pretty familiar footing, and agreed tolerably well, for he suspected nothing of my setting up. He wore his beard at full length, because somewhere in the Mosaic law it is said, "*Thou shalt not mar the corners of thy beard.*" He likewise kept the Seventh day, Sabbath; and these two points were essentials with him. I dislik'd both; but agreed to admit them upon condition of his adopting the doctrine of using no animal food. "I doubt," said he, "my constitution will not bear that." I assur'd him that he would be the better for it. He was usually a great glutton, and I Promised myself some diversion in half-starving him. He agreed to try; and we held for three months. We had our victuals dress'd, and brought to us regularly by a woman in the neighborhood, who had from me a list of forty dishes to be prepared for us at different times, in all which there was neither fish, flesh, nor fowl, and the whim suited me the better at this time from the cheapness of it, not costing us above eighteen pence sterling each week. I went on pleasantly, but poor Keimer suffered grievously, long'd for the flesh-pots of Egypt, and order'd a roast pig. He invited me and two women friends to dine with him; but, it being brought too soon upon table, he could not resist the temptation, and ate the whole before we came.

I had made some courtship during this time to Miss Read. I had a great respect and affection for her, and had some reason to believe she had the same for me; but, as I was about to take a long voyage, and we were both only a little above eighteen, it was thought that if a marriage was to take place, it would be more convenient after my return, when I should be, as I expected, set up in my business.

My chief acquaintances at this time were Charles Osborne, Joseph Watson, and James Ralph, all lovers of reading. The first two were clerks to an eminent scrivener or conveyancer in the town, Charles Brogden; the other was clerk to a merchant. Watson was a pious, sensible young man of great integrity; the others rather more lax in their principles of religion, particularly Ralph, who, as well as Collins, had been unsettled by me, for which they both made me suffer. More of Ralph hereafter.

The governor, seeming to like my company, had me frequently to his house, and his setting me up was always mention'd as a fixed thing. I was to take with me letters recommendatory to a number of his friends, besides the letter of credit to furnish me with the necessary money for purchasing the press and types, paper, etc. For these letters I was appointed to call at different times, when they were to be ready; but a future time was still named. Thus he went on till the ship, whose departure too had been several times postponed, was on the point of sailing. Then, when I call'd to take my leave and receive the letters, his secretary said the governor was extremely busy, but would be down at Newcastle before the ship, and there the letters would be delivered to me.

Ralph, though married, and having one child, had determined to accompany me in this voyage. It was thought he intended to obtain goods to sell on commission; but I found afterwards, that, thro' some discontent with his wife's relations, he purposed to leave her on their hands, and never return again. Having taken leave of my friends, and interchang'd some promises with Miss Read, I left Philadelphia in the ship. I ask'd the captain for those letters that were to be under my care. He said all were put into the bag together and he could not then come at them; but, before we landed in England, I should have an opportunity of picking them out; so I was satisfied for the present, and we proceeded on our voyage.

When we came into the Channel, the captain gave me an opportunity to examining the bag for the governor's letters. I found none upon which my name was put as under my care. I picked out six or seven, that, by the handwriting, I thought might be the promised letters, especially as one of them was directed to Basket, the king's printer, and another to some stationer. We arriv'd in London the 24th of December, 1724. I waited upon the stationer, who came first in my way, delivering the letter as from Governor Keith. "I don't know such a person," says he; but, opening the letter, "O! this is from Riddlesden." I was surprized to find these were not the governor's letters; and, after recollecting and comparing circumstances, I began to doubt his sincerity. I found Mr. Denham, who contracted a friendship for me during the voyage, and opened the whole affair to him. He let me into Keith's character; told me there was not the least probability that he had written any letters for me; he laught at the notion of the governor's giving me a letter of credit, having, as he said, no credit to give. On my expressing some concern about what I should do, he advised me to endeavor getting employment. "Among the printers here," said he, "you will improve yourself, and when you return to America, you will set up to greater advantage."

What shall we think of a governor's playing such pitiful tricks, and imposing so grossly on a poor ignorant boy! It was a habit he had acquired. He wish'd to please everybody; and, having little to give, he gave expectations.

RALPH and I were inseparable companions. We took lodgings together at three shillings and six-pence a week—as much as we could then afford. He found some relations, but they were poor, and unable to assist him. He had brought no money with him, so he borrowed of me to subsist.

Immediately I got work at Palmer's, then a famous printing-house in Bartholomew Close, and here I continu'd near a year. I was pretty diligent, but spent with Ralph a good deal of my earnings in going to plays and other places of amusement. We had together consumed all my pistoles, and now just rubbed on from hand to mouth.

At Palmer's I was employed in composing for the second edition of Wallaston's "Religion of Nature." Some of his reasonings not appearing to me well founded, I wrote a little metaphysical piece in which I made remarks on them. It was entitled "A Dissertation on Liberty and Necessity, Pleasure and Pain." It occasion'd my being more consider'd by Mr. Palmer as a young man of some ingenuity, tho' he seriously expostulated with me upon the principles of my pamphlet, which to him appear'd abominable.

I now began to think of getting a little money beforehand, and, expecting better work, I left Palmer's to work at Watts's, a still greater printing-house. Here I continued all the rest of my stay in London.

At my first admission into this printing-house I took to working at press, imagining I felt a want of the bodily exercise I had been us'd to in America. I drank only water; the other workmen, near fifty in number, were great guzzlers of beer. On occasion, I carried up and down stairs a large form of types in each hand, when others carried but one in both hands. They wondered to see, from this and several instances, that the *Water-American*, as they called me, was *stronger* than themselves, who drank *strong* beer! My companion at the press drank every day a pint before breakfast, a pint at breakfast, a pint between breakfast and dinner, a pint at dinner, a pint in the afternoon, and another when he had done his day's work. I thought it a detestable custom; but it was necessary, he suppos'd, to drink *strong* beer, that he might be *strong* to labor. I endeavored to convince him that the bodily strength afforded by beer could only be in proportion to the flour of the barley dissolved in the water of which it was made; that there was more flour in a pennyworth of bread than in a quart of beer. He drank on, however, and had four or five shillings to pay out of his wages every Saturday night for that muddling liquor. Thus these poor devils keep themselves always under.

Watts, after some weeks, desiring to have me in the composing-room, I left the pressmen; a bien venu or sum for drink, being five shillings, was demanded of me by the compositors. I thought it an imposition, as I had paid below; the master thought so too, and forbid my paying it. I stood out two or three weeks, was accordingly considered as an excommunicate, and had so many little pieces of private mischief done me, by mixing my sorts, transposing my pages, breaking my matter, etc., etc., if I were ever so little out of the room, and all ascribed to the chapel ghost, which they said ever haunted those not regularly admitted, that, notwithstanding the master's protection, I found myself oblig'd to comply and pay the money, convinc'd of the folly of being on ill terms with those one is to live with continually.

I was now on a fair footing with them, and soon acquir'd considerable influence. From my example a great part of them left their muddling breakfast of beer, and bread, and cheese, finding they could with me be supply'd from a neighborhood house with a large porringer of hot water-gruel, sprinkled with pepper, for the price of a pint of beer, viz., three halfpence. This was a more comfortable as well as cheaper breakfast, and kept their heads clearer. Those who continued sotting with beer all day, were often out of credit at the alehouse, and us'd to make interest with me to get beer. This, and my being esteem'd a pretty good jocular verbal satirist, supported my consequence in the society. My constant attendance recommended me to the master; and my uncommon quickness at composing occasioned my being put upon all work of dispatch, which was generally better paid.

At Watt's printing-house I contracted an acquaintance with an ingenious young man, one Wygate, who having wealthy relations, had been better educated than most printers. I taught him and a friend of his to swim at twice going into the river, and they soon became good swimmers.

I had from a child been ever delighted with this exercise, had studied and practis'd, aiming at the graceful and easy as

well as the useful. All these I took this occasion of exhibiting to them, and was much flatter'd by their admiration; and Wygate, who was desirous of becoming a master, grew more and more attach'd to me on that account. He at length proposed to me travelling all over Europe together, supporting ourselves everywhere by working at our business. I was once inclined to it; but, mentioning it to my good friend Mr. Denham, with whom I often spent an hour when I had leisure, he dissuaded me from it, advising me to think only of returning to Pennsylvania.

He now told me he was about to return to Philadelphia, and should carry over a great quantity of goods in order to open a store there. He propos'd to take me over as his clerk, to keep his books, in which he would instruct me, copy his letters, and attend the store. He added, that, as soon as I should be acquainted with mercantile business, he would promote me. The thing pleas'd me; therefore I immediately agreed on the terms of fifty pounds a year, Pennsylvania money; less, indeed, than my present gettings as a compositor, but affording a better prospect.

We sail'd from Gravesend on 23d of July, 1726, and landed in Philadelphia on the 11th of October. Mr. Denham took a store in Water-street, where we open'd our goods; I attended the business diligently, studied accounts, and grew, in a little time, expert at selling. We lodg'd and boarded together; he counsell'd me as a father, having a sincere regard for me. I respected and lov'd him, and we might have gone on together very happy; but, in the beginning of February, when I had pass'd my twenty-first year, he was taken ill of a distemper which at length carried him off. He left me a small legacy but the store was taken into the care of his executors, and my employment ended.

My brother-in-law, Holmes, being now at Philadelphia, advised my return to my business; and Keimer tempted me, with an offer of large wages by the year, and I clos'd with him. I found in his house these hands: Hugh Meredith, a Welsh Pensilvanian, thirty years of age, bred to country work; honest, sensible, something of a reader, but given to drink. Stephen Potts, a young countryman, bred to the same of uncommon natural parts, a great wit, but a little idle. These he had agreed with at extream low wages per week, to be rais'd a shilling every three months, as they improved in their business. I soon perceiv'd that the intention of engaging me at high wages was to have these raw, cheap hands form'd thro' me; and as soon as I had instructed them, then he should be able to do without me. I went on, however, very cheerfully, put his printing-house in order, which had been in great confusion, and brought his hands by degrees to mind their business and to do it better.

We never worked on Saturday, that being Keimer's Sabbath, so I had two days of reading. My acquaintance with ingenious people in the town increased. Keimer at first treated me with great civility. But I found that my services became every day of less importance, as the other hands improv'd in the business; and, when Keimer paid my second quarter's wages, he let me know that he felt them too heavy, and thought I should make an abatement. He grew by degrees less civil, frequently found fault, was captious, and seem'd ready for an outbreaking. At length a trifle snapt our connections; for, a great noise happening near the court-house, I put my head out of the window to see what was the matter. Keimer, being in the street, look'd up and saw me, call'd out to me in a loud voice and angry tone to mind my business, adding some reproachful words, that nettled me the more for their publicity, all the neighbors who were looking out on the same occasion, being witnesses how I was treated. He came up immediately into the printing-house, continu'd the quarrel, high words pass'd on both sides, he gave me the quarter's warning we had stipulated, expressing a wish that he had not been oblig'd to so long a warning. I told him his wish was unnecessary, for I would leave him that instant; and so, taking my hat, walk'd out of doors, desiring Meredith to take care of some things I left and bring them to my lodgings.

Meredith came accordingly in the evening, when we talked my affair over. He had conceiv'd a great regard for me, and let me know that he was sure his father would advance money to set us up, if I would enter into partnership with him. "I am sensible I am no workman," says he, "if you like it, your skill in the business shall be set against the stock I furnish, and we will share the profits equally."

The proposal was agreeable, and I consented; his father was in town and approv'd of it; the more as he saw I had great influence with his son, had prevail'd on him to abstain long from dram-drinking, and he hop'd might break him of that wretched habit entirely. I gave an inventory to the father, who carry'd it to a merchant; the things were sent for from London.

When the new types arrived, we found a house to hire near the market. We had scarce opened our letters and put our press in order, before George House, an acquaintance of mine, brought a countryman to us, whom he had met in the street inquiring for a printer. All our cash was now expended, and this countryman's five shillings, being our first-fruits, and coming so seasonably, gave me more pleasure than any crown I have since earned; and the gratitude I felt toward House has made me always ready to assist young beginners.

There are croakers in every country, always boding its ruin. Such a one then lived in Philadelphia; an elderly man, with a wise look and a very grave manner of speaking. This gentleman, a stranger to me, stopt one day at my door and asked me if I was the young man who had lately opened a new printing-house. Being answered in the affirmative, he said he was sorry for me because my expensive undertaking would be lost; for Philadelphia was a sinking place, the people already half bankrupt. He gave me such a detail of misfortunes now existing, or that were soon to exist, that he left me half melancholy. This man continued to declaim in the same strain, refusing for many years to buy a house because all was going to destruction; and at last I had the pleasure of seeing him give five times as much for one as he might have bought it for when he first began his croaking.

I should have mentioned before that, in the autumn of the preceding year, I had form'd most of my ingenious acquaintance into a club of mutual improvement, which we called the JUNTO; we met on Friday evenings. The rules that I drew up required that every member, in his turn, should produce one or more queries on any point of Morals, Politics, or Natural Philosophy, to be discuss'd by the company; and once in three months produce and read an essay of his own writing, on any subject he pleased. Our debates were to be under the direction of a president, and to be conducted in the sincere spirit of inquiry after truth, without fondness for dispute, or desire of victory; and, to prevent warmth, all expressions of positiveness in opinions, or direct contradiction, were after some time made contraband, and prohibited under small pecuniary penalties.

I received at this time from the Quakers the printing 40 sheets of their history, and upon this we work'd exceedingly hard. I compos'd of it a sheet a day, and Meredith worked it off at press; it was often eleven at night, and sometimes later, before I had finished my distribution for the next day's work, for the little jobbs sent in by our other friends now and then put us back. But so determined I was to continue doing a sheet a day of the folio, that one night, when, having impos'd my forms, I thought my day's work over, one of them by accident was broken, and two pages reduced to pi, I immediately distributed and compos'd it over again before I went to bed; and this industry, visible to our neighbors, began to give us character and credit; particularly, I was told, that mention being made of the new printing-office at the merchants' Every-night club, the general opinion was that it must fail, there being already two printers in the place, Keimer and Bradford; but Dr. Baird gave a contrary opinion: "For the industry of that Franklin," says he, "is superior to any thing I ever saw of the kind; I see him still at work when I go home from club, and he is at work again before his neighbors are out of bed."

George Webb, who had found a female friend that lent him wherewith to purchase his time of Keimer, now came to offer himself as a journeyman to us. We could not then imploy him; but I foolishly let him know as a secret that I soon intended to begin a newspaper, and might then have work for him. My hopes of success, as I told him, were founded on this, that the then only newspaper, printed by Bradford, was a paltry thing, wretchedly manag'd, no way entertaining, and yet was profitable to him; I therefore thought a good paper would scarcely fail of good encouragement. I requested Webb not to mention it; but he told it to Keimer, who immediately, to be beforehand with me, published proposals for printing one himself, on which Webb was to be employ'd. I resented this; and to counteract them, as I could not yet begin our paper, I wrote several pieces of entertainment for Bradford's paper, under the title of the Busy Body. By this means the attention of the publick was fixed on that paper.

Keimer began his paper, however, and, after carrying it on three-quarters of a year, with at most only ninety subscribers, he offered it to me for a trifle; and I, having been ready some time to go on with it, took it in hand directly; and it proved in a few years extremely profitable to me. This was one of the first good effects of my having learnt a little to scribble; another was, that the leading men, seeing a newspaper now in the hands of one who could also handle a pen, thought it convenient to oblige and encourage me.

But another difficulty came upon me which I had never the least reason to expect. Mr. Meredith's father, who was to have paid for our printing-house, was able to advance only one hundred pounds currency, which had been paid; and a hundred more was due to the merchant, who grew impatient, and su'd us all. We gave bail, but saw that, if the money could not be rais'd in time, the suit must soon come to a judgment and our hopeful prospects be ruined, as the press and letters must be sold for payment, perhaps at half price.

In this distress two true friends, whose kindness I have never forgotten, came to me separately, unknown to each other, offering each of them to advance me all the money that should be necessary to enable me to take the whole business upon myself.

These two friends were members of the JUNTO: Robert Grace, a young gentleman of some fortune, generous, lively, and witty; a lover of punning and of his friends; and William Coleman, then a merchant's clerk, about my age, who had the coolest, clearest head, the best heart, and the exactest morals of almost any man I ever met with.

Meredith, my partner, said to me at this time, "I see this is a business I am not fit for. I was bred a farmer, and it was a folly in me to come to town. I am inclined to follow my old employment. If you will take the debts of the company upon you, return to my father the hundred pounds he has advanced; pay my little personal debts, and give me thirty pounds and a new saddle, I will relinquish the partnership, and leave the whole in your hands." I agreed to this proposal.

As soon as he was gone, I recurr'd to my two friends; and went on with the business in my own name.

I NOW opened a little stationer's shop and began gradually to pay off the debt I was under for the printing-house. In order to secure my credit and character as a tradesman, I took care not only to be in *reality* industrious and frugal, but to avoid all appearances to the contrary, I drest plainly; I was seen at no places of idle diversion. I never went out a fishing or shooting; a book, indeed, sometimes debauch'd me from my work, but that was seldom, snug, and gave no scandal; and, to show that I was not above my business, I sometimes brought home the paper I purchased at the stores thro' the streets on a wheelbarrow.

Thus being esteem'd an industrious, thriving young man,

the merchants who imported stationery solicited my custom; others proposed supplying me with books, and I went on swimmingly. In the meantime, Keimer's credit and business declining daily, he was at last forc'd to sell his printing-house to satisfy his creditors.

My thoughts now turned to marriage, and I look'd round me and made overtures of acquaintance; but soon found that, the business of a printer being generally thought a poor one, I was not to expect money with a wife, unless with such a one as I should not otherwise think agreeable. In the mean time, that hard-to-be-governed passion of youth hurried me frequently into intrigues with low women that fell in my way, which was attended with some expense and great inconvenience, besides a continual risque to my health by a distemper which of all things I dreaded, though by great good luck I escaped it. A friendly correspondence as neighbors and old acquaintances had continued between me and Mrs. Read's family, who all had a regard for me from the time of my first lodging in their house. I piti'd poor Miss Read's unfortunate situation, who was generally dejected, seldom cheerful, and avoided company.

I considered my giddiness and inconstancy when in London as in a great degree the cause of her unhappiness, tho' the mother was good enough to think the fault more her own than mine, as she had prevented our marrying before I went thither, Our mutual affection was revived, and I took her to wife, September 1st, 1730. She proved a good and faithful helpmate, assisted me much by attending the shop; we throve together, and have ever mutually endeavored to make each other happy.

Spoonhandle

The story of Donny Mitchell

BY RUTH MOORE

SPOONHANDLE

THE DUCKS, a flock of old squaws, came scaling in so fast that Donny almost missed seeing them. From where he waited, crouched behind a boulder, he glanced around just in time to see them zoom into the cove like a fleet of little sea-planes.

Donny ducked his head with a jerk, then peeked carefully over the boulder. In the still November twilight, the cove lay like a sheet of glass, rippled only by the swimming birds. Donny's 13-year-old body shook a little and his hands, bare on the stock of the shotgun, trembled with cold and excitement.

But he patiently stalked the ducks for a closer shot, tearing down the rocky shore in a scrambling run when they dived, and throwing himself full length on the rocks when they reappeared on the water. Despite his caution, however, the birds seemed nervous and kept moving away from Donny's end of the cove. He saw that, even if he got to the edge without scaring them, it would still be a pretty long shot for Artie's old gun.

Oh, darn, he whispered. Darn, darn, darn. Donny kept on watching the birds with a longing that made moisture come into his eyes. If he could only shoot one, just one.

His third run brought him to the shore of the cove. He did not lie down this time, but stood and steadied his gun on a flat ledgetop. When the old squaws broke water, he let go with both barrels. The birdshot plowed into the water at least ten feet short of the flock. The cove exploded into tatters of foam as the birds churned for headway, standing on their tails. Then they were off, streaking for the sea. Donny stared after them bleakly, then slowly broke his gun at the breech and ejected the empty shells.

It wouldn't happen to a dog, he muttered. Not to a dog with a litter of pups. He kicked violently at a pebble. Noth-

282

ing ever went right any more. Not school, nor his plans, nor the new home he'd had such hopes of. Not even gunning. Cap'n My Mitchell, his great-uncle, had always said that, however long it was a-comin, change in a man's luck was all he could be sure of; but since Cap'n My's death it seemed to Donny there'd been nothing but bad luck and hard times.

He had lived with Uncle My at Bear Harbor, 20 miles down the Maine coast. His mother had died before he had known her; his father, shortly after, had been lost at sea. Uncle My had died two years ago, and the sale of his few things had brought hardly enough to bury him. For a while Donny had stayed with some neighbors. Then they had turned him over to the State Welfare. He was wild, they said; he didn't act right, didn't appreciate what was done for him. Better for somebody with authority to take him before it was too late.

The State Welfare sent Donny to an inland village to board with a storekeeper, who maybe in time would adopt him. Donny felt he couldn't stand it so far away from the water and he hated the storekeeper and his tight-faced wife. He stuck it out for six months and then ran away. The State cops picked him off a freight train outside of Portland.

In the past year and a half Donny had had three foster homes; it didn't look as if this new one with Mis Mary Mackay was going to be much different, although she did live on the coast of Big Spoon Island and only 20 miles above Bear Harbor, where he had lived with Uncle My. Mis Mackay was an old lady, a widow, living alone, who needed someone for company and to do her outdoor chores. She served him good meals and she was nice enough, except when he didn't mind her or slacked on his work.

Tonight, for instance, she would raise the deuce for sure when he got home. He'd sneaked off without doing the after-noon chores, and now he couldn't even take home any birds. She might have been easier to handle if he could have come into the kitchen holding up five-six sea birds, and saying: "I know I run off without milkin or fillin the woodbox, Mis Mackay, but I done it to get these birds for us."

But what was the use? She wouldn't know that evening

choretime was just when the birds were flying; or that today was the only day he could borrow Artie Osgood's gun. All she'd think about was her cussid old chores. What the heck, if she needed a hired man, why didn't she hire one? The trouble with all these people who got State boys to board, they wanted something for nothing—a boy to do their work and the State to pay them board besides.

His bitter thoughts were interrupted when he noticed someone in a ragged old hat moving toward him around the cove. As he watched, he recognized Willie Stilwell, one of the two Stilwell "boys" who batched it together on Little Spoon Island. Donny was startled. What was *he* doing here? Did he maybe have some ideas about that lobster car?

A week before, he and Artie Osgood had tried to swipe some lobsters out of Hod and Willie Stilwell's car. Artie had had the idea, saying that they could have a feed on the shore, and then sell the rest. But the lobster car had been locked, and while they were figuring how to get it open, Hod and Willie had come in from fishing, so they'd had to give it up. It had been fairly dark but Donny wasn't sure whether they'd seen anything.

Now, as Willie came closer, Donny saw that he had his shotgun cuddled in the crook of his arm and two ducks slung across his shoulder. Donny's alarm changed to bitterness. "Well, no wonder," he said. "I knew somethin scairt my old squaws."

"I don't b'lieve I did, did I?" Willie said amiably. "I shot these ducks a long time ago, before the old squaws ever thought of comin into the cove."

"Well, somethin scairt em," said Donny darkly. "I know I never."

"Nobody scairt em," Willie said companionably. "They was feedin out. I saw you creepin up on em, and it was a darned smart job."

Donny was mollified. Ole Willie had the name of being a smart gunner. If he said it was a good job of creeping up, it must have been.

In the two months since he had come to live with Mis

Mackay, Donny had heard a lot of gossip about Willie and Hod Stilwell. Both of them, Donny had learned, were "peculiar." Although the rest of the Stilwell family were somebody—they had money and big houses—Willie and Hod wouldn't have a thing to do with them. They'd gone off by themselves to an old camp on an island.

Artie Osgood, the boy Donny liked best in school, had told him a lot about Willie and Hod, the night they tried to break into the car. Artie was Myron Osgood the storekeeper's son. He never seemed to have any spending money either. It had seemed natural for Donny and him to go around together.

"Willie and Hod won't hurt nobody unless they get mad," Artie said. "But they say if they get mad they're an awful sight. You look close, sometime, you'll see they got a kind of a wild light in their eye."

Looking at Willie, Donny couldn't detect anything unusual in his eye. He would be kind of good-looking, tall like that, wide-shouldered and easy-moving, if it wasn't for them slouchy old clothes.

"If you had shot them ducks," Willie was saying, "how would you have brung em in without you'd had a dog or a boat?"

"I'd have swum out after em," Donny said fiercely. "I always swum out after the birds when I went gunnin with Uncle My."

Willie looked up quickly. "That wouldn't be Cap'n My Mitchell down to Bear Harbor, would it?"

"What's it to ya?" Donny said.

"Nothin to me. I just don't recollect ya." Willie glanced at him, surprised.

"I stay to Mis Mackay's. Mitchell's my name."

"Why," said Willie, with pleasure. "You're Cap'n My's great-nephew. I heard you was comin to stay to Mary's and I've seen you up around the wharf, but I never made the connection. I knew Cap'n Myron Mitchell well. Went to the Banks two seasons on his vessel."

"You did!" Donny was excited.

Willie got up, stretching his legs leisurely. "Well, well.

Cap'n My Mitchell! I knew your pa, too. He was a great gunner."

"That's what Uncle My always said. He was always braggin about pa." Donny's face darkened. "I guess you and me's the only ones left that care anything about that now."

"Shucks!" said Willie. "Lots of folks remember Granville Mitchell. Joe Sangor, lives down on the Point, does, I know for a fact. He was aboard the vessel your pa was lost off of. You ought t' go down and see him."

"That Portygee?" Donny said stiffly.

Willie regarded Donny with a keen, cool eye.

"Your pa," he said, "nor your Uncle My neither, never let nobody tell them whether a man was a decent feller. They found out for themselves. Joe's a heck of a good guy."

Willie stuck his shotgun-stock in his armpit and started off down the path. Suddenly he stopped and turned. "I was thinkin," he said, "Hod and me's got a chowder to finish up, and I don't b'lieve I can use these ducks. You like to have em?"

"Well, gee, I..." Donny stammered. Then he grinned and his eyes shone. "Gee, I sure would." He scooped up the birds Willie held out and raced off down the path.

Watching him go, Willie shook his head. The poor duffer, he muttered. I don't know's I ever see anyone so lonesome.

It was dark when Donny got home. As he came up the driveway, panting, he could see Mis Mackay through the lighted window, her gray head bent over her supper plate.

"Well!" she said, as he came through the door. "I'd give you up for lost. Where on earth you been?"

"Gunnin," Donny said briefly. "I got two birds. You want em?"

"Of course I want em. They'll go good. Hang em on a high nail in the shed, so's the cat won't get at em." She watched while Donny splashed briefly at the washbasin and sprawled into the chair across the table. She shook her head firmly as he piled his plate with three pork chops and four potatoes and started shoveling huge mouthfuls.

"Donny," she said, "you put one of them chops and two potatoes back on the plate. If you want a second helpin you can have it. No, not with your fingers. Now you set up straight and stop gobblin."

She wished, with a sigh, that she knew how on earth to handle him. If one of her own boys, now grown up and gone, had ever acted that way at the table, she'd have snaked him bald-headed; but she'd tried jawing Donny

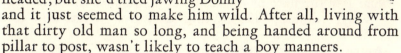

and it just seemed to make him wild. After all, living with that dirty old man so long, and being handed around from pillar to post, wasn't likely to teach a boy manners.

She noticed, as she sat thoughtfully eating, that Donny's ears were red and that his frantic mouthfuls had slowed down. Waiting for me to open up on him, the poor little scamp. Well, he'd have to have a talking-to, but she'd let him finish his supper in peace.

"Where'd you get the birds, down to Cat Cove?" Mary said at last.

"Uh-huh."

"You must have had to borrow a shotgun."

"Uh-huh."

Mary cut herself a piece of pie and a generous piece for Donny, and set the rest of the pie where he could reach it. "Anyone else out gunnin?"

"Just Willie Stilwell."

"Oh . . . Willie." Mary gave a little laugh. "He's a funny one. Didn't you think so?"

"Well . . ." Donny said. "Well, Mis Mackay . . ." He turned red and his voice, never very stable these days, squeaked into an upper register. "I don't 'low nobody to tell me whether a man's a good feller. I find out for myself."

"Why!" said Mary astonished. "That's a good idea, Donny, only you don't need to make it sound quite so sarsy."

Donny pushed back his chair from the table. "My father

and my Uncle My was like that," he went on, more loudly than he needed to, "and I figger it's a good way to be." He reached for his cap.

"Donny, you set right back down there." Now she'd have to do it. Yet how would she? A boy as sensitive as Donny, if he lost too much face in a place, he wouldn't be able to stay. So the querulous scolding she gave him for scamping his chores was brief. Then, ignoring his sullen silence, she added, "I was thinkin. It'd be awful handy to have a mess of birds off and on this winter. Why don't you use my boy Dave's gun, that's packed away in the closet upstairs?"

She saw the flare of joy in his eyes, quickly hidden.

"Why, I dunno," Donny said carefully. "What kind of a gun is it?"

Mary was already regretting her impulse. That gun had been the apple of Dave's eye. "All I know is, it's a good one," she said brusquely. "If you use it, Donny, you'll have to be awful careful of it. It's got to be cleaned and greased every time you use it."

Donny had been edging across the room while she was talking, and when she finished he opened the hall door quietly. Then she heard him go tearing up the stairs two at a time.

A moment later he called desperately down the hot-air register, "Mis Mackay! Oh, Mis Mackay! Which closet?"

A few weeks later Donny was splitting cordwood for the stove when Mrs. Mackay came around the house and bore down on him, obviously mad. He was going at his task with great effort, lifting the axe and letting it fall so that the blade barely pierced the bark each time and bounced off ineffectively.

"Donny," said Mary Mackay, "what's become of that root beer I made and put down suller?"

"I d'no what's become of it," Donny said. "I never touched it."

"Well, somebody's touched it. Somebody warn't satisfied with drinkin it all up, they even filled up the bottles with water, so's I wouldn't notice 't was gone."

"Maybe the yeast didn't work," said Donny hopefully. "There was a place I was to, up-country, Mis Mackay, they made root beer and it all just turned to water."

Mary eyed him grimly. "Donny, I'm sick and tired of your doin underhand tricks and then lyin out of it. You drunk up that beer and you filled those bottles with water."

"I never!" Donny's voice went shrill. "How do you know who might of broke into that suller some night when we was sleepin?"

"Oh, fiddle! You've got to stop this business, Donny, hear me? I've stood all of it I'm goin to."

"That's right, blame me! That's all you ever do, jaw and blame me for stuff I don't know nothin about."

It was true, he had drunk up the root beer and had spent long careful moments refilling the bottles. But the explanation he had worked out seemed perfectly reasonable to him. Somebody *might* have broken in. The fact that Mis Mackay refused to consider this logical possibility and preferred to blame him was only further proof that she picked on him. He felt deeply wronged, and suddenly, alone in the world, and a fat tear rolled down his cheek.

Mary, staring sternly at his figure of woe, sighed deeply. "It ain't the root beer I care about, for goodness' sake, Donny. You could have had all you wanted when it was ready. But why did you bother to steal it?"

"I never! It wasn't me that done it!"

"It's the same way with the cookies and the pie in the pantry," Mary went on. "I spose you think I don't know how you come sneakin downstairs at night and lug stuff up to hide in your bureau drawer. Why, the bottom of your drawer is covered with old stale crumbs! You don't have to steal, and besides, it tolls the mice!" The neat housewife in her awakened angrily. "If you don't stop it, Donny, I'm goin to lock the pantry door. So help me."

When she had finished and gone back into the house, Donny picked up the axe and flung it furiously into the woodpile. He followed with the bucksaw and saw it land with a satisfactory, vibrating crash. Let her try to catch him, the nosy old hen, he thought, starting down the shore road on a dead run.

His rage at being caught about the root beer was nothing, compared to the way he felt at her knowing of his visits to the pantry at night. He couldn't have explained the deep thrill he got out of creeping down the stairs, feeling out with his bare toes the creaky boards. For weeks he'd made a study of the noisy places in the stairs and floor, learning where he mustn't step. To swipe pie and cake at night gave him a sense of getting his own back, something that would be actually his.

The trouble was, he didn't own anything, not even his clothes. Every few months the Welfare Woman checked up on his wardrobe, and sent what she thought he ought to have. But she never consulted his own wishes. He never had any spending money. Sometimes Mis Mackay doled out 35 cents for the movies, but she always gave him just exactly 35 cents, so that he never had anything after the show for treat, like the rest of the boys. Even the shotgun she hadn't given to him outright. She was always reminding him it was her boy Dave's gun.

Nursing his grievances, Donny slouched along the shore road, his hands driven deep into his overalls pockets. Presently, walking aimlessly, he found himself in the clearing above the mussel-bar that led to Willie Stilwell's island.

As he made his way along the rocks he saw a small white punt hauled up in the jog where the mussel-bar met the beach. Either Willie or Hod had rowed over from the island. Donny guessed that whoever it was had gone on up to the village. He went down the beach cautiously and looked the punt over. Then he studied the cove on the opposite shore where Willie and Hod kept their lobster car. He and Artie Osgood had looked over the ground pretty carefully the other night. The car was locked, but he bet he could pry the padlock off.

Making as little noise as possible, Donny shoved the punt into the water and rowed across to the cove. He kept the punt in the dark water along the shadowy side of the bar. The staples on the padlock were big ones. He stuck the hand grip of an oar through one and pried, and felt it give with a punky splintering of water-soaked wood.

Willie Stilwell, walking back through the woods from Cat Cove, heard the splintering sound. Coming out on the shore where he had left his punt, he saw with surprise that the boat was over by the lobster car. Through the dusk he could see the dark outline of someone taking lobsters from the open trap door. Willie slipped behind a boulder. He was bewildered and shocked. He would never have believed anyone would be mean enough to swipe a man's lobsters.

Donny rowed silently ashore and hauled up the punt as he had found it. When he went past Willie's boulder, his windbreaker thrown sacklike over his shoulder and bulging with lobsters, Willie grabbed him firmly by the collar.

"It's you, is it?" Willie said. "I swear, boy, I wouldn't never of believed it."

"You le'me go!" Donny threshed furiously. "You dirty ol' bastid!"

Still holding Donny by the collar, Willie got out his jack-knife and opened it with his teeth. Donny gave a squawk of terror, but Willie merely reached and cut from the bushes a short, limber cane.

"If 't wasn't that Cap'n My was such a good man," he said, "I wouldn't bother with this. I'd take and hand you over to the sheriff."

The cane landed with a *thwack!* in the proper place. Donny let out an outraged yowl.

Willie did a thorough job. When he was through the boy stood blubbering, both fists stuck into his eyes.

"What did you think you was up to, stealin lobsters?" Willie asked. "My Lord, boy, don't you know that's a prison crime?"

His voice sounded reasonable and kind, not wild mad, the way Donny had thought he was. "I was just hungry," he said. "I only wanted a few to cook for supper."

"You had a lot more there than you could eat," Willie pointed out. "I guess you wanted to sell a few somewhere, didn't you?"

"Yes," Donny admitted. "I guess so." He couldn't imagine why he was telling on himself this way. But somehow he didn't want to lie; he'd done a rotten thing and he'd been thrashed good for it. For the first time in months Donny felt uncomplicated and simple, as if things had straightened out for him.

"How come you was hungry? Don't Mary feed ya?"

"Sure. She feeds me all right. Only tonight we had a fight."

"Oh." Willie nodded. He turned and started down the beach toward the punt. "You want to help me put them lobsters back in the car?" he asked over his shoulder. "After it's done we'll go over to my camp and have some supper."

Donny picked up the windbreaker full of lobsters and brought it down to the punt.

"Be a favor t' me if you was to row," Willie said. "I been bankin the house today and I'm tired."

"Sure." Scrabbling in over the side, Donny took the oars.

"You handle a punt pretty good," Willie said. "I guess Cap'n My learnt you how to row."

"Yes, he did. He learnt me a lot of things about a vessel, too. His idea was that maybe I'd be a skipper of a vessel sometime. Only—" Donny stopped.

'Only he died before he got you learnt, that it?" Willie said. "You know, I could use a boy that knows some of the things about the water that Cap'n My knew. I'd pay 25 cents an hour. What d'you do after school and Sat'd'ys?"

Donny looked sullen. "I help out Mis Mackay with her work."

"You think it over," Willie said. "After we eat we'll go ask her if she can spare you part of the time."

Mᴵꜱ ᴍᴀᴄᴋᴀʏ, Donny could see, was still mad. She didn't look up as he and Willie came in.

Willie said, "Evenin. I brought your boy back. He's been down to supper with me."

"It's a good thing he et somewhere," Mary Mackay said. She was sewing, and she bit off her thread with an angry little snap.

Willie was always ill at ease in the presence of a cross or positive woman. "I knew he'd run off," he went on, "but I was eatin supper so I fed him. I hope I ain't kept him too long."

"Well, I'll tell you," Mary said, "I was just about ready to call up the State Woman and tell her to take him away." She looked at Donny for the first time, a stony glance which seemed not to see him. "Donny, if you've had your supper, go up to bed. I'll talk to you in the morning."

"But Willie's—but he's got somethin to ask you," Donny said desperately. He and Willie had had a wonderful supper of fried eggs and potatoes and preserves. Willie had let him cook most of it, and afterward had shown him things in an old sea chest—a real swordfish sword, and some silver pirate earrings he'd bought in New Bedford, a long time ago.

"Ne'm mind, now," Willie said. "We'll talk it over later on. You run along to bed, like you're told."

"I got to know." Donny stood stubbornly.

"What is it you've got to know?" Mis Mackay eyed him. "I spose you know you smashed up that bucksaw, throwin it around?"

"He was figgerin out a way he could pay for it," Willie cut in smoothly. Misery in someone defenseless always put him on his mettle, and now the conversation had shown him a way to go. "I told him I could use a boy sometimes after school and Sat'd'ys and Sundays, pay him a quarter an hour. He said he'd like to have the job, only he had chores to do for you."

"That's right, he does," said Mary tartly.

"I wouldn't want to cut in on your time," Willie explained. "Only thing is, he wants to buy you a new saw and maybe earn a little of his own expense money."

"Well, he ain't a mite of use to me now," Mary said. She sounded mollified in spite of the sharpness of the words, and Donny took a deep breath. "At least, I'd know where he was part of the time."

"That's fine." Willie got up as if the matter were settled. He picked up his hat and his lantern. "First day she can spare you, you come on down, Don." He paused in the doorway and smiled. "Good night."

Donny had his first chance to go out trawling with Willie the following Saturday. Willie had told him to be at the mussel-bar at three o'clock sharp. But he had overslept, and it was a minute or so after three when he came tearing down to the landing. Willie was still waiting for him in the punt and Donny tumbled into it.

"My alarm never woke me up very good," he panted. "I hustled so's you wouldn't go off and leave me."

"I'd a hat to go in a minute," Willie said, "on account of catchin the low-water slack off the Rock."

"Well, I got here," Donny said relieved. Willie wouldn't have left him unless he'd had to. He wouldn't take it out on you because you were a few minutes late, the way a lot of people would. Willie rowed out to where Hod was waiting for them in the big dragger, idling off the point.

"Hi," Hod said briefly, as Willie and Donny clambered aboard. He kicked the gear lines, swung the boat in a wide circle, then headed down channel for the three-hour run to the fishing grounds.

"Calm's a clock, ain't it?" Willie said, sitting on the gunnel beside Donny. "Don't know when I've seen a prettier night."

"Some breakfast'd be prettier," Hod said over his shoulder. "How about it, Donny?"

Donny didn't know Hod very well—not the way he knew Willie. He'd seen him often around the fish wharf, and had admired the width of his shoulders and his lean, rangy height. But Hod never had much to say to people and Donny had been worrying about being aboard a boat with him for a whole day. But now he could see it would be all right.

"I sure could eat," he said, grinning.

Willie started for the cabin. "Come on down and help me wog up some fried ham."

The trim cabin, with its bunks and camp stove, was a wonder to Donny. With Willie's supervision, he got a crackling fire going in the stove, and soon the cabin was filling up with the rich smoke of frying ham. Nothing had ever smelled so good, Donny thought, not even wild ducks roasted on the beach with Uncle My. He tended the ham with cautious absorption, and was relieved when it came out all right.

"Guess we'll have to ship you steady as cook if you can fry eggs like you can ham," Willie said.

He and Willie ate first. Then they went back on deck to steer while Hod came down for breakfast.

"I d'no b't you're goin to need a set of oilskins, ain't you?" Willie said, as they came out into the cold air again. "You take the wheel while I go see 'f the' ain't an extry set in the locker."

He did not wait for Donny to say whether he could steer the big boat. He just left the wheel and went below. Donny braced up to the wheel, a chill of excitement and apprehension racing down his back. Jeepers, he thought, what if I whang her onto a lobster buoy or a rock? He peered tensely out past the boat's steady bow, and for a moment he felt that it was all a gray blur. Then he realized that he could see better. The gray blur became a wide stretch of smooth water and the white horizon came down to meet and blend with it, until it looked as though you'd sail right off the water on to the sky. Jeepers, Donny thought, it's big.

For the first time he was conscious of the deep, steady drone of the engine and of the power that his hand controlled. He moved the wheel a little and felt the boat swerve; looking back, he saw a delicate curve appear in the straight creamy moonlit wake.

"Here's your oilskins," said Willie's voice at his elbow. "Shove em on."

"Can I steer some more?"

"Be a favor to us if you would," Willie said. "The's a

couple trawls left to bait, and I was wondering how we'd manage if you didn't know how to steer."

"You could tell me the course," Donny said, struggling into the oilskins, which were way too big for him. "Uncle My, he showed me how to read a compass. I never steered a boat by one, but—"

"Sou' sou' east," Willie said. Donny found the south-southeast bearing on the compass, lined it up with the snubby mooring post on the boat's bow and held it there. The wake, which had done some snaking around, straightened out and stayed straight.

Paying no further attention to Donny, Hod and Willie began to break out the trawls and the bait barrels. Presently the tip of the bright gold sun appeared on the horizon.

Hazlett's Rock, their destination, was a rugged table-topped ledge, half an acre long, thrusting out of deep water 25 miles from the coast. As they approached it, Hod came to stand by Donny's elbow.

"You can run in close," he said. "The water makes off deep."

The Rock was coming nearer fast. Donny was beginning to feel a little shaky, but now Willie took the wheel and Hod threw over the first trawl buoy with its fluttering, faded marker-flag. The engine, barely ticking over, drove the boat ahead slowly. The ground line of the trawl with its hundreds of baited hooks paid out steadily from the tub. For a moment the hooks seemed to lie motionless on the water; then they sank slowly.

They set nine tubs of trawl and then drifted while they waited for the low-water slack and had a midmorning lunch. Then it was time to go back and haul in the first trawl.

As they slid alongside the buoy and Hod gaffed it in, Donny felt a mounting excitement. If there were any fish on The Ridges today, the boat might go home with kidboards loaded down. Or the hooks might come up empty—or else fouled with something worthless, such as dogfish or skates.

When the first hooks came in, they carried nothing but shreds of sea-flea chewed bait. Straining out over the side

until Willie, afraid he would fall
overboard, reached out and clutched
the baggy seat of his oil-pants,
Donny could see other bare hooks
coming up in slow procession. The
entire trawl was empty, except for
one lone skate. "H'm," said Willie.

The next trawl was more of the
same, and the third one started out
to be no different. Then, halfway
up, the heavy ground line took a
sudden lunge into the sea. Hod tried
to hold it, giving line slowly, and
Willie, suddenly watchful, said excitedly, "Let him run, boy!"

He grabbed a bait knife and began as fast as he could to cut
the hooks off the trawl. Donny had never seen hands move so
quickly. But suddenly the line began to burn through Hod's
hands so fast that Willie couldn't catch the hooks. For a
moment there was a flurry of flying line and then the line
went slack.

"He gone?" asked Willie tensely. "He didn't hook you,
did he?"

Hod began to take in steadily on the line, and as it came
aboard Willie methodically cut off the hooks. The line stayed
slack, then suddenly it straightened out and cut through the
water with a *z-zing*.

"No, by gosh, he ain't gone!" Hod shouted. He braced
back and held the line, this time not having to bother with
hooks. Slowly he horsed it in, now gaining, now losing line,
but gaining more than he lost.

"Hauls like a halibut," he said, panting. "If it's a shark
it's a jeasly big one." The line yielded itself in a series of hard
jerks and rushes.

"He's drownin out some," Willie said. He picked up a
stout-handled gaff and peered anxiously down into the water.
Then his body tensed with excitement.

"By gorry, I can see him! It's a halibut bigger'n Hazlett's

Rock!" Willie poised the gaff. "Easy, boy. E-e-easy, there. Let him run a little, haul up his head. Oh, you sonova, you great big beautiful sonova—Look out!"

Donny climbed to the roof of the coop. From there, deep down, swirling in the green-black light, he could see something that looked as big as the bottom of the ocean, something now dark, now white, as it turned back and belly upward to the pull of the line.

"Dong him in," Willie crooned. "Git him up here where I can whang this gaft into his gills. E-e-easy. Dong him in!"

The flat monstrosity, feeling doom with the surface of the water, started down, and Hod lost 20 feet of line. He was breathing hard and the sweat was running down his face. He got the lost line back and then, with a tremendous lash of foam, the head of the halibut broke water.

"Put the gaft to him," croaked Hod, and Willie sank it deep into the vulnerable soft gills. Together they heaved upward. The great gasping head appeared at the gunnel. Then Hod freed a hand from the line, picked up a heavy hardwood club, and hit the halibut twice in the middle of his thick triangular head. The big fish ceased his lashing, and the men quickly hauled him over the side.

"Jeepers!" Donny said, staring with awe at the dead fish. "Look at his head. It wouldn't go into a bucket!"

Donny shared the pride and the excitement when the boat pulled up to the fish wharf in the afternoon, and the other fishermen gathered around, bug-eyed, to see the big halibut.

"Biggest one we've had here in ten years," said Nick Driver, the wharf boss, watching the arm of his weighing scales teeter to a balance. "Two hundred 'n fifteen pounds. Figger that out at—um—cents a pound, plus 2400 hake—" He scratched busily on a piece of paper—"Hun'd'n thirteen dollars. Come in the office, I'll give you the cash."

Willie came out of the office, spreading a fat roll like a fan. "You sure bring us luck, Don. Guess you'll have to come along again. Here's yours." He held out a ten-dollar bill.

"Oh, gee," Donny said, awestruck. "I never earnt that much. I had too good a time. I don't—"

"Take it," Willie said. "You earnt it fair, all the work you done for us. How about next Sat'd'y, if Mis Mackay can spare ya?"

"Oh, sure, "Donny said. His face broke into a wide grin.

Ann freeman, walking through the village for the first time since her return home, saw with surprise and shock that it had changed considerably in the six years she had been away. Not the spruce woods and the pastures—they were as she remembered them—but the hayfields and the houses were different. The long grass was uncut, and gables peeled paint, roofs spilled shingles.

Hard times were slow getting to an out-of-the-way, almost self-sufficient place like Big Spoon Island; but once they got there, they stayed. The Mackay place, Ann noticed with satisfaction, still was neat, but the hayfields that had been old Bob Mackay's pride and joy were choked with new-growth alders. Bob, though, was dead and his sons gone to the city. Very likely Mary Mackay, living there alone, couldn't handle the place by herself.

As Ann passed the Mackay house, she saw a skinny tall boy come out of the barn. He reached the road with a flying leap, and almost plowed into her.

"Hi," she said, dodging. "You're in a hurry, I guess."

But the boy merely glared at her, hesitated, then darted into the thick bushes on the other side of the road. My gosh! Ann thought. What could he have been up to?

Mary Mackay's front door opened and Mary herself in shawl and rubbers came vigorously down the driveway. "Hello," she said. "Oh, it's Ann Freeman. I heard you was home. Did that young limb of Satan come out this way?"

"Who?" Ann asked. "There was a kid—"

"That's him," said Mary grimly. "Which way did he go?"

Ann was astonished at the change in Mary Mackay. The Mary she remembered had been a kind, motherly soul with a tolerant hand over her turbulent brood. About this woman there was something implacable, and Ann was shocked that a grown woman could be so deeply angry at a boy.

"Whose boy is it, Mary?" she asked. "I don't seem to place him. Has he been pestering you?"

"He's that Mitchell boy I took to board for the State," Mary said, her lips tight. "He's done nothing but pester me ever since he come."

"Boys that age are little hellions," Ann said. It would help Mary, she saw, to air the grievance, so she listened sympathetically.

"I told him he could take a job down to Willie Stilwell's," Mary went on, "if he didn't soldier on his chores for me. So he spends every spare minute he's got down on that island. He never has time to do *nothin* for me. Last Sat'd'y he went out fishin with Willie, and this week he planned t' go again. Only I warned him that he couldn't go if he didn't do his work, and he never. So this mornin I told him he couldn't go today. He started to sarse me, then, and if the's one thing I won't stand from a kid, it's sarse."

"I don't blame you," Ann said.

"I locked him in the woodshed and told him he could stay there till he made up his mind to mind me. He's that stubborn, he stayed there all forenoon. Then, just now, he climbs out the window. And if I could of got my hands on him, I'd of shook the daylights out of him." Mary pulled herself up short. "There!" she said, looking a little sheepish. "I swore I wouldn't git mad at him again, but I guess I can't help it."

"It does anyone good to get mad once in a while," said Ann.

Mary nodded doubtfully and sighed. She felt better, Ann saw. "I swear, I'm weak's a kitten. I ain't seen you for a long time, Ann, and all I do is blow off my troubles. Come int' the house and set awhile, won't you?"

Ann thanked her and explained that she couldn't right now. "I will soon, though," she promised.

"You do that," Mary said. "I'm going back and wait for that boy to come home. I've made up my mind I'm goin t' take a good strong stand with him. He'll mind me, or he'll go back where he come from!"

The scamp, Ann thought, walking thoughtfully along the

Spoonhandle road. He's got her so wrought up she's ready to fly. She was sorry for Mary, yet her real sympathy swung perversely in the opposite direction. The Mitchell boy didn't look mean; he looked like a decent, intelligent kid. He had looked, Ann thought, more desperate than anything else.

After barging into Ann Freeman, Donny ran all the way to the beach and waded across the mussel-bar to Willie Stilwell's island. The expression in his eyes startled Willie.

In a voice close to tears Donny told him the story of his fight with Mis Mackay. "She says I can't come no more," he finished. "She says I got t' give up my job down here."

Willie's eyes were serious and thoughtful. "I can't let you come down here if she says no. You and me both's going t' be in awful bad if we do somethin she says not to."

Donny looked at him. "Maybe you're scared of her. I ain't."

"Hold on, son. I'll go see her again. Maybe we can talk her into it. But if you been scampin your chores, Don, she's right."

"All right," Donny said bitterly. "If you can stand it, I guess I can." He turned and ran, charging across the mussel-bar without stopping, though the tide had started to flow and the water was halfway to his knees.

It was a few days before Willie had time to call on Mis Mackay. When he did he found her hardened against him.

"Donny's got to learn to mind me," she said stiffly. "Besides I need him here to help me."

"Well, I'm sorry," Willie said. "He's a nice boy and I've enjoyed havin him around."

"He must show you a side he don't show me, then."

"Why, I don't know why he would," Willie said slowly. "He's always tellin me what a nice home he's got up here."

She made no reply, and Willie saw it was no use.

"You wun't change your mind?" he asked, pausing at the door. "I had a feelin he was gittin interested in learning about the boat and things. Sometimes when you interest a boy you have less trouble with him."

"No," Mary said firmly. "S' far as I can see, it's just made him more sarsy, if anything."

Donny, watching from an upstairs window, saw Willie walking slowly back down the road. He had heard every word, listening tensely down the hot-air register. Well, there it was. Willie hadn't even put up an argument. If he'd only made just a little bit of a fuss Donny was all prepared to start over again—he'd even try harder with Mis Mackay's chores. But Willie didn't want him bad enough to fight for.

You couldn't trust anyone, Donny thought. For a while, being around with Willie and Hod, he'd begun to feel at home and liked again, the way he had with Uncle My. Now it was over, and he ought to have known better than to count on it. Tears came into Donny's eyes, but he brushed them angrily away. He sat bleakly on the bed staring at his shoes. He'd planned on buying himself some new shoes with his own money, and he could have done it, too, out of his ten dollars if he hadn't had to replace *her* lousy old bucksaw.

He thought resentfully of the way she'd handled that—to get the most out of him, he told himself. The old bucksaw he had busted was worth about three dollars at the most. But she had ordered a bran-new saw that cost eight dollars, and she made him pay it, the old skinflint. That left him two dollars. The brown buckskin shoes he had set his heart on—instead of the black brogans the State Woman always brought—cost three dollars and a half.

It's *her*, he said to himself. She don't want me to have a good time. Now she's lost me my job, she owes me money, and I'll git it out of her, somehow.

The next day, when he took the vegetable man's change, she didn't see him. But the second time, she came in just as he was pocketing 35 cents she'd left on the sideboard. Donny stared at her, his eyes round with horror. But she didn't say anything then or later. She just walked on by him and into the other room.

Mis Mackay's first impulse was to telephone to the Welfare and have them take Donny away. But then she would have to admit that she had failed with him. She had been brought up to believe that there wasn't a human being who wouldn't respond in time to kindness. To give up that conviction would have shaken her to her foundations. She decided to give him a good talking-to; but, when the time came she found she couldn't do it. There was something indecent in having another person know that you knew he was a thief. She could scold him about stealing pie and cake—but how could you accuse him of stealing money and ever look him in the face again?

In the end Mis Mackay did nothing. She took to keeping her money in a locked drawer. Suspicious of Donny, watching his every move in the house, she lost the little respect and liking she had for him and, finally, the kindness with which she had hoped to accomplish so much. It did not occur to her that if Donny had been her boy Dave, she would not have thought him a thief at all, but merely a naughty boy who had made a mistake.

WILLIE STILWELL kept thinking about Donny. He was convinced that something had to be done, that somehow or other a hand could be held out. But he realized that he couldn't do it. Mary Mackay and Donny, had seen to that. In his dilemma his thoughts turned to Ann Freeman.

Ann was now one of his nearest neighbors. She'd had to find a quiet place to work, free from a carping father who didn't think much of book-writin womenfolks, and Hod had been helping her fix up an old fishing shack on the shore. The shack was pretty run-down. Late one afternoon Willie stopped by to find her pottering on it discouragedly.

"I was comin back from gunnin," he said, "and I thought I'd drop by and see how you're makin out."

Actually he had been wandering around Cat Cove, hoping for a sight of Donny. But the Cove had been deserted.

Willie stood his gun carefully in a corner, advanced on the wall and tapped it here and there with his knuckles. "That wall don't 'mount to much. Goin t' let in some cold this winter. Know what I'd do? I'd get some plasterboard and seal this room up tight."

"Oh, Lord," Ann said, "I've already spent more than I should—"

"H'm. I got some plasterboard over'n my barn chamber, left over from the time I fixed my house. 'T wouldn't take much, and Hod'n I could put it on for you tomorrow."

"Oh, I couldn't let you do that."

"Why not? I don't know nothin I'd ruther do than fix up old buildins. Cost you, say, four dollars."

"Oh," Ann said. "But would that be enough, Willie?"

"All I'd want," he said. "If you're walkin up the road now, I'll go along with you far's my turnoff."

As they walked up the wood road, Ann tried to match her steps to his effortless stride.

"You know that Mitchell boy lives to Mary Mackay's?" he asked at last.

"Why no. I've seen him, but I don't know him."

"He's been helpin me with odd jobs, off'n on this fall. I got t' know him quite well. He's a good little kid," Willie said. "He ain't been down for quite a spell. I guess Mary got an idea he was spendin too much time with me."

"I'd think she'd be glad to have him spend time with you."

"Well, no," Willie said. "Hod and I live kind of apart. Not that I'm diff'rent 'n anybody else, but if you live apart folks git to thinkin that you are."

"Do you really like to live apart, Willie?" Ann asked.

"Yes. I do. Y'see I ain't a violent man. I can't stand the pull an haul between people. I found that out a long time ago, so I come away by myself."

They had come to the narrow path that led down to Willie's landing, and he stopped, shifting his gun from one arm to the other. "What I started out to say, I think somethin may be botherin that Mitchell boy pretty bad. He's a little bit wild and he might quite easy be wilder. Mary Mackay's an awful good woman, but she's like a lot of good women, a kid has to be her own before she can see that ordinary devilishness ain't a sign of a crim'nal."

"Could someone do something, you think?" Ann asked.

"Might," Willie said. "I'd hate for Donny t' git into trouble. He ain't got a soul t' turn to, and he ain't what you could call bad. Right now, I run of an idea he could jump either way."

"I don't know what I could do," Ann said doubtfully. "Maybe I could drop by Mary Mackay's."

"Wish you would, sometime," Willie turned and went down the bank to his punt. He did not look back at her.

Maybe they think he's peculiar, Ann thought, but he's one of the kindest men I've ever seen.

He was one of the shrewdest, too, but she did not know that. Willie, according to his estimate of what a good trade should be, had just made one. Four dollars, of course, wouldn't begin to pay for the plasterboard and for putting it on. But in return for his favor, he had found Ann to lend him a hand with Donny Mitchell. And she was the only one he could think of who had the brains and the insight not to go at Donny with a steam shovel.

Mary mackay was sitting in her kitchen, feeling lonesome and abused, when Ann came to see her. Soon the talk got around to Donny. It was as if Ann had loosed the waters behind a dam. In calling the roll of Donny's sins, however, Mary did not say that he was a thief. That lay in her heart, deep buried and festering.

In the midst of her bitter recital, footsteps sounded outside the door and Donny came in. He hesitated wildly at the door when he saw there was company.

"This is Ann Freeman," Mary said abruptly. "I guess you ain't met her."

Donny said, "Uh," and ducked his head.

"We almost bumped into each other one day," Ann said, smiling at him. "I was hoping you'd come in," she said on sudden impulse. "I thought I'd take Sam over to Bellport on a Christmas party, next Saturday afternoon—movies and things." Sam was Ann's 15-year-old brother. "He wants you to go along too. How about it? Can you make it?"

Donny stared at her incredulously. "Sam? Sam *Freeman?*"

"That's what he said." Ann nodded. It wasn't true, and Ann realized she'd have to hop home fast and square it with Sam.

"Well, uh," Donny said. He rubbed his chin against his collar. "Thanks. I can't go this Saturday."

"You can't *go?*" asked Mary sharply. "Why on earth not?"

"I told a feller down to the wharf I'd help him shift some bait." Donny's voice was a mumble.

"Never mind, then," Ann said. "Maybe next Saturday?"

"I guess maybe I'll have to let you know," Donny said. "I ain't sure about that Saturday, either."

He was deeply embarrassed, Ann saw, anxious to get out of sight, and it seemed only kindness to let him go. "Fine," she said casually. "You do that."

When she left Mary Mackay, Ann hurried home to tell Sam what she had done. Sam, it turned out, didn't even like Donny. "Oh, my Lord!" he said. "What got into you, Ann?"

"Look, Sam! I know it was a dirty trick without asking you first. You've probably got your Saturdays planned up to the hilt."

"I've got basketball practice, that's what I've got." Sam was the star of the high school team. "We work *every* Saturday afternoon. Besides, I wouldn't be caught dead—"

Ann pleaded. "Sam, help me out, please. I know that kid's getting into trouble, and he hasn't got a soul to help him."

"Sure he is. But why should we stick our necks out?" he growled.

"What's he doing that's so bad?"

"Oh, I d'no." Sam looked stubborn, then said suddenly. "Well, look. A couple of times he and Artie Osgood have had stuff to peddle—like jackknives and gloves. New ones. Artie told me how they got them—he never could keep his mouth shut. But don't tell, Ann, or the cops would be after them."

"No," she said, feeling a little cold. "I won't tell."

"I gave em both merry hell, last week. Said they needn't bring their stuff around to me." He looked thoughtful. "I guess Donny must've thought it was pretty funny, me askin him to go to the movies."

"M'm. I guess so." Ann was silent a moment, thinking. "Look, Sam. This is how it is." Hoping that the story would reach him, she told Sam what Donny's life at Mary Mackay's must be like, and she added some speculations of her own. "All right," he said. "I'll see what I can do. How about some Friday night, maybe?"

"That'll be swell. You're my favorite brother, Sam.'

They needn't have bothered, as it turned out. Donny met Ann the next day and said politely that he was sorry, his Saturdays were full up for the next few weeks.

DONNY MITCHELL's Saturday plans had nothing to do with shifting bait. Instead he and Artie Osgood crossed over to Bellport, on the mainland, then hitchhiked to Ferriston, the nearest city of any size. As they rode in the big refrigerator truck which had given them a lift, Artie talked easily; the trips to Ferriston didn't seem to bother him at all, or the things they'd sold or hidden away.

The time would come, Donny promised himself, when he'd stop worrying, too. Not about getting caught but about what Uncle My would think if he could know what Donny was doing. I don't care what Willie Stilwell or anyone thinks, he mused morosely. They can let me alone. When they're all rottin on dry fish and potatoes, I'll be ridin around in my Cadillac.

They got off at the town square in Ferriston. "Come on," Artie said. "And see you don't turn green, like you done last time."

The boys went along the main street and loitered in front of a sporting goods store. Through the window they could see three clerks in the store, all busy with customers. Going in, they stood idly by a counter, ostensibly waiting for a clerk.

Artie let his eyes rove around the store. "Over there," he said furtively. "Them hunting knives."

Finally a clerk came toward them. "What can I do for you?"

"Like to see some rawhide laces," Artie said politely. "Long ones for high-topped boots."

He was a nice-looking boy, neatly dressed in a blue windbreaker and dark-blue pants. His pleasant round face and frank blue eyes made a good impression on people.

"This way, please," said the clerk.

Artie made a long business of choosing just the right quality and length of rawhide. "Got a good pair of leather-tops," he told the clerk, smiling shyly. "Want to fit em out right."

"Good idea," said the clerk. He showed everything the store had in rawhide laces.

Donny, as if understanding that his friend would be quite a while, ambled off to another counter and looked at some sneakers. Idly, he watched the busy clerks, leaning back against the showcase on which the hunting knives lay in their tan leather sheaths.

"Those'll be swell," Artie said at last. He paid for the laces and as he waited for change he called to Donny. "Hey, Bill, come here and look at the swell boxin gloves."

Donny came slowly and stood looking, without seeing anything. He could feel a drop of sweat trickling coldly along his nose, but he did not dare wipe it away.

Outside, they walked to the corner, turned around it and ducked into an alley.

"Get one?" Artie asked.

"Two," said Donny jerkily. "One apiece."

"Chee-*zis!* If you ain't the one," Artie panted. "Me, I'd never of dared try for two."

On an obscure bench in the city park, they wrapped the knives neatly in brown paper which Artie carried flattened in his windbreaker, and tied the package with string to look as if it had been purchased in a store. All afternoon they "shopped" in stores scattered widely in the city, accumulating a variety of brown paper parcels which they stuffed in the fronts of their windbreakers. It was nothing unusual to see two boys loaded down with wrapped bundles, in town shopping a couple of days before Christmas. They ate supper at a diner, and took an early evening train back to Bellport.

Donny lay back on the plush seat and closed his eyes. He was so tired the calves of his legs were trembling, and his undershirt was clammy with sweat. He wished Artie would

shut up and let him rest, but Artie was on top of the world
and talked continuously.

"Aw, dry up," Donny flared up at last.

Artie started to say something, but the look in Donny's eye
suddenly impressed him. The rest of the way he was silent,
while Donny looked morosely out the window.

On christmas morning Sam Freeman mooched down through
East Village looking for Donny Mitchell. He still didn't
think much of the embarrassing role his sister had mapped
out for him. Why should he bother with a smart-alecky little
heel who didn't have the sense to keep out of jail? But Ann's
arguments, and tears, had won him over. He'd do what he
could.

So here he was, on Christmas Day, out looking for Donny.
He found him down at the fish wharf talking to Artie Osgood.
Well, that's fine, Sam said to himself. Kill two birds with one
stone. He paused briefly as he passed them, and spoke out of
the corner of his mouth. "Want to see you two. Meet me out
on the end of the wharf."

"What for?" Artie said, eyeing him suspiciously.

But Sam moved on to the wharf and sat down on the stringpiece at the very end. He grinned a little, waiting for them to
follow, as they did presently.

"What's eatin you?" Artie asked.

"Shut up and listen," Sam said. "There's a guy I know got
a cousin over in Ferriston, his father's one of the Ferriston
cops." He saw that both Donny and Artie had frozen, staring
at him.

"Before school closed for Christmas vacation," Sam went
on, "the cops had some storekeepers visit all through the
Ferriston schools trying to spot two kids who'd been shop-
liftin."

He waited, letting it sink in.

"They don't know who you are, or where you live, but the
storekeepers are on the lookout for you. They'll know you if
they see you again." He got up. "That's all. I thought I'd
tip you off."

"How'd you know about it?" Donny asked, breathlessly.

Sam jerked his head at Artie. "*He* told me. You ought to know by this time he can't keep his trap shut. They got the Bellport storekeepers primed too. Any two kids that come into any store from now on, somebody'll have an eye peeled on em, and don't you forget it."

Artie was staring at him with a stiff face, but looking at Donny, Sam was amazed to see tears moistening the corners of his eyes.

"Thanks a lot, Sam," Donny said.

"Don't thank me," Sam said savagely. "You ought to know better than to get in such a mess, you dumb little fool." He started off along the wharf, then turned around. "When'll you be comin to high school, Don?" he asked abruptly.

"Next—next fall. If I pass."

"Well, pass, then," Sam said. "You got a swell build for a basket-ball center, and we'll need some new blood on the team next year." He started on, then looked back again. "You two dopes!" he said. "You ain't so damn tough."

Sam and Ann Freeman would have been astounded if they had known how closely their little scheme actually described the activities of the Ferriston police.

Some three months later, Donny sat on the stringpiece of the fish wharf, listlessly dangling his feet and thinking over the events of the morning. The March weather was warm, but the gusty little breeze made him wish he hadn't shucked his heavy underwear. If Mis Mackay'd been up and around he wouldn't have dared dig out his summer stuff; but she had been in bed for two weeks with bronchitis, almost pneumonia, and Jory, her boy Dave's wife, had come down from Somerville to nurse her.

Today Mis Mackay was sitting up for the first time, and as he was going out she had called to him and in a quavering old-woman's voice had told him the news:

"Jory thinks I ought t' close up this place and go back to Massachusetts with her and Dave. So, Donny, I guess the Welfare'll have to find you another place to stay."

Donny had mumbled in reply, "One place's good's another, I guess"; and now, sitting on the deserted wharf, he said it again to himself. The only thing, it was too bad not to enter high school with the kids he knew; and another high school might not have such a swell basketball team as Bellport. Donny had thought a lot about making the team ever since Sam Freeman had told him he might have a chance.

And he had thought a lot about Sam Freeman too. Sam had been pretty decent to him during the winter, and he liked Sam now a lot better than he did Artie Osgood. Since Christmas, he and Artie seemed to make each other kind of sick. Donny couldn't get it out of his mind that Artie had told.

He heard a slow step behind him and turned to see Willie Stilwell sauntering along the wharf.

"Hi," Willie said.

"Hi."

Donny hadn't seen Willie, to speak to, since he'd run out on him last fall. He'd gone out of his way to avoid him. At first, when he'd been so sore at Willie, he hadn't wanted to see him. Now, avoiding him had gone on so long, he felt embarrassed. Somehow, he didn't feel sore any more.

Willie sat down on the stringpiece near him, folding his long legs. "Cold, ain't it?" he volunteered.

"Ayeh," Donny said. He went on talking before he thought. "I put on my summer underclo'es this mornin."

"You did?" Willie grinned. "Y'know," he said confidentially, "I did, too. Now I wisht I hatn't."

"So do I," Donny said.

"How's Mis Mackay?"

"She's better." Just being with Willie, Donny found, was all at once making him feel better, the way it used to. "She's goin away soon's she gits well," he said in a low voice.

"That so?" Willie nodded slowly. "Well, she's gitting along and that's a big place for an old lady to handle." There was a silence. "That kind of changes matters for you, don't it?"

Donny said, "Oh, I don't care where I go. One place is same's another."

"How'd you like to come down and live with Hod and me? Say we could fix it?" he heard Willie's voice say.

"Why, I d'no." Donny couldn't believe what he heard.

"We'd like it fine," Willie went on. "We missed you when you didn't come down no more. You think it over." He got to his feet and started slowly down the wharf. "Me, I've always wanted a boy of my own. I never thought I'd have the chance to get Granville Mitchell's boy. You say the word go, we'll start things rolling." After Willie had gone, Donny sat with his eyes closed, picturing how it would be to live in the same house with Willie and Hod. Hod was pretty wonderful —it took a *man* to handle a 200-pound halibut. He liked Hod a lot. But Willie, he thought, Willie was somebody you could feel about the way he used to feel about Uncle My.

As Donny sat musing about his incredible good fortune, a car drove up and stopped and heavy steps started down the wharf. Two men came past the sheds on one side and two others on the other. Three of them were strangers, but the fourth was Myron Osgood.

"There he is, the little hellion," Myron said. "Don't let him get away."

Donny gave a wild look around. There wasn't anyone else on the wharf. It was him! They were after him! He darted over to the corner and stood there with his back to the piles panting and staring.

"This here's Mr. Morrison, the Chief of Police over to Ferriston," Myron said. "You can tell him how you got my boy Artie to go over there with you and steal all them things out of the stores last Christmas."

"I don't know nothin about it," Donny said sullenly.

"We'll see whether you do," Myron sputtered. He was so mad his face was a dirty-gray color. "Artie never would of, without you to egg him on. You take him along, Mr. Morrison, and we'll see what he says when he faces Artie."

In the front room of Myron Osgood's house, Artie was crying on the sofa, his face globbered with tears. When he saw Donny he burst out into fresh sobs, and for a moment he couldn't speak.

"There, you see how bad he feels," Myron said. "You can tell he ain't nothin like this tough young devil."

"He got me into it," Artie sobbed. "He said he'd knock my head off if I didn't." Donny's glance at Artie was cold and impersonal, and Artie burst out with louder accusations. "He stole all the things, too. You ask them men in the stores. They'll tell ya that I was always busy buyin somethin. It was him took everything."

"How about that?" the police chief said to Donny.

"I d'no," Donny said. "I wasn't there."

"He's lyin," Artie said. "He stole all the stuff."

"Look here." Morrison took hold of Donny's shoulder and whirled him around. "This boy was over to Ferriston this morning and one of the storekeepers recognized him. Don't you think he'll recognize you as well? Artie, here, may get out of it because he's owned up. You better too." But Donny merely shook his head and closed his mouth tight.

"All right. We may as well be on our way. You'll hear from us in a few days, Mr. Osgood."

"I'd like t' hev it kept as quiet's possible, Mr. Morrison," said Myron distractedly. "After all, I'm second selectman of the town, and if this got around—it ain't as if Artie was a real bad kid. He was egged on."

"Well, the storekeepers'll be decent about it, I think," said Morrison, "especially if you make up the money they lost. First offense and all, I don't think they'll prosecute. You'll have to bring your boy over, though, to the hearing."

"I guess you understand I'll be awful grateful for anything you can do." Myron began fumbling awkwardly in his pockets.

Morrison grinned. "Okay. When the time comes. Under the circumstances, I guess we can keep the hearing a private one. Nobody'll know about it." He slipped a stubby hand under Donny's armpit. "Come on, son."

"I hope," said Myron vindictively to Donny, "that you go to jail. I hope they shove you just as far as the law allows." His outraged voice brought out each word with harsh and separate emphasis.

"You don't need to worry about that," Morrison said. "The State don't take no funny business from State wards. They figger if the kids can't behave it ain't no use to fool around. They slap em straight into reform school."

"Well, I'm glad to hear it," Myron said. "That's where any kid belongs that goes around makin crim'nals out of honest people's children."

When the days went by and Willie did not hear from Donny he decided that his latest effort hadn't been any use. Then, in mid-April, passing by Mary Mackay's house on his way up to Myron Osgood's, he saw that the front windows were boarded up.

Mary must've gone away, he thought. Now, that's funny. Seem's as though Donny would've come down to say good-bye before he let em take him somewhere's else. But there, he mused, I d'no why I'd expect it, seein he ain't been near me all winter. Turning into Myron's, Willie wondered what kind of a place the Welfare had found for Donny, and if there'd be any way of getting in touch with him.

He passed the time of day while Myron was wrapping his groceries.

"See Mary Mackay's gone away." Willie commented.

"Ayeh," Myron said. "Went last Sunday."

"Wonder what she done with her boy?"

Myron, adding up figures, didn't answer. "Sent him back where he come from, I hope," he said finally. "Dollar-three. That right?"

"M'm." Willie handed him the money. "Your boy was kind of side-kicks with him, wasn't he? I was wonderin if he left Artie his address?"

He was unprepared for Myron's outburst. "No, he never! And Artie don't have no more truck with him, see?" Myron flushed a little under Willie's mild, inquiring gaze.

"He bother you bout somethin, Myron?"

"I don't want t' say no more about him. But I tell you this, Willie, any more of them State kids in this town, it's over my dead body."

"That so?" Willie gathered up his groceries.

"Yes, by gosh, that's so!" Myron said angrily. "That kid was wilder'n a hawk. What's more, the' warn't nobody to hold responsible, when it come to payin for any damage he might of done."

"Well," Willie said. "See you, Myron."

He went back down the shore road, carrying his bundles, and wondering. Funny for Myron to be so tore out. He wasn't usually unreasonable about kids' ructions. Must be that Artie and Donny had done something that Myron had had to pay for.

Willie was sure something was peculiar, a week or so later, when he got a letter from Donny. It was written on a plain piece of tablet paper, and quite a lot was crossed out with heavy, inky scratches.

> Box 5047, Ferriston
>
> Dear Willie:
> I guess you will be surprised to hear from me, but I thought I would write seein I didn't get a chance to come down and see you before I left. I am with some very nice people on a farm back of Ferriston. They are awful good to me—

He had crossed out something here, and Willie was able to make out, under the scratches, "and they have a Cidilac car."

Now why would he scratch that out, Willie wondered. Could be Donny'd started out to make things sound better than they were and then had decided not to lie. Willie read on:

> I am doing all right in school.

A long, scratched-out part followed, hard to decipher, but Willie finally figured it out: "They are letting me finish up eighth grade here, so I will be ready for high school work in the fall." After Donny had crossed it out, he had written:

> I am most through the eighth grade now, so I guess I will enter the high school here next fall. I hope they will have a good basketball team, but I bet it won't be as good as Bellport. I wanted you to know that I would have liked it fine to come and live with you and Hod, and the only reason I didn't was—

The next few sentences were inked over so heavily that Willie couldn't make them out. He went on reading the rest of the letter:

—because I couldn't. I guess these folks here wanted me awful bad. But I sure would of liked it fine. I am kind of lonesome here, they don't let you go out much. If you see Sam Freeman, say hello for me to him, will you?

Yours
Donald Mitchell

Willie sat for a while, with the letter in his hand.

"*They don't let you go out much.*"

"*They're letting me finish up the eighth grade here—*"

Willie folded the letter into his pocket and went down the shore to his punt. He rowed around the point to Ann Freeman's cove, went ashore and knocked at the door of the shack.

"I'm botherin you," he smiled, as she opened it.

"I'm glad to see you, Willie. Come on in."

Willie got out the letter. "Like to have you read this," he said. "See what you make of it."

Ann read the letter once, and then, carefully, again.

"I don't know, Willie. I—oh, there's something about it that makes me want to cry."

Willie nodded. "Guess that's just it," he said. "Sam wouldn't know nothin, would he?"

"If Sam did, he'd have told me, I'm sure. The kids have been wondering where Donny went so fast, without saying good-bye to anyone."

"They was some trouble," Willie said. "Myron Osgood is mad enough at Donny to kill him."

Ann thought fast. "Willie, I haven't said anything—Sam and I promised not to. But you know you asked me last winter to see if I could do anything."

Willie nodded, and she went on quickly, telling him about Artie Osgood, the Ferriston stores, and the scheme she and Sam had cooked up at Christmastime. "Sam said he was pretty sure it stopped them. So far as he's been able to tell, they stayed away from Ferriston all winter."

"Mm-hm. I guessed 't was somethin of the kind." Willie got up. "Too bad it couldn't of been stopped before it begun." He put the letter back in his pocket. "I'll go see 'f the's anything to be done about it. Seems as though, fella like me, all he does is go proguein around the aidges, after it's too late."

"That's more than most people bother to do, Willie," Ann said warmly.

AFTER leaving Ann, Willie went to see another old friend. Josh Hovey was sitting at his roll-top desk making out his payroll, when Willie came in through the door. Josh owned the Bellport boatyard. He was a fat ordinary-looking man, and glancing at him no one would suspect the size of the check he could put his name to, or that his boatyard was famous up and down the coast. In a quiet way Josh was a power in the town, if not in the state. Few people remembered now that in the old days he and Willie Stilwell had been dorymates on a Grand Banks fishing vessel.

"Willie, you old son-of-a-gun!" he bellowed. "I ain't seen you since Adam was a doll. I'd sure like to shake your hand."

Willie grinned. "Well, I might let you," he said. "If you was t' do me a favor, Josh."

"You can hev anything out a me you want," Josh said. "Except my wife."

"Well," Willie said, "what would the address of Box 5047, over to Ferriston, be? You know?"

"H'm." Josh pulled his telephone toward him, called the postmaster and asked about the address. He listened a few seconds, nodded, said, "Thanks, Greg," and hung up.

"Well, Willie," he said. "It's the box of the State Industrial School for Boys, over in Ferriston Hills."

Willie sat quiet a moment. "Been quite a while since I asked you any favors, Josh," he said. He went on, telling briefly the story of Donny Mitchell, and ending up with the details of what he wanted to do.

Josh listened glumly. "Don't that beat hell!" he said. "Granville Mitchell's boy!"

"Ayeh."

"And you want to adopt him? *Legal* adoption? Willie, you're crazy."

"Ayeh."

"My God, Willie, they wun't let ya. They're carefuller of them State wards than if they was virgin maidens. Ain't the' a law that you have t' be a married couple?"

"I d'no, Josh. That's why I come to you."

"Well," Josh said. "I'll do what I kin. I know Judge Elliot. He'll say if it's an impossibility. Might take a few months. Might cost somethin. Oh, blast!" Josh levered himself out of his chair and went with Willie to the door. "Willie, you old sog," he said affectionately, "come agin. Been an awful spell sence we went fishin together, ain't it?"

Willie grinned. "Ayeh," he said. "It has."

"And you gi'me back my faith, by God, you do," Josh said. "Er—August, Willie. Maybe September. I'll drop you a postal card."

Back at home, Willie sat down at his kitchen table to compose, for almost the first time in his life, a long letter.

Little Spoon Island
April 22, 1937

Dear Donald:

Hod and I are haking almost every day now and we about loaded the boat when we struck a streak for three days running out on the Otter Bank. That's a good ways off-shore. It's so far out that the land to the westard looks like a fogmull. They's good fishing there, if you know just where to set the trawls. I been wishing you was along with us, for with them big loads we sure have needed a third hand the last three days.

Last week Hod and I went up to Winker's Island after trap ballace, when we had her loaded we had to wait for tide so I walked round shore to a camp I used to go gunning to way back in the blackberry bushes. That camp sure is handy to use if you want to go gunning and Winker's Island is an awful good place for birds. They's a cove there that freezes over in the wintertime, and sometimes of a cold morning, early, I seen that cove so black with ducks you couldn't see the ice. This fall I plan to go over there with my gun. I hope by that time you'll be home here to go with me. Maybe we could talk it up to Sam Freeman to go too, and stay all night in that camp.

There was a lot more, of news about the town—about various people Willie thought Donny might be interested in. Sam Freeman said he thought the Bellport basketball team would win the state championship next year. Sam said to say hello.

> I'm glad you got a good place and the people are nice people. But whenever you can, I want you to be good and darn sure you can come home here and stay with me. Hod and I missed you something fierce and they's a lot of things we ain't done and a lot of things I like I ain't had a chance to show you. We'll plan on them when you come. I'm glad you want to come and stay with me. Now I know you do, I can start the ball rolling to fix it with the Welfare people. When the time comes.
>
> Yours lovingly
> Willie Stilwell.

When Donny first got the letter, he tore through it once as fast as he could to find out if Willie knew he was in the reform school. He stopped when he read, "I'm glad you've got a good place." Willie didn't know. Donny felt an almost choking sense of relief; then the realization came to him slowly that if Willie knew he wouldn't want him.

Yet in spite of himself Donny began to picture the camp among the blackberry vines Willie's letter had told about, and the black ducks covering the ice in that cove. And he thought about the morning he'd steered Willie's boat out to Hazlett's Rock and watched the sun come up out of the water. But it all seemed dim and far away.

Early in August Josh Hovey sent Willie a postcard instructing him to drop by on the 15th. Willie took the boat alone that day and went over to Bellport. The first person he saw, when he walked into Josh's office on the boatyard wharf, was Donny Mitchell, sitting beside Josh's desk.

"Well, Willie, you old sog," Josh boomed. "I been showin this young feller around my boatyard. He can't make up his mind whether he wants to run a boatyard or skipper a vessel when he gits back a little meat on his bones."

"That so?" Willie said, quietly. He didnt like the way

Donny looked, thin as a rail and with that unfocused look around his eyes. "Well, there's plenty of time for him to make up his mind, Josh."

Josh said: "You and him'll have to go around to see Judge Elliot, Willie. Papers to sign, what-not. Everything's fixed."

Josh didn't say anything about the hard time he had had to get everything fixed, or mention costs, or the fact that he himself had gone sponsor for Donny, putting the whole weight of his name behind him.

"All right," Willie said. "Appreciate it, Josh. Come on, Don."

They walked the three blocks to Judge Elliot's office without saying anything. The Judge was business-like. Everything, as Josh had said, was fixed.

"About his name," the Judge said. "You want to change it to Stilwell, I suppose."

Willie glanced at Donny, but Donny was looking at the floor. "That's up to him," Willie said. "I'd like it if he wants to. If he don't, it's his business."

"How about it, young man?"

The Judge didn't care for Donny, Willie saw; and he decided he didn't care much for the Judge. "It ain't a thing that's got to be settled right away, is it?" Willie said. "I'll let ya know." He signed his name where he had to, picked up his copy of the adoption papers and stuck them in his pocket.

"That's all," said the Judge. "Now, young man, I don't want to hear any more of your—" he began, and Willie, seeing how Donny flushed up, cut in briskly.

"Thanks, Judge," he said. "We'll be on our way. Come on, Don."

"Thank the good Lord," Willie said, when they were out in the street. "Don, I don't think much of them clo'es you got on, for a hot day. What say we go down the street here and git rid of a little money?"

They bought a new dark-blue suit for dress-up, sweaters, shirts, underwear, shoes and overalls. Donny let himself be fitted at the clothing store without showing much preference.

He did run his hand over a tan waterproof windbreaker, feeling its texture.

"How about it?" Willie asked. "You like that one?"

Donny shook his head. "It's airplane cloth," he said wistfully, "but it's eight dollars."

"Stick it in the bundle," Willie said to the salesman. "Why don't you put on a suit of them overhauls and a work shirt? Likely we might end up fishin before we go home."

Donny went into the dressing room to change, but he remained listless. Willie was worried about him. Maybe with good handling he'd let out what was goweling him. "You look slick," he said when Donny came back dressed in the stiff new blue denims. "Where's the suit you wore in here?"

Donny flushed. "I left it in there."

"Well, tell the man he can chuck the damn thing overboard," Willie said. "We don't want it."

He divided up the bundles with Donny and led the way to the wharf, where he had tied up the boat. He said nothing until they had cast off and the boat was drumming down the harbor and Donny stood silently beside him in the coop. He'd grown taller, Willie saw, and his face had lengthened with his thinness. He had a way now of biting his lips tight shut. Well, Willie thought, give him time.

"How'd you like to take a run to Cat Cove and see 'f we can dong us up a school of mackerel?" he said. "Want to?"

"Ayeh," Donny said.

"Which d'you rather do—fix up the mackerel jigs and grind the chum, or steer while I do it?"

"I guess I'd like to steer."

He put his hands on the wheel, and Willie saw his shoulders straighten a little.

Maybe that'll fix it up, Willie thought. He went on talking while he dug a rusty old meat grinder out of the locker, fixed it to a board over a bait tub and began grinding the herring for bait, letting the chum drop down into the tub. The meat grinder had a rhythmic squeak, and presently Willie, seeing he couldn't think of any more to say, began to sing in time to it.

Oh, we have a ship that sail-ed, upon the Lowland Sea,
And she goes by the name of the Golden Vanit-ee,
And we fear she will be sunk-en by the Spanish enemy,
As she sails in the Lowlands Low.

"You know that song, Don?" he asked.
"Yes."
"One of Uncle My's, warn't it?"
"Yes."

Then up and spoke our cabin boy and loudly outspoke he,
And he said to our captain, "What will you give to me,
If I'll swim 'longside of the Spanish enemy
And sink her in the Lowlands Low?"
"Oh, I will give you silver and I will give you gold,
And my own fair young daughter your bonny bride shall be,
If you'll swim 'longside of the Spanish enemy,
And sink her in the Lowlands Low."

Donny stirred suddenly at the wheel. "Quit singin it, will you?" he said in a strangled voice.

"Why, sure, boy," Willie said, quickly. "Hard to tell, anyway, which is me and which is the meat grinder."

They made the remainder of the trip to Cat Cove in silence, and Willie stopped the boat just outside the entrance to the cove and dropped the anchor. "You want to be the one to keep the chum going?" he asked. "Or will I?"

"I don't care."

"I will, then. Nasty job, anyway." They sat through the long afternoon, with time out for lunch. Willie ate heartily, trying not to notice that the boy only picked at his food. Willie was getting more and more worried. Something was pretty wrong with Donny. Willie wondered what he'd better do, mechanically throwing out his mackerel jig, and hauling it in again. Donny sat hunched over his line, letting it dangle in the water. Once or twice Willie jogged him a little. "God, boy, you don't never want to let a mack'rel jig stay still."

But mostly he let him alone.

At four o'clock Willie couldn't stand it any longer. "What is it, Don? Git it outa your system, boy."

"I been in the reform school," Donny said weakly, his

hands clenched tightly on the gunnel. "I been thinkin how I could tell you."

"Why, I know that," Willie said. "I knew it before I wrote ya that letter. I found out by gittin Josh Hovey to look up that post-office-box number for me."

"Who else knows?"

"Josh," Willie said. "Myron Osgood and Artie—don't worry about them mentionin it, either. That's all."

"Don't it make no difference to you?" Donny's voice was almost inaudible.

"Not in the way you're thinkin about," Willie said. "I'm sorry you had to go."

"I thought you wouldn't want me if you knew."

"Hell," Willie said. "You made a mistake. I don't say it warn't a bad one, and it wouldn't do to make it again. But look, Artie made the same mistake. The difference was he had someone to stick up for him. As for me not wantin you, I had a chance to back out when I found out where you was, didn't I?"

At that moment Willie's line snapped taut with a zing. He let out an excited yell and a look of exaltation came over his face. His fish, seeing he hadn't been holding his line taut, got away; but Donny's line, the next moment, jerked out through the water.

"Fried catfish into the Holy Land!" Willie gasped. "They've struck!"

He dug excitedly in the bottom of the chum-tub and sent his jig flying over the side again. Donny boated his fish, a bright-striped mackerel, 18 inches long, and Willie moaned at the sight of it.

"If we ain't gone and donged up a school of big ones when the bait's most gone!" His line zinged, and he hauled in, slatting off the mackerel and throwing his jig over again almost with the same motion.

For a few minutes the spray flew, the fish biting the jigs as fast as they hit the water. Then the chum was all gone and the school flashed away. Willie, seeing them go, suddenly picked up the empty chum-tub, and heaved it after them. The tub struck the water on its side and filled and sank at once. Then, realizing what he had done, Willie stood astounded. "Godsake," he said. "That was a good tub."

Donny, in the stern, found himself laughing. He doubled over, shouting, his eyes filling with tears. Slowly the astonishment left Willie's face; in a moment he laughed, too.

"Nothin like a school of mack'rel to git a man excited," he said. "How many'd we git, Don?"

"I think I got ten," Donny said proudly.

"Well, I caught seven I know about," Willie said. "I guess you wiped my eye out."

They gathered up the flopping fish from the platform, but all they could find was 15.

"Maybe I only caught eight," Donny said.

"Could of been ten," Willie pointed out. "I git too excited to count, anyway."

Donny drew a deep breath. "Look, if you want to fill in my name the same as yours on them papers, it's all right with me."

"You sure? Mitchell's a fine name."

"I been thinkin it over. I guess I'd rather."

Willie wiped his hands on a piece of engine waste, dug the papers out of his pocket and filled in the blank space with heavy block-printed letters. "Donald Mitchell Stilwell."

"There," he said, holding it up for Donny to see. "That looks kind of good, don't it?"

He let Donny start the engine and showed him how to kick her over slowly, while he eased up on the anchor rope.

"I know that song," Donny said, after a while, as they skirted the foot of the island. "I don't care if you sing it."

So Willie sang the whole thing through again, and then they sang it through together. The boat droned homeward through the lengthening shadows of the afternoon to the tune of the doleful ballad:

So his messmates hauled him up, but on the deck he died,
And they wrapped him in his hammock that was so fair and white,
And they lowered him overboard and he drifted with the tide,
And he sank into the Lowlands Low.

Biography of the Unborn

A Condensation from the Book by

MARGARET SHEA GILBERT

This book won for its author the $1000 prize for the "best book on a scientific subject for general reading," awarded by The Williams & Wilkins Company, leading publishers of scientific and medical works

Genesis

L IFE BEGINS for each of us at an unfelt, unknown, and un-honored instant when a minute, wriggling sperm plunges headlong into a mature ovum or egg. So extremely small is the single sperm that all the sperm required to produce the next generation in North America could be contained in a pinhead. Yet the quiet ovum, electrified by the entrance of this strange creature, reacts with violent agitation, releasing the man-forming potencies that are inherent in the human egg cell. It is at this moment of fusion of the sperm and ovum (a process called fertilization) that there arises a new individual who contains the potentialities for unnumbered generations of men.

If this rendezvous between ovum and sperm is missed, both are destined to die. And so long and hazardous is the course which the sperm must travel through the female sex ducts to reach the ovum that millions of sperm fail for each one that succeeds.

At this moment of fertilization there has been determined not only the existence of a new human being, but also his sex and individuality. By the union of sperm and ovum, he has inherited a mixture of the physical traits of both parents, as well as those hereditary traits which he in turn will transmit to his offspring.

FIRST MONTH
Out of the Unknown

OUT OF the unknown into the image of Man—this is the miraculous change which occurs during the first month of human life. We grow from an egg so small as to be barely visible, to a young human embryo almost one fourth of an inch long, increasing 50 times in size and 8000 times in weight.

326

We change from a small round egg cell into a creature with a head, a body and, it must be admitted, a tail; with a heart that beats and blood that circulates; with the beginnings of arms and legs, eyes and ears, stomach and brain. In fact, within the first 30 days of our life almost every organ that serves us during our allotted time (as well as some that disappear before birth) has started to form.

Shortly after fertilization the great activity which was stirred up in the egg by the entrance of the sperm leads to the division or "cleavage" of the egg into two cells, which in turn divide into four and will go on so dividing until the millions of cells of the human body have been formed.

In addition to this astounding growth and development we must also make our first struggle for food. For this purpose a special "feeding layer"—the trophoblast—forms on the outer edge of the little ball of cells, and "eats its way" into the tissues of the uterus. As these tissues are digested by the trophoblast, the uterus forms a protective wall—the placenta —which coöperates with the trophoblast in feeding the growing embryo. The maternal blood carries food, oxygen (the essential component of the air we breathe) and water to the placenta, where they are absorbed by the trophoblast and passed on to the embryo through the blood vessels in the umbilical cord. In return, the waste products of the embryo are brought to the placenta and transferred to the mother's blood, which carries them to her kidneys and lungs to be thrown out. In no case does the mother's blood actually circulate through the embryo—a prevalent but quite unfounded belief.

Meanwhile the new individual has been moving slowly along the path of changes which it is hoped will make a man of him. While the trophoblast has been creating a nest for the egg in the uterine wall, the inner cell-mass has changed from a solid ball of cells into a small hollow organ resembling a figure 8—that is, it contains two cavities separated in the middle by a double-layered plate called the embryonic disc which, *alone*, develops into a human being. The lower half of our hypothetical figure eight becomes a small empty vesicle, called the yolk-sac, which eventually (in the second month) is severed from the embryo. The upper half forms a water-sac (called the amnion) completely surrounding the embryo except at the thick umbilical cord. The embryo then floats in a water-jacket which acts as a shock-absorber, deadening any jolts or severe blows which may strike the mother's body.

Having now made sure of its safety, the truly embryonic part of the egg—the double-layered plate—can enter wholeheartedly into the business of becoming a human being. Oddly enough, it is his heart and his brain, in their simplest forms which first develop.

Almost at once (by the age of 17 days at most) the first special cells whose exact future we can predict appear. They are young blood cells, occurring in groups called blood islands which soon fuse to form a single tube, the heart-tube, in the region that is to be the head end of the embryonic disc. This simple tube must undergo many changes before it becomes the typical human heart, but rather than wait for that distant day before starting work, it begins pulsating at once. First a slight twitch runs through the tube, then another, and soon the heart is rhythmically contracting and expanding, forcing the blood to circulate through the blood vessels in the embryonic disc. It must continue to beat until the end of life.

About the same time the nervous system also arises. In the embryonic disc a thickened oval plate forms, called the neural plate, the edges of which rise as ridges from the flat surface and roll together into a round tube exactly in the middle of what will be the embryo's back. The front end of this tube will later develop into the brain; the back part will become the spinal cord. Thus, in this fourth week of life, this simple tube represents the beginning of the nervous system—the dawn of the brain that is to be man's most precious possession.

The embryo now turns his attention to the food canal. The hungry man calls this structure his stomach, but the embryologist briefly and indelicately speaks of the gut. The flat embryonic disc becomes humped up in the middle into a long ridgelike pocket which has a blind recess at either end. Very shortly an opening breaks through from the foregut upon the under surface of the future head to form the primitive mouth, though a similar outlet at the hind end remains closed for some time.

Within 25 days after the simple egg was fertilized by the sperm, the embryo is a small creature about one tenth of an inch long with head and tail ends, a back and a belly. He has no arms or legs, and he lacks a face or neck, so his heart lies close against his brain. Within this unhuman exterior, however, he has started to form also his lungs, which first appear as a shallow groove in the floor of the foregut; his liver is arising as a thickening in the wall of the foregut just behind the heart; and he has entered on a long and devious path which will ultimately lead to the formation of his kidneys.

The development of the human kidneys presents a striking example of a phenomenon which might be called an "evolutionary hangover." Instead of forming at once the type of organ which he as a human will use, the embryo forms a type which a much simpler animal (say the fish) possesses. Then he scraps this "fish organ" and forms another which a higher animal such as the frog uses. Again the embryo scraps the organ and then, perhaps out of the fragments of these preceding structures, forms his own human organ. It is as if, every time a modern locomotive was built, the builder first made the oldest, simplest locomotive ever made, took this engine apart, and out of the old and some new parts built a later locomotive; and after several such trials finally built a modern locomotive, perhaps using some metal which had gone into the first. Scientists interpret this strange process common to the development of all higher animals as a hasty, sketchy repetition of the long process of evolution.

By the end of the month the embryo is about one fourth of an inch long, curled almost in a circle, with a short pointed tail below his belly, and small nubbins on the sides of his body—incipient arms and legs. On the sides of his short neck appear four clefts, comparable to the gill-slits of a fish—another "evolutionary hangover." Almost all the organs of the human body have begun to form. In the head the eyes have arisen as two small pouches thrust out from the young brain tube. The skin over the front of the head shows two sunken patches of thickened tissue which are the beginning of a nose. At a short distance behind each eye an ear has started to develop—not the external ear, but the sensitive tissue which will later enable the individual to hear. In 30 days the new human being has traveled the path from the mysteriously simple egg and sperm to the threshold of humanity.

SECOND MONTH
The Face of Man

FROM TADPOLE to man: so one might characterize the changes that occur during the second month of life. True, the embryo is not a tadpole, but it looks not unlike one. The tailed bulbous creature with its enormous drooping head, fishlike gill-slits, and formless stubs for arms and legs, bears little resemblance to a human form. By the end of the second month, however, the embryo has a recognizable human character, although it is during this period that the human tail reaches its greatest development. In this month the embryo increases sixfold in length (to almost an inch and a half) and approximately 500 times in weight. Bones and muscles, developing between the skin and the internal organs, round out the contours of the body.

But the developing face and neck are the main features that give a human appearance, however grotesque. The mouth, now bounded by upper and lower jaws, is gradually reduced in size as the fused material forms cheeks. The nasal-sacs gradually move closer together until they form a broad nose. The eyes, which at first lie on the sides of the head, are shifted around to the front. During the last week of the month eyelids develop which shortly afterwards close down.

The forehead is prominent and bulging giving the embryo a very brainy appearance. In fact, the embryo is truly brainy in the sense that the brain forms by far the largest part of the head. It will take the face many years to overcome this early dominance of the brain and to reach the relative size the face has in the adult.

The limbs similarly pass through a surprising series of changes. The limb "buds" elongate, and the free end of the limb becomes flattened into a paddlelike ridge which forms the finger-plate or toe-plate. Soon five parallel ridges separated by shallow grooves appear within each plate; the grooves are gradually cut through, thus setting off five distinct fingers and toes. At the same time, transverse constrictions form within each limb to mark off elbow and wrist, knee and ankle.

The human tail reaches its greatest development during the fifth week, and the muscles which move the tail in lower animals are present. But from this time it regresses, and only in abnormal cases is it present in the newborn infant. Along with the muscles develop the bones. In most instances of bone development a pattern of the bone is first formed in cartilage, a softer translucent material, and later a hard bony substance is laid down in and around the cartilage model. As a sculptor first fashions his work in clay and then, when he knows that his design is adequate, casts the statue in bronze, so the developing embryo seems to plan out its skeleton in cartilage and then cast it in bone. This process continues through every month of life before birth, and throughout childhood and adolescence. Not until maturity is the skeleton finally cast.

Perhaps the most interesting feature of the second month of life is the development of the sexual organs. At the beginning of the month there is no way of telling the sex of the embryo except by identifying the sex chromosomes. By the end of the month the sex is clearly evident in the internal sex organs and is usually indicated externally. The most surprising aspect of sexual development is that the first-formed organs are identical in the two sexes. Even milk glands start to develop in both sexes near the end of the second month. Nature seems to lay down in each individual all the sexual organs of the race, then by emphasizing certain of these organs and allowing the remainder to degenerate, transforms the indifferent embryo into male or female.

Is each human being, then, fundamentally bisexual with the organs and functions of the apparent sex determined at fertilization holding in abeyance the undeveloped characters of the opposite sex? Laboratory experiments with sex-reversal in lower animals suggest that there may be various degrees of sexual development, even in mankind, and that between the typical male and female there may occur various degrees of intersexuality.

So the second month of life closes with the stamp of human likeness clearly imprinted on the embryo. During the remaining seven months the young human being is called fetus, and the chief changes will be growth and detailed development.

THIRD MONTH

Emergence of Sex

Now THE future men assert their ascendency over the timid female, for the male child during the third month plunges into the business of sexual development, while the female dallies nearer the neutral ground of sexual indifference. Or if sexual differences are overlooked, the third month could be marked the "tooth month," for early in this period buds for all 20 of the temporary teeth of childhood are laid down, and the sockets for these teeth arise in the hardening jaw bones.

Although six months must pass before the first cry of the infant will be heard, the vocal cords whose vibrations produce such cries now appear, at present as ineffective as a broken violin string. Only during the first six months after birth do they take on the form of effective human vocal cords. It must be remembered that during the period of life within the uterus no air passes through the larynx into the lungs. The fetus lives in a watery world where breathing would merely flood the lungs with the fluid that cushions the embryo in its sac, and the vocal cords remain thick, soft and lax.

The digestive system of the three-months-old fetus begins to show signs of activity. The cells lining the stomach have started to secrete mucus—the fluid which acts as a lubricant in the passage of food through the digestive organs. The liver starts pouring bile into the intestine. The kidneys likewise start functioning, secreting urine which gradually seeps out of the fetal bladder into the amniotic fluid, although most of the waste products of the fetus's body will still be passed through the placenta into the mother's blood.

Overlying the internal organs are the bones and muscles which, with their steady development, determine the form, contours, and strength of the fetal body. In the face, the developing jaw bones, the cheek bones, and even the nasal bones that form the bridge of the nose, begin to give human contours and modeling to the small, wizened fetal face. Centers of bone formation have appeared in the cartilages of the hands and feet, but the wrists and ankles are still supported only by cartilage.

No longer is there any question about whether or not the fetus is a living, individual member of mankind. Not only have several of the internal organs taken on their permanent functions, but the well-developed muscles now produce spontaneous movements of the arms, legs and shoulders, and even of the fingers.

FOURTH MONTH

The Quickening

DEATH THROWS its shadow over man before he is born, for the stream of life flows most swiftly through the embryo and young fetus, and then inexorably slows down, even within the uterus. The period of greatest growth occurs during the third and fourth fetal months, when the fetus grows approximately six to eight inches in length, reaching almost one half its height at birth. Thereafter the rate of growth decreases steadily.

However, the young fetus is not a miniature man, but a gnomelike creature whose head is too large, trunk too broad, and legs too short. At two months the head forms almost one half of the body; from the third to fifth months it is one third, at birth one fourth, and in the adult about one tenth the body height.

Nevertheless, the four-month fetus is not an unhandsome creature. With his head held more or less erect, and his back reasonably straight, he bears a real resemblance to a normal infant. The face is wide but well modeled, with widely spaced eyes. The hands and feet are well formed. The fingers and toes are rather broad, and are usually flexed. At the tip of each finger and toe patterned whorls of skin ridges appear —the basis of future fingerprints and toeprints. As might be expected, the pattern of these skin ridges is characteristically different for each fetus; at four months each human being is marked for life with an individual, unchangeable stamp of identity.

The skin of the body is in general dark red and quite wrinkled at this time; the redness indicates that the skin is so thin that the blood coursing through the underlying vessels determines its color. Very little fat is stored in the fetus's body before the sixth month, and the skin remains loose and wrinkled until underlain by fat.

Now the still, silent march of the fetus along the road from conception to birth becomes enlivened and quickened. The fetus stirs, stretches, and vigorously thrusts out arms and legs. The first movements to be perceived by the mother may seem to her like the fluttering of wings, but before long his blows against the uterine wall inform her in unmistakable terms that life is beating at the door of the womb. For this is the time of the "quickening in the womb" of folklore.

FIFTH MONTH
Hair, Nails and Skin

Man is an enigma; indivisible and yet complex; he is composed of hundreds of separate parts that are constantly dying and being renewed, yet he retains a mysterious "individuality." The human being may be compared to a coöperative society whose members band together for mutual support and protection, presenting a common front to the external world, and sharing equally in the privileges and responsibilities of their internal world. Division of labor, specialization, and the exchange of produce are just as important in the society of cells and organs as in the society of men. The digestive organs convert the materials taken in as food into the components of living cells. The circulating fluids of the body form an extensive transportation system. Nerves are the cables of the communications system while the brain is the central exchange. The potent endocrine glands determine the speed and constancy of many activities. Over-lying all of the body's specialized systems is the skin—the protector, conservator, and inquirer of the society of organs.

Now that the internal organs are well laid down, the skin and the structures derived from it hasten to attain their final form. The surface of the skin becomes covered with tough, dried and dead cells which form a protective barrier between the environment and the soft tissues of the body. Even as in life after birth, the outer dead cells are being constantly sloughed off and replaced from below by the continually growing skin. Sweat glands are formed, and sebaceous glands, which secrete oil at the base of each hair. During the fifth month these glands pour out a fatty secretion which, becoming mixed with the dead cells sloughed off from the skin, forms a cheesy paste covering the entire body. This material, called the *vernix caseosa*, is thought to serve the fetus as a protective cloak from the surrounding amniotic fluid, which by this time contains waste products which might erode the still tender skin.

Derivatives of the skin likewise undergo marked development. Fine hair is generally present all over the scalp at this time. Nails appear on the fingers and toes. In the developing tooth germs of the "milk teeth," the pearly enamel cap and the underlying bonelike dentine are formed.

But the most striking feature of the month's development is the straightening of the body axis. Early in the second month the embryo forms almost a closed circle, with its tail not far from its head. At three months the head has been raised considerably and the back forms a shallow curve. At five months the head is erectly balanced on the newly formed neck, and the back is still less curved. At birth the head is perfectly erect and the back is almost unbelievably straight. In fact, it is more nearly straight than it will ever be again, for as soon as the child learns to sit and walk, secondary curvatures appear in the spinal column as aids in body balance.

The five-month fetus is a lean creature, with wrinkled skin, about a foot long and weighing about one pound. If born (or, strictly speaking, aborted) it may live for a few minutes, take a few breaths, and perhaps cry. But it soon gives up the struggle and dies. Although able to move its arms and legs actively, it seems to be unable to maintain the complex movements necessary for continued breathing.

SIXTH MONTH

Eyes That Open on Darkness

Now THE expectant parents of the six-months-old human fetus may become overwhelmingly curious about the sex of their offspring, especially when they realize that the sex is readily perceived in the fetus. Yet to the external world no sign is given.

During the sixth month the eyelids, fused shut since the third month, reopen. Completely formed eyes are disclosed which, during the seventh month, become responsive to light. Eyelashes and eyebrows usually develop in the sixth or seventh month.

Within the mouth, taste buds are present all over the surface of the tongue, and on the roof and walls of the mouth and throat, being relatively more numerous than in the infant or adult. It seems odd that the fetus, with no occasion for tasting, should be more plentifully equipped, and some biologists believe that this phenomenon is but another evidence of the recurrence of evolutionary stages in development, since in many lower animals taste organs are more widely and generously distributed than they are in man.

The six-month fetus, if born, will breathe, cry, squirm, and perhaps live for several hours, but the chances of such a premature child surviving are extremely slight unless it is protected in an incubator.* The vitality, the strength to live, is a very weak flame, easily snuffed out by the first adverse contact with the external world.

SEVENTH MONTH
The Dormant Brain

Now the waiting fetus crosses the unknown ground lying between dependence and independence. For although he normally spends two more months within the sure haven of the uterus, he is nonetheless capable of independent life. If circumstances require it and the conditions of birth are favorable, the seven-month fetus is frequently able to survive premature birth.

One of the prime causes of the failure of younger fetuses to survive birth is believed to be the inadequate development of the nervous system, especially of those parts concerned in maintaining constant rhythmic breathing movements, in carrying out the sequence of muscular contractions involved in swallowing, and in the intricate mechanism for maintaining body temperature.

The human nervous system consists of a complex network of nerves connecting all the organs of the body with the brain and spinal cord, the centralized "clearing-house" for all the nervous impulses brought in from the sense organs and sent out to the muscles. By the third month of life special regions and structures have developed within the brain: the cerebellum, an expanded part of the brain that receives fibers coming mostly from the ear; and two large saclike outpocketings, the cerebral hemispheres, which are the most distinctive feature of man's brain. They are destined to become the most complex and elaborately developed structures known in the nervous system of any animal. They are alleged by some to be the prime factor in man's dominance over other animals.

At seven months these hemispheres cover almost all the brain, and some vague, undefined change in the minute nerve

---

*See "Incubator Babies," The Reader's Digest, December, '37, p. 91.

cells and fibers accomplishes their maturation. Henceforth the nervous system of the fetus is capable of successful functioning.

The seven-month fetus is a redskinned, wrinkled, old-looking child about 16 inches long and weighing approximately three pounds. If born he will cry, breathe, and swallow. He is, however, very susceptible to infection and needs extra protection from the shocks which this new life in the external world administers to his delicate body. He is sensitive to a light touch on the palm. He probably perceives the difference between light and dark. Best of all—he has a chance to survive.

EIGHTH AND NINTH MONTHS

Beauty That Is Skin-Deep

Now THE young human being, ready for birth, with all his essential organs well formed and able to function, spends two more months putting the finishing touches on his anatomy, and improving his rather questionable beauty. Fat is formed rapidly all over his body, smoothing out the wrinkled, flabby skin and rounding out his contours. The dull red color of the skin fades gradually to a flesh-pink shade. The fetus loses the wizened, old-man look and attains the more acceptable lineaments of a human infant.

Pigmentation of the skin is usually very slight, so that even the offspring of colored races are relatively light-skinned at birth. Even the iris of the eye is affected; at birth the eyes of most infants are a blue-gray shade (which means that very little pigment is present) and it is usually impossible to foretell their future color.

The fetus is by no means a quiet, passive creature, saving all his activity until after birth. He thrashes out with arms and legs, and may even change his position within the somewhat crowded quarters of the uterus. He seems to show alternate periods of activity and quiescence, as if perhaps he slept a bit and then took a little exercise.

Exodus

J UST WHAT specific event initiates the birth sequence remains unknown. For some weeks or even months previous to birth, slow, rhythmic muscular contractions, similar to those which cause labor pains, occur in a mild fashion in the uterus. Why the uterus, after withstanding this long period of futile contractions, is suddenly thrown into the powerful, effective muscular movements which within a few hours expel the long-tolerated fetus remains the final mystery of our prenatal life. It is quite probable that the birth changes occur as a complex reaction of the mother's entire body, especially those potent endocrine glands which may pour into the blood stream chemicals that stimulate immediate and powerful contraction of the uterine muscle.

There is nothing sacrosanct about the proverbial "nine months and ten days" as the duration of pregnancy; but 10 per cent of the fetuses are born on the 280th day after the onset of the last true menstrual period and approximately 75 percent are born within two weeks of that day.

As soon as the infant is born, he usually gasps, fills his lungs with air and utters his first bleating cry, either under the influence of the shock which this outer world gives to his unaccustomed body or from some stimulus administered by the attending doctor. The infant is still, however, connected through the umbilical cord with the placenta lodged within the uterine wall. Their usefulness ended, the placenta and umbilical cord are cut off from the infant. The stump soon degenerates, but its scar, the defect in the abdominal wall caused by the attachment of the cord to the fetus, remains throughout life as the navel—a permanent reminder of our once parasitic mode of living.

The newborn infant is by no means a finished and perfect human being. Several immediate adjustments are required by the change from intra-uterine to independent life. The lungs at birth are relatively small, compact masses of seemingly dense tissue. The first few breaths expand them until they fill all the available space in the chest cavity, and as the numerous small air sacs are filled with air, the lungs become light and spongy in texture. But it is not yet a complete human lung, for new air sacs are formed throughout early childhood, and even those formed before birth do not function perfectly until several days of regular breathing have passed.

The heart, which is approximately the size of the infant's closed fist, gradually beats more slowly, approaching the normal rate of the human heart. Shortly after birth the material which has been accumulating in the intestine during the last six months of fetal life is passed off. One peculiarity of the newborn infant is that the intestine and its contents are completely sterile; the elaborate and extensive bacterial population present in the intestine of all human beings appears only after birth.

Neither tear glands nor salivary glands are completely developed at birth; the newborn infant cries without tears, and his saliva does not acquire its full starch-digesting capacity until near weaning time. The eyes, although sensitive to light, have not yet acquired the power of focusing on one point so that the newborn infant may be temporarily cross-eyed.

Thus the first nine months of life are completed. The manifold changes occurring during this period form the first personal history of each member of the race. It is the one phase of life which we all have in common; it is essentially the same for all men.

Anna and the King of Siam

A CONDENSATION FROM THE BOOK BY

MARGARET LANDON

THOUGH stranger by far than most imaginative fiction, *Anna and the King of Siam* is a true story, based on authentic records, of an English woman's adventures at the fabulous court of one of the last of the Oriental despots.

Toward evening of a day in 1862, a steamer from Singapore was completing its slow and careful passage up the winding Chow Phya River to Bangkok, capital city of Siam.

Leaning against the rail was an Englishwoman with her small son, a boy of about six. Her dress of lavender mull had a neat high collar and modest wrist-length sleeves. She was slender and graceful as she stood there with a light breeze ruffling her full skirts. Only her dark eyes, turned toward the shore, betrayed anxiety.

The ship dropped anchor near a long white wall over which towered dimly, tier on tier, the roofs of the Royal Palace. The Englishwoman looked at them, oblivious of the innumerable rafts, junks and ships that filled the river.

Presently out of the deepening shadows flashed a long gondola, beautifully carved like a dragon, with torches reflected on the rhythmic dip of rows of wet paddles. From its deck an official mounted the side of the steamer. A length of rich red silk folded loosely about his person did not reach his ankles. He wore no coat. His brown skin gleamed in the torchlight. He was followed by a dozen attendants who sprawled on the deck like toads, doubling their arms and legs under them. As if at a signal every Asiatic on the ship, coolies and all, prostrated himself.

The captain of the steamer stepped forward.

"Mrs. Leonowens, may I present His Excellency, Chao Phya Sri Suriyawong, Prime Minister of the Kingdom of Siam? Your Excellency, Mrs. Anna Leonowens."

The Englishwoman bowed slightly. The torches flickered across the firmly modeled face of the Prime Minister. He beckoned a young attendant, who crawled to him as a cur approaches an angry master. A rapid flow of unintelligible syllables, and the attendant turned to Anna Leonowens and addressed her in English:

"Are you the lady who is to teach the royal family?"

She inclined her head slightly. "I am."

"Have you friends in Bangkok?"

"I know no one in Bangkok at all."

Again there was a quick exchange in Siamese. The Englishwoman could not know that the owner of the proud black eyes, which watched her so intently, understood perfectly what she said.

The interpreter spoke to her again: "What will you do? Where will you sleep tonight?"

"I don't know," she replied, holding her voice steady by an effort of will. "I am a stranger here. But I understood from His Majesty's letter that a residence would be provided for me on my arrival."

Interpreter and lord surveyed her insolently. The lord spoke, the interpreter translated. "His Majesty cannot remember everything," he said indifferently. "You can go wherever you like."

The Prime Minister strode down the gangway, followed by his slaves and minions. The dragon boat with its flickering torches and flashing paddles disappeared into the night.

For a moment Anna could only stand there watching, completely stunned by the callousness of her reception.

Hardly more than a year before, her husband, a young British army officer serving in the Far East, had died suddenly, leaving Anna and their two small children penniless. For a time she had tried running a school for officers' children in Singapore, but it was hard going; the officers sent their children willingly but often forgot to pay the fees. So when King Monghut of Siam, through his Consul, had offered her the post of governess to the royal children, she had accepted. After arranging to have her daughter, Avis, go with friends to England, to school, and accompanied by little Louis and two family servants, she had set forth.

Repeatedly she had been warned against coming to this land of darkness and mystery, with its slavery, its harems, and its deep-rooted distrust of foreigners. Now, as the last faint splashings from the retreating paddles died on the night air, her whole being was filled with overpowering dread. If only she had listened to her friends in Singapore! Then resolutely she put fear away. Whatever happened, she was determined to stay.

THE British consul in Bangkok, Sir Robert Schomburgk, was out of town and could be of no help. Fortunately, the ship's captain was able to suggest a temporary refuge with the English harbor master, Captain John Bush. Anna's trunks were put ashore, and in spite of the lateness of the hour she was given a pleasant welcome by Mrs. Bush.

But Anna could not sleep. The next morning, after a restless night, she sought the harbor master's advice on what to do.

"This is Siam," Captain Bush explained. "The important point here is to be able to wait until things come to you. Don't worry! The King's put out money for your passage. He'll demand your services in good time."

Breakfast was hardly over, indeed, when a messenger arrived to summon Anna. The Prime Minister, or Kralahome as was his native title, was awaiting her.

The Kralahome was to receive them in the audience room of the palace, a huge room reached through a series of spacious saloons, all hung with luxurious draperies and crystal candelabra and filled with the slightly oppressive fragrance of many flowers. As she entered, Anna caught sight of a number of young girls peeping at them from behind the velvet curtains which hung from ceiling to floor. A large group of male attendants crouched in the antechamber. Some were in the poor clothing of servants or slaves. Others were handsomely dressed and seemed to be younger relatives of the Kralahome. There was a subdued bustle of excitement, the peering of many dark eyes. Anna and Louis stood in the middle of it, uncertain and apprehensive. Suddenly the Kralahome appeared. He was seminude as on the night before. Some sixth sense acquired from long years in the Orient suggested to Anna that this indicated an absence of respect for her, but his manner was not unfriendly as he held out his hand and addressed her in English. "Take a seat, sir."

She grasped the proffered hand, and smiled involuntarily at the "sir." Its incongruousness diverted her from her fears and restored a measure of balance to her thoughts. She decided to come at once to the point. Turning to the interpreter who crouched beside her on the floor, she said:

"Will you ask your master to present my request for a quiet house or apartment to His Majesty as soon as possible? The King, in his letter, promised me a residence near the Palace."

Instantly the Kralahome's manner changed. He spoke to her directly. "You are not married?"

"My husband is dead."

"Then where will you go in the evening?"

"Not anywhere, Your Excellency," she answered shortly, pricked by the insinuation. "I simply desire some privacy and rest for myself and my child when my duties have been fulfilled." She turned to the interpreter. "Tell your master that his rights do not extend to prying into my domestic concerns. His business with me is in my capacity of governess only. On other subjects I decline conversation."

Immediately she doubted the wisdom of having struck out so sharply. Her instinctive reaction had blinded her momentarily to the knowledge that Orientals usually opened a conversation with a series of personal questions, and that the Kralahome's seeming impertinence may have implied nothing more than a conventional desire to be polite. Still it was important to establish at once her right to respect and privacy. The Kralahome shrugged his shoulders slightly. "As you please," he said coldly. Then with a bow, he turned and disappeared behind a mirror.

As soon as the Kralahome had withdrawn, the interpreter got up from his crouching position.

"Good morning," he said.

"Good morning," she replied coldly. "I thought you were a servant."

He drew himself up offended. "I am the Kralahome's half brother. Come this way, please. Rooms have been prepared."

The apartment was comfortably furnished in the European manner and opened on a quiet piazza, shaded by fruit trees in blossom, and overlooking an artificial lake stocked with colored fish. After a while, dinner was brought in and set on a table by little pages. It seemed to be a mixture, European foods prepared especially for them and curries and sauces that were obviously Siamese.

Their boxes and trunks had been brought up from the boat, and Anna was still busy unpacking the next day when she received a call from Mr. Robert Hunter, secretary to the British Consul. Anna at once sought his aid in getting an audience with the King. The secretary agreed to do what he could, but warned her that it might take several weeks. His Majesty, he explained, was busy with the ceremony which would raise his oldest son, Prince Chulalongkorn, to official rank and make him, in effect, the Crown Prince.

"Will he be one of my pupils?" asked Anna.

"I think he will," Mr. Hunter assured her.

For the first time since her arrival, Anna felt encouraged. Her decision to come to Siam had not been dictated entirely by the need for employment. She had felt a sense of destiny. The movement in the United States to free the slaves had struck in her a sympathetic chord. Perhaps the opportunity to teach in the harem meant that she would be able to inculcate into her pupils her own deep sense of the sacredness of the human soul, and the evil of any system which permitted one person to own another. If the young heir was to be her pupil she could hope, at least, to mold him a little.

While the negotiations proceeded, Anna set about studying the language and life about her. Every day or so her apartments suffered a tumultuous invasion from the ladies of the Kralahome's harem. They rarely left without booty in the form of trifles which they had begged or taken.

Even to the fastidious Englishwoman, they were not unattractive. Except for their clipped hair and black teeth, the result of constant chewing of betel nut, many of the girls satisfied Western ideas of beauty with their clear olive complexions and their dark almond-shaped eyes.

Anna's greatest difficulty was in explaining to them the reason for her presence in Siam. Besides the Siamese girls of good family, many Chinese and Indian girls were purchased annually by agents for the King's harem. It was known also that there was a standing order for "an Englishwoman of beauty and good parentage." It seemed to them incredible that Anna was here merely to teach the children of the royal family, not to enter the harem.

The head wife, however, a woman of 40, was possessed of considerable intelligence. Sometimes she invited Anna to call at her pretty house in the women's quarters. Around the palace and within it more than a thousand of the prince's retainers lived. There were also several hundred slaves to be directed. This miniature city was her responsibility.

As the days passed, Anna grew to admire her more and more. She was mild in her manner, but very efficient. The big establishment moved easily with something of the calm which distinguished its mistress. Anna was especially impressed with her unfailing kindness to the younger women of her husband's harem. She lived among them as happily as if they were her daughters, sharing their confidences, comforting them, pleading their cause with the Kralahome.

Iт was arranged at length that Anna should be presented at court by Captain John Bush, the harbor master.

Anna approached the interview with trepidation. She had already begun to learn something of this strange king whom his subjects called the "Lord of Life." He had come to the throne after 30 years in the priesthood and during this period he had devoted himself to the study of Western science. Now

his progressive scientific learnings were
combined with a traditional Oriental des-
potism, capricious and cruel.

The Royal Palace was across the river
from the Kralahome's. As always, the
river was teeming with activity. A large
party of priests was bathing in the river.
Other priests, standing on the bank were
wringing out garments they had just
finished washing. Graceful girls with vessels of water balanced on their heads were passing along the road that bordered the quay, while others carried bundles of hay or baskets
of fruit. Noblemen in gilded sedans, borne on the backs of
sweating slaves, were hurrying toward the late afternoon
audience. In the distance Anna glimpsed a troop of spearmen,
the sun glittering on their weapons.

At the Palace landing, Captain Bush, Anna and Louis
walked through a covered gangway to a narrow street bounded on either side by high brick walls. Captain Bush pointed
out the famous landmarks—the temple of Wat Bo with a
reclining figure of Buddha 150 feet long and 40 feet high over-
laid with gold plate, and the Wat Phra Kaeo, temple of the
Emerald Buddha, most fabulous of all the gorgeous temples
of Siam and the King's private chapel.

As they entered the Palace audience chamber, a flood of
late afternoon sunlight swept through the spacious hall from
high, crowned windows, upon a throng of noblemen dressed
in gold-encrusted silks of various colors. All were crouched
on their elbows and knees with their heads down, facing the
golden throne at the far end. On it sat the King. He was of
medium height and excessively thin, dressed in cloth of gold.
As he sat cross-legged and motionless, he appeared to have
been carved of a piece with the glittering throne.

The King caught sight of them at once. He bounced erect
and advanced rapidly down the length of the hall. His feet
were encased in gold slippers turned up at the toe and crusted
with gems that refracted little gleams of light.

When he reached them, Captain Bush, on his knees like the

others, performed his office:"Your Majesty, the English governess, Mrs. Anna Harriette Leonowens, and her son, Louis."

Anna curtsied deeply, and then balanced herself as best she could with bent knees in the froglike position she had been told would be acceptable.

Suddenly the King stretched his arms at full length and pointed at her nose.

"How old shall you be?" he asked loudly.

The unexpected question took Anna completely by surprise. Faced with the prospect of a cross-examination into her private life in front of the hundreds of kneeling men, however, her mind made several quick revolutions.

"One hundred and fifty years old, Sire," she answered.

The King's beady jet eyes scrutinized her face minutely, then lighted with quick understanding.

"In what year were you borned then?" he asked sharply.

Instantly she struck a mental balance and gravely replied, "In 1712, Your Majesty." This was like a child's game.

Amazingly the King, instead of appearing angry with her for evading his question, laughed delightedly. After addressing a few quick words to the nearest courtiers, who smiled at the carpet beneath their noses, he seized Anna's hand and dragged her rapidly down the length of the Audience Hall through a curtained door at the back. Louis clung desperately to her skirt. At this undignified pace they flew along a succession of covered passages, in which crouched shriveled and grotesque duennas and a few younger women. All had modestly covered their faces with their scarves. When Anna and Louis were quite out of breath the King stopped at last before one of a series of curtained recesses. He pushed open the velvet hangings.

On the floor was a kneeling woman. Like the women in the corridors her face was covered with her scarf. She had a childlike body as finely made as a Dresden figurine. The King drew aside the pleated silk in front of her face. Her features were as delicate as her figure, and very beautiful.

"This is one of my wives," the King announced. "It is our pleasure to make her a good English scholar."

Something about the young woman won Anna completely. She cast in Anna's direction a look of such genuine joy as she prostrated herself before them, that Anna left her with a mingled feeling of affection and pity. How revolting to be dependent for one's innocent desires upon the caprice of this withered grasshopper of a king! Suddenly the Palace—marble and gold and rich fabrics, jewels and glistening tiles—seemed filled with the shadow of slavery and oppression.

As the King led them back through the corridors toward the great hall, dozens of children had come out of the inner precincts of the Palace. The King addressed them indulgently, but it was Louis who drew them. They descended upon him, chattering, laughing and shouting. He pulled back shyly as they reached out to touch him, but they only pressed closer. They fingered his clothing, his hair, his skin, his shoes and his strange white hands.

"I have 67 children," the King said proudly, as they reached the Audience Hall and Louis was free at last. "You shall educate them for me, and as many of my wives also as may wish to learn English. And I have much correspondence in which you must assist me."

Anna was appalled at the prospect of such a multiplicity of duties, but thought it best to reserve any protests.

"I will send for you later," the King finished.

Anna curtsied, and even Louis managed a bob of the head. Then with Captain Bush they withdrew and were shortly out in the evening air. Anna breathed deeply. The King had seemed kindly disposed, and he was certainly not without a sense of humor. But he was a curious man, obviously unpredictable and autocratic.

After months of delay, a day was finally set which, in the opinion of the court astrologers, was propitious for the formal opening of the school. Meanwhile Anna, unable to endure the waiting and inaction, had taken to teaching the children in the Kralahome's palace. Her industry mystified the Prime Minister.

"Siamese lady no like work. Love play. Love sleep," he explained.

The new school was to be held in a large pavilion, standing in a grove of orange and palm trees. At the appointed time Anna took Louis by the hand and entered hesitantly. A colossal golden image of the Buddha dominated the great chamber. In the center stood a long table, finely carved, and some carved and gilded chairs. The King and most of the ladies of the court were present, with a few priests.

The King received Anna and Louis kindly, pointing to two seats that had been prepared for them. At a word from the King some female slaves appeared, crawling expertly across the floor with boxes of slates, pencils, ink, pens, and the familiar Webster's blue-backed speller, which they shoved up onto the long carved table. Then at another indication from the King, the priests took up a chant.

Finally a ruffle of music from an unseen orchestra announced the entrance of the princes and princesses who were to be Anna's pupils. They advanced in the order of their age. The King took them gently by the hand and presented them to Anna.

The ceremony ended, his Majesty spoke briefly to the children, then departed with the priests. A few moments later slaves arrived and bore the royal children off. To Anna's astonishment, not only the tiny children but the bigger boys and girls of eight, nine, and ten apparently quite unaccustomed to walking even short distances, were carried away in the arms of women as if they had been infants.

A week from the day of the formal opening, the serious business of school began. The youngest of the royal children was only five, the oldest ten.

The lesson went forward in an orderly manner until a number of young women were brought in to be taught like the children. It was soon evident that their teacher was much more interesting to them than their books. They fingered her

hair and extracted some of the hairpins. They felt Anna's
dress, and her rings. She discovered two of them flat on their
stomachs trying to peek under her skirt. Then a slave
crouched down in front of Anna and pointed at the Englishwoman's nose, so different from her own flat one. She
wanted to know, it seemed, whether Anna's nose had grown
long from much pulling, and also whether it had to be
arranged every morning to keep it so. This interruption
stopped all work until a grim duenna entered from the outer
porch. Her wrathful expression instantly restored order.

In the days that followed, some of the concubines began
to drift away, already bored with learning. Many of the royal children, however, quickly showed promise of becoming
excellent scholars, especially Prince Chulalongkorn, the heir
apparent, a handsome and well-behaved boy of ten, and his
pretty little sister, Princess Chanthara Monthon, whom
everyone called "Fa-hing," or Celestial Princess.

From the first, geography was the study that appealed
most to the royal pupils. Up to now the only map they had
ever seen was an old one prepared by a former prime minister
who was a better politician than cartographer. It was five
feet long and three wide. In the center was a ground of red,
20 by 12 inches. A human figure as long as the red patch was
cut out of silver paper and pasted on it. This was the King of
Siam. On his head had been placed an enormous crown with
many points, indicative of his vast possessions. When, at
Anna's request, the King provided a large English globe, it
was hard for them to see Siam reduced to a mere speck on the
earth's surface. The only thing that comforted them was that
England, their teacher's country, was smaller yet.

As the children's horizon widened, Anna sedulously hunted
and brought to class any unusual objects which might help
them gain some idea of the outside world—a lump of coal,
which they could compare with charcoal; a strip of fleece
from a sheep, with pictures of a carder and spinning wheel,
and of a modern mill; samples of yarn and woolen cloth.

One day a steamer had brought the King a box of ice from
Singapore. Anna obtained some for an object lesson. The chil-

dren examined the novelty with a great deal of interest, and as word of it spread women from the harem crowded into the school to see it. They giggled to find it cold; then they watched it melt and turn into water. They found no difficulty in believing that water froze in the colder countries of the world until it was possible to walk on it. But when Anna said that rain in such countries froze as it fell and became a white substance that the people called snow, the whole school was indignant. Not until she got the King himself to testify that he had frequently read of the phenomenon in books of travel, was her reputation for veracity re-established.

One day, since it was part of the King's plan that the royal children understand European customs, she invited about 30 of her pupils to an English tea party. For the event she had decorated her dining room with English flags, and put quantities of flowers on the tables, which were spread with tea, coffee, homemade cakes, English preserves, bread and butter.

When the royal pupils arrived each was accompanied by many slaves. As the motley throng streamed through the doors Anna vainly tried to enforce order, but her voice was lost in the din. The princes and princesses examined the tea tables with interest. Some poked their fingers into the preserves to feel their consistency. Some handled the cakes and set them down again. Then, without having eaten anything, they spread through the place with their slaves, laying hands on everything that struck their fancy.

There would hardly have been a needle, a vase, a picture or a handkerchief left if the boom of the clock striking from the high tower across the street had not announced the close of day. There was a rush for the Palace. The slaves snatched up their royal charges and vanished as unceremoniously as they had come. The house was in ruins. She hadn't a pair of scissors, a spool of cotton, a pin or a thimble left.

The next day a procession of slaves from the Palace, brought boxes of tobacco, camphor and snuff, and other compensatory offerings from the mothers of the children. Most of the gifts were of ten times the value of the things taken. The only trouble was that they were of no earthly use.

IN ADDITION to the school, King Mongkut soon began to demand Anna's assistance with his English and French letters. His Majesty's correspondence was enormous. His interest in the scientific knowledge of the West, especially astronomy, was the source of many exchanges with learned men all over the world. But the bulk of the correspondence had been undertaken for diplomatic reasons. In the 19th century both France and England were reaching out for the Malayan peninsula. Almost alone among his Siamese contemporaries, the King had realized early that Siam's traditional foreign policy of isolation and exclusion had to be revised if the country's independence was to be maintained.

Some years before, he had negotiated the first modern treaty with England and had subsequently entered into a lengthy correspondence with Queen Victoria.

In his efforts to further relations with the outer world, he had not neglected the United States. The King had once read that in the traveling menageries, which were very popular in the rural areas of the United States, the elephant was regarded as the most remarkable of the animals on display. He wrote promptly to President Lincoln, offering to send several pairs of young elephants, and suggesting that as they increased they could serve as beasts of burden.

Although Mr. Lincoln already had a great deal on his hands with the Civil War, his reply was courteous:

> . . . This government would not hesitate to avail itself of so generous an offer if the object were one which could be made practically useful. Our political jurisdiction, however, does not reach a latitude so low as to favor the multiplication of the elephant, and steam on land, as well as on water, has been our best and most efficient agent in internal commerce. . . .
>
> Wishing for your Majesty a long and happy life, and for the generous and emulous people of Siam the highest possible prosperity, I commend both to the blessings of Almighty God.
>
> Your good friend,
> ABRAHAM LINCOLN

Washington, February 3, 1862

The work of handling the King's correspondence was delicate and difficult because His Majesty was both fickle and tyrannical. It seemed impossible to please him, He would write letters, sign them, affix his seal, and dispatch them in his own mailbags to Europe, America, or elsewhere. Then, later, he would order Anna to write to the parties addressed to say that the instructions they contained had been an error —*her* error of translation or transcription.

One thing she insisted on. She must be allowed to stand upright in his presence. The froglike crouch that had been permitted her as a special dispensation was intolerable for more than a few minutes. The King agreed. He specified, however, that she must sit down when he did, on a chair if he sat on a chair, on the floor if he sat on the floor.

One day she received a peremptory summons from the King. He was expecting a visit shortly from Lord John Hay, Commodore of the British fleet in the Indian Ocean. To ingratiate himself with the distinguished visitor, he had decided on a step, unprecedented for Siam, of allowing him to see some of the country's prettiest girls. In order that he would not go back to Queen Victoria and report that the King was a barbarian, however, Anna was to educate the young women in European etiquette and costume. A barber would remove the black betel stains from their teeth.

The next morning the schoolroom was converted into a sewing room. Silks, jewels, flowers, laces and brocades were placed at Anna's disposal. The only omission was material suitable for undergarments. When Anna remonstrated, the chamberlain simply replied there was not time to make any.

The Princess Phanrai, an aunt of Prince Chulalongkorn, had been chosen as most suitable of the women to receive the commodore, along with five pretty girls as maids in waiting. All thought it great fun to have hoop skirts like Anna.

The King sent the royal barber to scrape the teeth of the six until they were as white as milk, while a Chinese artist painted their skins white also. Their heads were covered with wigs of European hair, curled in the latest fashion, and bound with ropes of pearls, rubies and diamonds. With the addition of jeweled brooches, necklaces and bracelets, they were really a dazzling sight. Anna knew a brief pang of regret that there had been no time for undergarments, although a critical examination reassured her that the heavy brocades were so thick that no one could have guessed the omission.

Then it was time for their drill in European etiquette. They were to sit behind a magnificent crimson curtain, wrought with gold, that had been hung across the temple. When the curtain was drawn and His Majesty made the presentation, they were to rise, bow and retire backward. Somebody had told the King that no one ever turned his back when presented to Queen Victoria, but withdrew face forward. His Majesty was imperative, therefore, in requiring this on his own behalf and that of the English Ambassador.

Over and over Anna made the girls practice the simple maneuver, but they were too nervous to mind. There was a rumor that all Englishmen were bearded—very repulsive to a beardless people—and that many of them had evil eyes, terrible blue eyes that could look straight into the souls of their victims and trap helpless spirits forever.

Unfortunately Lord John did wear a full beard and a heavy mustache, which mingled and flowed down upon his breast, leaving only his eyes and nose visible. On the day of the reception when the curtain was drawn, the Siamese girls, shocked, sat frozen in their chairs.

Lord John Hay was also taken completely by surprise. He was quite unprepared to find what seemed in the half-light of the temple to be European ladies in the royal harem of Siam. As if to make sure, he raised his monocle to his right eye and began to examine them from head to foot as the King made the presentation.

Then he bowed profoundly in his most courtly manner. The girls, instead of rising and bowing, uttered shrieks of terror, clapped their hands over their faces, peering between their extended fingers. Seeing that the creature continued to gaze at them calmly through his glass eye one of them cried, "The evil eye!" With one accord they threw their skirts over their heads to protect them, and fled from the temple.

Afterward Anna was much relieved when the King let her

off with a fairly mild rebuke for not having acquainted the girls with the English custom of "spying glass."

"Our women are too modest to let a strange man look on their faces," he told her.

B<small>Y THE</small> time Anna's first year in Siam was drawing to a close the dim life of the Palace had come into focus. The Palace itself, which at first had seemed too complex to be understood, was in reality a walled and fortified city, rectangular in shape, covering more than a square mile.

The northern section comprised the seat of government. In it were the armory, the government offices, the exchange and the supreme courts of justice. Only here were men allowed to come and go freely on official business.

The heart of the royal city, where the King lived, was so placed that it could be approached from the outside through heavily guarded gates. Completely surrounding the King's palace were formal terraced gardens with orange and pomegranate trees. The leaves of ilexa and oleander cast pointed shadows on the marble pavements. Porcelain jars were planted with water lilies in every form and color, purple and gold, and pale pink,  and white. There was the perpetual splashing of fountains. Stone basins caught the overflow and in the basins gold fish glittered like gems.

From the royal palace a covered passage led to the harem. No man was permitted to enter the harem city, except the King and priests who came under guard for religious functions. King Mongkut, more liberal than his predecessors, sometimes allowed his ladies to go out for such an important occasion as the cremation of one of their parents. But for most of them the harem was the world—a world of women, nine thousand of them within the confines of its high walls.

Within the Palace the King was the disk of light around which everything revolved. What he did determined what the women of the harem did. He rose at five. So, therefore, did most of his household. Then, after a scanty meal, the King withdrew to his private temple for an hour of meditation.

This service over, he retired for a nap, attended by a fresh detail of ladies in waiting. Those who had been on duty through the night were dismissed, not to be recalled for two weeks or a month unless as a mark of special favor.

When he woke, his breakfast was served with intricate formality. Twelve women knelt before great silver trays filled with 12 varieties of food—soups, meats, game, poultry, fish, vegetables, cakes, jellies, preserves, sauces, fruits and teas. Each tray was passed to the head wife, who removed the silver cover, and at least seemed to taste the contents. Then advancing on her knees she set the dishes one by one on the table before the King.

Actually the King ate very little of the lavish food. During the long seclusion in the Buddhist cloister he had acquired abstemious habits, and ordinarily contented himself with a modest bowl of boiled rice.

Often at breakfast he discussed with Anna the news of the day, the American Civil War, Napoleon's expedition to Mexico, "Chinese" Gordon.

Anna soon came to admire the King's intellectual attainments. She believed him to be the most systematically educated of any crowned head of that day, either Oriental or European. But she was often repelled by his extreme skepticism about people. He had no faith whatever in the integrity of any human being. Invariably if Anna rose to the defense of a friend he saw in her magnanimity some seeking for personal advantage. "Money, money, money! It will buy anything," he would growl, as if her friends had bribed her to uphold their cause before the King.

The love of children was his one constant virtue. Often he would take them in his arms and embrace them, making droll faces at the babies. Yet while the King was an affectionate father to those of his children whose mothers had pleased him, he could not forgive any child a mother who had not.

In spite of the paralyzing fear the women seemed to feel in

the King's presence, it took an enormous number of women guards to keep discipline. If there was too much giggling and whispering behind a curtain, one of the female police would lay a whip lightly on the shoulders of the more noisy. The whip was administered as often as three times during an audience. And the moment the King retired, the women scattered like a flock of geese, rushing away to their homes as if they had just escaped from an unpleasant duty.

ONE MORNING Anna found her pupils in a state of great excitement. During the annual roundup of elephants in the forest a white elephant had been sighted. To the Siamese, this was an event of supreme national importance, since it was universally believed that a white elephant was the reincarnation of some deceased King or hero.

As the news spread over the city, King and peasant, master and slave congratulated each other in jubilation. Prayers and offerings were made in all the temples. The town crier who shouted the news along the streets was showered with gifts of money, cloth, rice and bottles of perfumed oil.

Seventy-five royal barges and a hundred boats were provisioned with a week's supplies to take the entire royal household to the place where the white elephant had been found. Anna obtained permission to go along.

Before sunset the cortege set off for the old capital of Ayuthia. There the court transferred to horses and rode for miles through beautiful country to the stockade, or kraal, where the roundup had taken place. To the hysterical joy of the royal party a great salmon-colored beast heaved and trumpeted in the sea of gray and black ones crowded into the kraal.

The next morning the trapped animals were removed from the stockade. The white elephant was left alone, tied with silken cords. Immediately a wide path was begun for him through the country he must traverse to the river on his royal progress to Bangkok. A few days later a gold cloth was laid on his back and the triumphal return to the capital was begun. Even the King played second fiddle to the new "prince." In front of the elephant young girls danced and sang and played musical instruments; a number of men performed feats of strength and skill, tumbling, and wrestling. Other men fanned him and fed him. Priests prayed for him. When he reached Bangkok the lordly beast was ceremoniously knighted with a title which meant "Handsome Lord of Powerful Family." Gold rings were fastened around his tusks, a gold chain was hung around his neck, and a purple velvet cloak, fringed with scarlet and gold, was thrown over him.

A magnificent new stable had been commenced at once for the "prince." He was assiduously fed with the finest herbs, the tenderest grass, the sweetest sugar cane, the mellowest bananas, and the most delicious cakes, served on huge trays of gold and silver. His water was perfumed with jessamine. It was all too much for him. He was taken with a severe attack of indigestion during the seventh night, and although the King's doctor was summoned he died in a few hours.

No man dared to carry the catastrophic tidings to the King. But the Kralahome, always a man of prompt expedients and unfailing presence of mind, called up thousands of slaves and pulled down the new stables. They worked in nervous haste, terrified by fear that the King might come before they were through. It was not until the cool of the late afternoon that he appeared, to see for himself the progress of the building which had been nearly completed the night before. He stood rooted to the ground when his gaze met nothing but vacancy. The truth flashed upon him at once and with a cry of pain he sank down upon a stone and wept bitterly.

Immediately, the whole nation went into mourning. The dead animal was shrouded in white linen and laid on a bier. It was then floated down the river with much wailing and many dirges to be deposited in the Gulf of Siam.

WHENEVER Anna passed within the massive gates of the harem the oppressive feeling settled upon her that here was a jail in which women and children innocent of crime were imprisoned for life. Not all of them were unhappy, perhaps. But to Anna it was revolting that these women had no more control over their lives than the beasts of the field.

One morning she set off to attend an important religious festival. By some mischance, she took the wrong road. Suddenly she found herself in a dark alley, from which the only exit appeared to be a door of polished brass in a high brick wall. Half-afraid that she was trespassing in some forbidden place, she pushed open the door, then stepped over the sill into a paved courtyard.

In the middle of a garden a woman was sitting on the ground. She was nursing a naked child about four years old. When the woman saw Anna she raised her head with a convulsive movement. She clasped her bare arms around her child and stared at Anna with fixed, truculent eyes. She was large, strongly made and swarthy. She looked more like a gargoyle carved from dark stone and set there to frighten intruders than a human being. Her features were gaunt, and long matted hair hung around her shoulders.

Anna stood trembling a little, but as she looked at the woman and child she forgot her fear in a choking surge of pity. The woman was naked to the waist, and chained by one leg to a post driven into the ground, without the least shelter under the burning sky. The chain was of cast iron and heavy.

For a moment Anna was unable to command her voice. At last she asked the woman her name.

"*Pai sia!*" ("Go away!") was the savage reply.

Undisturbed, Anna sat on the blistering pavement beside the woman and child. Very gently she asked the child's name.

"His name is Thuk (Sorrow)," the woman answered reluctantly, turning away. But the defiant look in her face had already softened. Gradually, under Anna's sympathetic prompting, her story came out. Her name, she said, was L'Ore. Born a slave, her freedom had been purchased by an Indian merchant who had seen her and fallen in love with her. The woman began a life of happy freedom. Her mistress, however, had never been reconciled to the idea of letting her go.

One day, about three months after her marriage, she was seized, gagged, bound hand and foot, and brought back to this place. Her mistress ordered her chained to this post, where she remained until her child was born. A month later

she was chained again, and her child was brought to her to
nurse by a slave until he could come alone. Only the slave
and her mistress knew where she was. She had been chained
there now for four years.

Deeply shaken by L'Ore's recital, Anna resolved to lay
her case before the King. Fortunately she had recently bought
a gift, a small book entitled *Curiosities of Science*, which she
had intended to present to him at their next meeting.

The King was very much pleased with the book and in a
burst of magnanimity agreed to investigate L'Ore's case.

Not long afterward, L'Ore, was restored to her own home.
As a result, Anna found herself famous overnight. Slaves
going into the city from the Palace on business told the story.
Common people, fell on their faces as she passed. They
crawled to her with their petitions as she sat on her piazza in

the evening. When she entered the temple
schoolroom she found at her place and
on her chair flowers plucked by slave
hands and woven into garlands. From
now on she was known to the humble
people of Palace and city as the "White
Angel." "Go to the house of the White
Angel and she will help you," became a
message of hope whispered in the ears of
the distressed.

Even the highly placed ladies of the harem came to her
secretly with their grievances. She found herself between the
oppressor and the oppressed. Day after day she was called
upon to resist the cruelty of the judges. In cases of torture,
imprisonment, extortion, she tried again and again to excuse
herself from interfering, but still the mothers or sisters implored her until she had no choice left but to try to help them.

Sometimes, in these enterprises, Anna acted as the accom-
plice of the head wife, Lady Thiang, a person of broad sympathy and discretion. Whenever Lady Thiang thought that
the King was ready to loose the whip on one of the women of
the harem, she would quickly summon Anna. Anna would
go immediately to His Majesty, book in hand, to consult him

about a translation from the Sanskrit or Siamese. She kept a store of such questions ready. Transparent as the device was, or perhaps because of its simplicity, it usually worked. Often, absorbed in the question she raised, he would turn with comical abruptness from curses and abuse and motion the culprit, still kneeling before him, out of the room with an absent-minded wave of his hand.

Her pleading was not always successful, however. One day a former pupil, the Lady Tuptim, a young girl of 16 of whom Anna was especially fond, was reported to be in terrible trouble. Unable to endure any longer the life of the harem, not only had she refused the attentions of the King but had escaped from the palace. Worse than that, she was discovered to be hiding in a monastery. For a woman to defile a monastery with her presence could only mean death.

There was nothing anybody could do for her. Yet once again when friends of Tuptim's threw themselves on her mercy, Anna found herself, with a sickening sense of powerlessness, promising to be at the trial to do what she could.

When the prisoner was brought in, Anna was stupefied by the transformation in the pretty girl. Her hair was cut close to her head, and her eyebrows had been shaved off. Her cheeks were hollow and sunken, her eyes cast down. Her hands were manacled, and her little bare feet could hardly drag the heavy chains fastened to her ankles.

The evidence against her was overwhelming. Not only was she discovered in the priestly garments she had used as a disguise, but a piece of paper was found stitched inside with the name of Phra Palat, one of the priests, written on it.

To the judges there was no question of the nature of the sin which had been committed, or of the guilt of both parties. Yet Tuptim steadfastly refused to implicate the priest.

The grandeur of the fragile childlike woman as she hurled defiance at the judges affected Anna so powerfully with a conviction of her innocence that she hurried from the court-room to lay the case before the King.

The King was in his breakfast hall. The smell of food made Anna dizzy as she toiled up the lofty staircase, for she had not stopped to eat that morning before hurrying to the court, but she walked quickly forward, fearing that she might lose courage if she deliberated for a moment.

"Your Majesty," she began, "I have just come from the trial of Tuptim, and I am convinced that she is innocent of the crime of which she is accused."

The King looked at her out of the glittering narrow eyes that reminded her so often of a bird's.

"You're mad!" he said. He regarded her with a cold stare, full of suspicion, and then leaned over and laughed in her face. She started to her feet as if he had slapped her. In his angry face she saw something revolting, something fiendish that she had never seen before. He was not interested in the merits of Tuptim's case. His sense of decency and justice were gone, swallowed in a bestial need to sate in blood the injured pride of the scorned male. Anna was seized with an inexpressible horror of him. She was stupefied and amazed at the naked evil she had seen within the King's heart. Thought and speech had left her. She turned to go.

But the King had read what her face said. Her disgust had shocked him back to normal and instantly he made one of his characteristic about-faces. "Madam," he ordered, "come back! I grant your petition. The woman will be condemned to work in the rice mill for the rest of her life. I will send my decision to the court in a few minutes. You do not need to return there. You had better go to school now."

Anna could not thank him. Her revulsion was too great. Her head throbbed and she felt dizzy. She went away without a word. Instead of going to the schoolroom Anna went home. She felt too ill to do anything but go to bed.

It was two o'clock when she awoke. The sound of a crowd milling around drew her to the window. She was startled to see two scaffolds being set up on the plaza close to her house. Workmen were driving stakes and bringing up strange machines under the instruction of high officials. A vast throng of men, women and children had collected to see the spectacle, whatever it might be.

Anna summoned her maid and asked the reason for all the

preparation and commotion. The maid reported that a priest and a guilty princess were to be tortured for the improvement of public morals. The King had reversed his decision!

Anna learned later that she had hardly left the King before the proceedings of the trial had been laid before him. When he read them he flew into a violent rage that included Anna as well as the concubine and the priest. He ordered the two Siamese tortured publicly and then executed, but he could think of no way of punishing the Englishwoman except by having the scaffolds set up directly under her windows.

A little before three o'clock the instruments of torture were arranged beside the scaffolds. Soon a loud flourish of trumpets announced the King with all his court. Women police dressed in scarlet and gold took up their posts to guard the ladies of the harem. Suddenly the crowd sent up a cry. Guards had come from the Palace enclosure with the two prisoners. The priest, apparently too weak to walk alone, was hoisted upon the scaffold to the right, while Tuptim tranquilly ascended the one to the left without assistance. She looked down calmly at the rabble who flocked close to gloat over the spectacle. Something in the girl's attitude stilled them. Anna felt that a kind of unwilling awe was being drawn out of them by Tuptim's quiet steadiness.

Two trumpeters, right and left, blared forth the crime of which the pair were accused. The crowd was mute, not to lose a single word of the sentence. Again the trumpets sounded, and the judgment that had been passed, was announced. The spell was broken. A great shout went up from the crowd as the executioner mounted a raised platform to apply the torture to Tuptim. The blows began to fall. For the first few moments it seemed as if the agony would prove too much for her powers of endurance. She half turned from the royal spectator at the window. Her body writhed involuntarily and she tried to hide her face in her hands. But almost immediately, by a supreme effort of will, she stood erect again, and her voice rang out across the square like a deep toned silver bell: "The holy Buddha knows all. We are innocent!"

She just managed to finish speaking before she pitched forward with a piercing cry which went through Anna like a sword. The girl lay insensible until physicians restored her to consciousness, and then the torture was resumed. Once again her voice rang out in protest.

One by one every excruciating device that would agonize but not kill was used to wring a confession from Tuptim. But every torture, every pang, failed to bring forth anything but her incomparable courage. She confessed nothing, she asked for no mercy. The last words Anna heard her cry were: "I have not sinned!"

After this Anna neither heard nor saw anything more. Consciousness simply left her. She was still lying on the floor, crumpled and weak, when a slave from the Palace came in secret to tell her of Tuptim's and Palat's end. Neither had confessed anything under torture, and at last torture had been abandoned for fear it would extinguish life before the flames could be applied. They had been dragged through the streets and burned publicly outside the wall of the cemetery, The common people who followed had been terribly affected by the sight of Tuptim's fortitude, until at the last there were no scoffers left.

Anna did not see the King for a month after Tuptim's death. At last one day he summoned Anna to his presence. Never had she felt so cold, so hard, so unforgiving. He took no notice of her manner, but as soon as he saw her continued their previous conversation as if no interval had occurred.

"I have much sorrow for Tuptim," he said, and Anna saw that with his usual quixotic change of attitude it was true. His face was genuinely sad. "I shall now believe that she is innocent. I have had a dream, and I had clear observation in my vision of Tuptim and Palat floating together in a great wide space, and she bent down and touched me on the shoulder, and said to me, 'We were pure and guiltless on earth, and look, we are happy now.' I have much sorrow, Mem, and respect for your judgment. Now I shall cause monument to be erected to the memory of Palat and Tuptim."

On the spot where they had died two tall and slender *chedis* were erected by the King's order. Each bore the inscription:

"Suns may set and rise again, but the pure and brave Palat and Tuptim will never more return to earth." Believing as he did in the endless cycle of birth and rebirth that ended only in the attainment of Nirvana, his words were a testimony to his conviction that Tuptim and Palat had escaped by their purity from the wheel of reincarnation.

As time passed, Anna often felt the need to leave Siam. For five years now she had not seen her daughter Avis, and Louis needed to be placed in a boarding school with a regular routine. Then, too, there was her health. For some time now she had been subject to violent bouts of fever. On doctor's orders, the King had reluctantly agreed to reduce her hours of work, But even the limitation on time could not protect her from his extravagant demands.

Once she had felt herself in actual danger from the King's capricious temper. One afternoon, following a disagreement over a letter, the King's private secretary appeared with a paper listing several accusations that she was to acknowledge and sign. Among trivial charges of disobedience, ingratitude and "thinking evil," was a charge that she had "walked over the head of His Majesty."

Anna read the ridiculous accusations, her anger kindling. How tenacious was the King's memory of any slight fault! How easily he forgot faithful service! Once, long ago, before she understood palace etiquette, the King had expressed a desire for a certain book. She had remembered that it was in the room above where His Majesty had been working earlier in the day and, supposing that she was obeying his wish, she had hurried upstairs after it. All unthinking she had entered a room directly over the one in which the King was sitting, secured the book and come downstairs, expecting him to be pleased. But she had "walked over his head." To her surprise the attending women were shaking in terror. With trembling lips they had assured her that if she ever committed such a breach of royal etiquette again she would be cast into a dungeon.

The other charges were equally farcical. She handed the document back to the King's messenger without a word.

Shortly afterward she received an anonymous note telling her that the King's anger had grown by her refusal to sign the paper. He had shouted to his assembled courtiers, "Will no one rid me of this woman?" Anna called her servants to lock all doors and told them to admit no one. Afterward she laughed at herself, and in retrospect her fears seemed imaginary. Yet had they been? Or had she sensed an actual peril that had passed when the King's anger passed?

She had stayed on, in spite of everything, because she was deeply absorbed in the education of young Prince Chulalongkorn. But even this relationship would soon have to end. The Prince was growing into a young man, and would have to devote himself entirely to his official duties.

With the Prince, at least, she had felt a sense of accomplishment. Recently they had had a long talk about Abraham Lincoln. The story of the great humanitarian was familiar to him from the constant references she had made to it through the years.

"Mem *cha*," he said, his eyes shining with determination, "if I live to reign over Siam I shall reign over a free and not an enslaved nation."

Anna looked at the ardent face of the boy in front of her and hoped that he would live to accomplish his dream.

At first the King would not hear of her going. "Mem, you are lazy! You are ungrateful!" he reproached her. It took her six months to win his grudging consent, and even then he would not permit her to go unless she promised faithfully to return when her health permitted.

Before she left, one of her favorite pupils from the harem, Lady Son Klin, invited Anna to dinner. Remarkably receptive to occidental ideas of freedom, Son Klin had been so deeply affected when Anna had introduced her to *Uncle Tom's Cabin* that not only had she undertaken to translate it into Siamese but she had decided to adopt its author's name as part of her own. All her notes to Anna were signed "Harriet Beecher Stowe Son Klin."

All through dinner Anna seemed to sense an air of suppressed excitement. When dinner ended, Lady Son Klin rose and led Anna out to her garden.

There in rows knelt all her slaves, 132 men, women and children. Each of them was dressed in entirely new garments. Lady Son Klin had freed them all.

Anna stood silent. There was a lump in her throat. If she had done nothing more than teach this one woman, she knew now that her five hard years had been amply repaid by what she had seen this night.

Anna had put off telling most of the women and children that she was going until the time was near. The day she made her announcement she had hardly the courage to face them. For some time most of them refused to believe her. When they could doubt it no longer they gave her such a demonstration of their love and devotion that she was overcome. Gifts of every sort poured in with embarrassing profusion. Many sent small sums of money to help Anna on the journey. The poorest and humblest slaves brought rice cakes, dried beans, sugar. In vain Anna tried to tell them as gently as possible that she could not take all these things with her.

The King himself had been silent and sullen until the morning of her departure. At the end he relented. He embraced Louis and gave him a silver buckle, and a bag containing a hundred dollars to buy sweetmeats on the way. Then turning to Anna he said: "Mem, you much beloved by our common people, and all inhabitants of Palace and royal children. Everyone is in affliction of your departure. It shall be because you must be a good and true lady. I am often angry on you, and lose my temper, though I have large respect for you. But nevertheless you ought to know you are difficult woman, and more difficult than generality. But you will forget, and come back to my service, for I have more confidence on you every day. Good-bye."

Anna could not reply. Her eyes were full of tears. She realized that what she had not thought possible had taken place.

She and the King were more than employer and employe, King and governess—they were friends.

A few days later Anna and Louis left Bangkok. Many friends accompanied her to the steamer. Then she and Louis, watched the shore line fade to a thin gray shadow.

Anna never returned to Siam. A year after she left, the King died.

After placing Louis in school in England, Anna had gone, on doctor's advice, to America, where the climate was more bracing. Her first article describing some of her experiences at the court of King Mongkut appeared in *The Atlantic Monthly*, in June 1869, and was followed by two books, *The English Governess at the Siamese Court* and *The Romance of the Harem*. Instantly she was in demand as a lecturer, and for many years she divided her time between writing and lecturing.

Thirty years after she left Siam in 1867, King Chulalongkorn visited London and Anna Leonowens saw her most distinguished pupil again. The King had reigned for 29 years, a grave, quiet, determined man who had accomplished much against great odds. He had ended the Siamese custom of prostration and curbed the privileges of the nobles. He had initiated reforms which would eventually abolish slavery. Schools had been established all over the kingdom. Missionaries had been encouraged to start hospitals and schools. Law courts had been reorganized. Gradually, educated officials were replacing old feudal administrators. Young men were sent abroad for study, and teachers from Europe and America were imported. Already in his lifetime the Siamese were beginning to say that Chulalongkorn was their greatest king.

It was thus with a feeling of deep gratitude and humility that Anna heard the King say it was through the principles laid down in her teaching that he had formed the plans by which he had transformed his kingdom.

HOW TO WIN FRIENDS
and
INFLUENCE PEOPLE

A CONDENSATION FROM THE BOOK

DALE CARNEGIE

President of the Carnegie Institute of Effective Speaking and
Human Relations, New York City; author of "Public Speaking,"
"Little Known Facts About Well Known People," etc.

Criticism Is Futile

I N MAY 1931, when "Two Gun" Crowley was captured—after being besieged by 150 policemen with machine guns and tear gas—Police Commissioner Mulrooney declared that this desperado was one of the most dangerous criminals in the history of New York. "He will kill," said the Commissioner, "at the drop of a feather."

But how did "Two Gun" Crowley regard himself? While the police were firing into his apartment, he wrote a letter addressed "To Whom It May Concern." In this letter he said: "Under my coat is a weary heart, but a kind one—one that would do nobody any harm."

A short time before this, Crowley had been having a necking party on a country road out on Long Island. Suddenly a policeman walked up to the parked car and said: "Let me see your license."

Without saying a word, Crowley drew his gun, and shot the policeman dead.

Crowley was sentenced to the electric chair. When he arrived at the death house at Sing Sing, did he say, "This is what I get for killing people"? No, he said: "This is what I get for defending myself."

The point of the story is this: "Two Gun" Crowley didn't blame himself for anything.

Is this an unusual attitude among criminals? If you think so, listen to Warden Lawes of Sing Sing: "Few criminals regard themselves as bad men. Most of them attempt to justify their anti-social acts even to themselves, consequently stoutly maintaining that they should never have been imprisoned at all."

If the desperate men behind prison walls don't blame themselves for anything—what about the people with whom you and I come in contact?

Personally I had to blunder through a third of a century before it even began to dawn upon me that, 99 times out of a hundred, no man ever criticizes himself for anything, no matter how wrong he may be; and that criticism is futile because it puts a man on the defensive, and usually makes him strive to justify himself.

Criticism is also dangerous, because it wounds a man's precious pride, hurts his sense of importance, and arouses his resentment.

When I was very young and trying hard to impress people, I wrote a foolish letter to Richard Harding Davis. I was preparing a magazine article about authors; and I asked Davis to tell me about his method of work. I had just received a letter with this notation at the bottom: "Dictated but not read." I was quite impressed. I felt the writer must be very busy and important. And as I was eager to make an impression on Richard Harding Davis, I ended my own short note, "Dictated but not read."

He never troubled to answer the letter. He simply returned it with this scribbled comment: "Your bad manners are exceeded only by your bad manners." True, I deserved his rebuke. But, being human, I resented it. I resented it so sharply that when I read of the death of Richard Harding Davis ten years later the one thought that still persisted in my mind—I am ashamed to admit—was the hurt he had given me.

When dealing with people, remember you are not dealing with creatures of logic, but with creatures of emotion, creatures bristling with prejudices and motivated by pride and vanity. And if you want to stir up a resentment tomorrow that may rankle across the decades and endure until death, just indulge in a little stinging criticism—no matter how certain you are that it is justified.

Benjamin Franklin, tactless in his youth, became so diplomatic, so adroit at handling people that he was made American Ambassador to France. The secret of his success? "I will speak ill of no man," he said, "and speak all the good I know of everybody."

As Dr. Johnson said: "God Himself, sir, does not propose to judge man until the end of his days."

Why should you and I?

We Want to Be Important

PROFESSOR John Dewey, America's most profound philosopher, says the deepest urge in human nature is the "desire to be important." Remember that phrase, "the desire to be important." It is a gnawing and unfaltering human hunger. It was this desire that led the uneducated, poverty-stricken grocery clerk, Abraham Lincoln, to study law; that inspired Dickens to write his immortal novels. It makes you want to wear the latest styles, drive the latest car, and talk about your brilliant children.

People sometimes become invalids in order to win sympathy and attention, and get a feeling of importance. Some authorities declare that people may actually go insane in order to find, in the dreamland of insanity, the feeling of importance that has been denied them in the harsh world of reality.

If people are so hungry for a feeling of importance, imagine what miracles you and I can achieve by giving them honest appreciation. The rare individual who honestly satisfies this heart hunger will hold people in the palm of his hand.

Andrew Carnegie paid Charles Schwab the unprecedented salary of a million dollars a year. Because Schwab knew more about the manufacture of steel than other people? Nonsense. Schwab told me himself that he had many men working for him who knew more about steel than he did, and that he was paid this salary largely because of his ability to deal with people. And what is his secret?

"I consider my ability to arouse enthusiasm among the men," he said, "the greatest asset I possess, and the way to develop the best that is in a man is by appreciation. There is nothing that so kills the ambitions of a man as criticism from his superiors. So I am anxious to praise but loath to find fault. I have yet to find the man, however exalted his station, who did not do better work and put forth greater effort under a spirit of approval than under a spirit of criticism."

Sincere appreciation was one of the secrets of Rockefeller's success in handling men. For example, when one of his partners, Edward T. Bedford, lost the firm a million dollars by a bad buy in South America, John D. might have criticized; but he knew Bedford had done his best. So Rockefeller found something to praise; he congratulated Bedford because he had been able to save 60 percent of the money he had invested. "That's splendid," said Rockefeller. "We don't always do as well as that upstairs."

The truth is that almost every man you meet feels himself superior to you in some way; and a sure way to his heart is to let him realize that you recognize his importance. A line in *Reunion in Vienna* runs, "There is nothing I need so much as nourishment for my self-esteem." We nourish the bodies of our children and friends; but how seldom do we nourish their self-esteem!

No! I am not suggesting flattery. Flattery ought to fail and usually does. But flattery is from the teeth out. Sincere appreciation is from the heart out.

Let's cease thinking of our own accomplishments, our wants. Let's try to figure out the other man's good points. Give him honest, sincere appreciation for them and he will cherish your words years after you have forgotten them.

Emerson said: "Every man I meet is my superior in some way. In that, I learn of him."

What the Other Fellow Wants

TOMORROW you will want to persuade somebody to do something. Before you speak, remember there is only one way under high Heaven to get anybody to do anything. And that is by making them *want* to do it.

Andrew Carnegie was a past master at influencing people by talking in terms of what the other person wants. To illustrate: His sister-in-law was worried sick over her two boys at Yale, who neglected to write home and paid no attention to their mother's letters. Carnegie offered to wager a hundred dollars that he could get an answer by return mail, without even asking for it. Someone called his bet; so he wrote his

nephews a chatty letter, mentioning casually in a postscript
that he was sending each a five-dollar bill.

He neglected, however, to enclose the money.

Back came replies by return mail.

This strategy appealed, of course, to a relatively low motive; but it is often possible to influence people by appealing
to the highest motive possible to the situation. When the late
Lord Northcliffe found a newspaper using a picture of himself which he didn't want published, he wrote the editor a
letter. But did he say, "Please do not publish that picture of
me any more; I don't like it"? No, he appealed to the respect
all of us have for motherhood. He wrote, "Please do not publish that picture of me any more. My mother doesn't like it."

When John D. Rockefeller, Jr., wished to stop newspaper
photographers from snapping pictures of his children, he
didn't say: "I don't want their pictures published." No, he
appealed to the desire, deep in all of us, to refrain from harm-
ing children. He said: "You know how it is, boys. You've
got children yourselves. And you know it's not good for
youngsters to get too much publicity."

Charles Schwab had a mill manager whose men weren't
producing their quota of work. "How is it," Schwab asked,
"that a man as capable as you can't make this mill turn out
what it should?"

"I don't know," the man replied, "I've coaxed the men;
I've pushed them; I've sworn and cussed. They just won't
produce." It happened to be the end of the day, just before
the night shift came on.

"Give me a piece of chalk," Schwab said. Then, turning to the
nearest man: "How many heats did your shift make today?"

"Six." Without another word, Schwab chalked a big figure six on the floor and walked away. When the night shift
came in, they saw the "6" and asked what it meant. "The
big boss was in here today," the day men said. "He asked us
how many heats we made, and we told him six. He chalked
it down on the floor." The next morning Schwab walked
through the mill again. The night shift had rubbed out "6,"
and replaced it with a big "7."

When the day shift reported for work, they saw a big "7" on the floor. So the night shift thought they were better than the day shift, did they? Well, they would show the night shift a thing or two. They pitched in with enthusiasm and when they quit that night, they left behind them an enormous, swaggering "10." Shortly this mill, that had been lagging way behind in production, was turning out more work than any other mill in the plant.

The principle? "The way to get things done," says Schwab, "is to stimulate competition. I do not mean in a sordid, money-getting way, but in the desire to excel."

Back in 1915 when Woodrow Wilson determined to send a peace emissary to counsel with the war lords of Europe, William Jennings Bryan, Secretary of State, the peace advocate, longed to go. He saw a chance to make his name immortal. But Wilson appointed Colonel House, and it was House's thorny task to break the news to Bryan. "Bryan was distinctly disappointed," Colonel House records in his diary, "but I explained that the President thought it would be bad for anyone to do this officially, and that his going would attract a great deal of attention and people would wonder why he was there."

You see the intimation? House practically tells Bryan that he is too important for the job—and Bryan is satisfied. Colonel House, adroit, experienced in the ways of the world, was following one of the important rules of human relations: Always make the other man happy about doing the thing you suggest.

Don't Argue

AT A BANQUET one night the man next to me told a story in which he used the quotation, "There's a divinity that shapes our ends, rough-hew them how we will," and attributed it to the Bible. He was wrong. And to display my superiority, I corrected him. He stuck to his guns. From Shakespeare? Absurd! That quotation was from the Bible. An old friend of mine, seated at my left, was a Shakespearean scholar. The story-teller and I agreed to submit the question to him. My friend listened, kicked me under the table and said: "Dale, you are wrong. The gentleman is right. It is from the Bible."

On our way home that night, my friend explained: "Of course that quotation is from Shakespeare, Dale; but we were guests at a festive occasion. Why prove to a man he is wrong? Is that going to make him like you? Why not let him save his face? He didn't ask for your opinion. Why argue with him? Always avoid the acute angle."

"*Always avoid the acute angle.*" I sorely needed that lesson because I had been an inveterate arguer. During my youth, I had argued with my brother about everything under the Milky Way. In college I studied logic and argumentation, and later taught them in New York. As a result of it all, I have come to the conclusion that there is only one way to get the best of an argument—and that is to avoid it. Nine times out of ten, an argument ends with each of the contestants being more firmly convinced than ever that he is absolutely right. You can't win an argument. You can't win because even if you win it, you lose it, for you will never get your opponent's good will.

Moreover, my experience has been that it is all but impossible to make *any* man—regardless of his I.Q. rating—change his mind by a verbal joust. For example, Frederick S. Parsons, an income-tax consultant, had been disputing and wrangling for an hour with a government tax inspector. An item of $9000 was at stake. Mr. Parsons claimed that this $9000 was a bad debt, the inspector that it must be taxed.

"This inspector was cold, arrogant and stubborn," Mr. Parsons said. "The longer we argued, the more stubborn he became. Finally I said, 'I suppose that this is a very petty matter in comparison with the really important and difficult decisions you are required to make. I've made a study of taxation myself. But I've had to get my knowledge from books. You are getting yours from the firing line of experience. I sometimes wish I had a job like yours. It would teach me a lot.' I meant every word I said. Well, the inspector straightened up in his chair, leaned back, and talked for a long time about his work, telling me of the clever frauds he had uncovered. His tone gradually became friendly; and presently he was telling me about his children. As he left, he advised me that he would consider my problem further, and give me his decision in a few days. He called at my office three days later and informed me that he had decided to leave the tax return exactly as it was filed.''

This tax inspector was demonstrating one of the most common of human frailties. He wanted a feeling of importance; and as long as Mr. Parsons argued with him, he got his feeling of importance by loudly asserting his authority. But as soon as his importance was admitted, and the argument stopped, and he was permitted to expand his ego, he became a sympathetic and kindly human being.

I have quit telling people they are wrong. And I find it pays. Few people are logical. Most of us are prejudiced, blighted with preconceived notions. When we are wrong, we may admit it to ourselves. And if we are handled gently and tactfully, we may admit it to others and even take pride in our frankness. But not if someone else is trying to ram the unpalatable fact down our esophagus.

When You're in the Wrong

WHEN one is at fault, it is frequently disarming to admit it quickly. Ferdinand E. Warren, a commercial artist, used this technique to win the good will of a petulant art director. "Recently I delivered him a rush job," Mr. Warren told me, "and he phoned me to call at his office immediately. When I arrived, I found just what I had anticipated—he was hostile, gloating over his chance to criticize. He demanded with heat why I had done so and so. Trying a new strategy, I simply said, 'I am at fault and there is absolutely no excuse for my blunder. I have been doing drawings for you long enough to know better. I'm ashamed of myself.'

"Immediately he started to defend me. 'Yes, you're right, but after all, this isn't a serious mistake—'

"I interrupted him. 'Any mistake may be costly. I should have been more careful. I'm going to do this drawing over.'

"'No! No!' he protested. 'I wouldn't think of putting you

to all that trouble.' He praised my work, assured me that he wanted only a minor change, a mere detail—not worth worrying about. My eagerness to criticize myself took all the fight out of him. Before we parted, he gave me a check and another commission."

The First Person Singular

MANY OF the sweetest memories of my childhood cluster around a little yellow-haired dog with a stub tail. Tippy never read a book on psychology. He didn't need to. He had a perfect technique for making people like him. He liked people himself—and his interest in me was so sincere and genuine that I could not keep from loving him in return.

Do you want to make friends? Then take a tip from Tippy. Be friendly. Forget yourself. People are not interested in you. They are interested in themselves—morning, noon, and after dinner. The New York Telephone Company made a detailed study of telephone conversations to find out which word is the most frequently used. It is the personal pronoun "I." It was used 3900 times in 500 telephone conversations. "I," "I," "I," "I," "I."

That is why you can make more friends in two months by becoming interested in other people than you can in two years by trying to get other people interested in you.

This was one of the secrets of Theodore Roosevelt's astonishing popularity. Roosevelt called at the White House one day when the President and Mrs. Taft were away. His honest liking for humble people was shown by the fact that he greeted all the old White House servants by name, even the scullery maids.

"When he saw Alice, the kitchen maid," writes Archie Butt, "he asked her if she still made corn bread. Alice told him that she sometimes made it for the servants, but no one ate it upstairs.

"'They show bad taste,' Roosevelt boomed, 'and I'll tell the President so when I see him.'

"Alice brought a piece to him on a plate, and he went over to the office eating it as he went and greeting gardeners and laborers as he passed. They still whisper about it to each other, and Ike Hoover said with tears in his eyes: 'It is the happiest day we have had in nearly two years.'"

It was this same intense interest in the problems of other people that made Dr. Charles W. Eliot of Harvard one of the most successful presidents who ever directed a university. One day a freshman, L. R. G. Crandon, went to the president's office to borrow $50 from the Students' Loan Fund. The loan was granted. "Then"—I am quoting Crandon—"President Eliot said, 'Pray be seated.' To my amazement, he continued, 'I am told that you cook and eat in your room. Now I don't think that is at all bad for you if you get the right food and enough of it. When I was in college I did the same. Did you ever make veal loaf? That, if made from sufficiently mature and sufficiently cooked veal, is one of the best things you could have, because there is no waste. This is the way I used to make it.' He then told me how to pick the veal, how to cook it slowly, with such evaporation that the soup would turn into jelly later, then how to cut it up and press it with one pan inside another and eat it cold."

Does this attitude work in business? Does it? I could cite scores of illustrations.

Charles R. Walters, of one of the large banks in New York City, was assigned to prepare a confidential report on a certain corporation. He knew of only one man who possessed the facts, the president. As Mr. Walters was ushered into his office, a young woman stuck her head through a door and told the president that she didn't have any stamps for him that day.

"I am collecting stamps for my 12-year-old son," the president explained.

Mr. Walters stated his mission, and began asking questions. The president was vague, general, nebulous. The interview was brief and barren. Mr. Walters didn't know what to do. Then he remembered that the foreign department of his bank collected stamps, taken from letters pouring in from every continent.

"The next afternoon I called on this man again," said Mr. Walters, "and sent in word that I had some stamps for his boy. He greeted me radiating smiles. 'My George will love this one,' he kept saying as he fondled the stamps. 'And look at this. This is a treasure.'

"We spent half an hour talking stamps, and then he devoted more than an hour of his time to giving me every bit of information I wanted—without my even suggesting it."

If we want to make friends, let's put ourselves out to do things for other people—things that require time, energy and thoughtfulness.

Be a Good Listener

I RECENTLY MET a distinguished botanist at a dinner party. I had never talked to a botanist before, and I literally sat on the edge of my chair the whole evening while he spoke of hashish and potatoes and Luther Burbank and indoor gardens. Midnight came. I said good night and departed. The botanist then turned to our host and paid me some very flattering compliments. I was "most stimulating," a "most interesting conversationalist."

An interesting conversationalist? I had said hardly anything at all. I couldn't have said anything if I had wanted to without changing the subject, for I know nothing about botany. But I had done this: I had listened intently, because I was genuinely interested. And he felt it. Naturally that pleased him, That kind of listening is one of the highest compliments we can pay.

And that is the secret of success alike in social conversation and in a business interview. Remember that the man you are talking to is a hundred times more interested in himself and his wants and problems than he is in you and your problems. His toothache means more to him than a famine in China. Think of that the next time you start a conversation. And if you want people to like you, be a good listener. Encourage them to talk about themselves.

The Magic of Names

I ONCE ASKED Jim Farley the secret of his success. He said, "Hard work," and I said, "Don't be funny."

He then inquired what *I* thought was the reason for his success. I replied: "I understand you can call 10,000 people by their first names."

"No. You are wrong," he said. "I can call 50,000 people by their first names."

Make no mistake about it. That ability helped Mr. Farley put Franklin D. Roosevelt in the White House. During the years that Jim Farley traveled as a salesman for a gypsum concern, he built up a system for remembering names. Whenever he met a new acquaintance, he found out his complete name, the size of his family, the nature of his business, and the color of his political opinions. He got all these facts well in mind, and the next time he met that man, he was able to slap him on the back, inquire after the wife and kids, and ask him about the hollyhocks in the back yard. No wonder he developed a following!

He had discovered early in life that the average man is more interested in his own name than in all the other names on earth put together. Remember that name and call it easily, and you have paid him a subtle and very effective compliment. But forget it or misspell it—and you have placed yourself at a sharp disadvantage.

Andrew Carnegie, by the time he was ten years old, had discovered the astonishing importance people place on their own names. And he used that discovery to win coöperation. He had a nest of little rabbits, but nothing to feed them. Then he had a brilliant idea. He told the boys in the neighborhood that if they would pull enough clover and dandelions to feed the rabbits he would name the bunnies in their honor.

The plan worked like magic; and Carnegie never forgot it. When Carnegie and George Pullman were battling each other for supremacy in the sleeping car business, the Steel King again remembered the lesson of the rabbits.

The Central Transportation Company, which Andrew Carnegie controlled, was fighting with the company Pullman owned. Both were struggling to get the sleeping car business of the Union Pacific Railroad, bucking each other, slashing prices, and destroying all chance of profit. Both Carnegie and Pullman had gone to New York to see the board of directors of the Union Pacific. Meeting Mr. Pullman one evening in the St. Nicholas Hotel, Carnegie suggested a merger of the two companies. He pictured in glowing terms the mutual advantages of working with, instead of against, each other. Pullman listened attentively, but was not wholly convinced. Finally he asked, "What would you call the new company?" and Carnegie replied promptly: "Why, the Pullman Palace Car Company, of course."

Pullman's face brightened. "Come into my room," he said. "Let's talk it over." That talk made industrial history.

One of the simplest, most obvious, and most important ways of gaining good will and making people feel important is by remembering names. Yet how many of us do it? Half the time we are introduced to a stranger, chat a few minutes, and can't even remember his name when we say good-bye. Most people don't remember names for the simple reason that they don't take the time and energy necessary to concentrate and repeat and fix names indelibly in their minds.

Napoleon III of France boasted that he could remember the name of every person he met. His technique? If he didn't hear the name distinctly, he said, "So sorry. I didn't get the name clearly." Then, if it was an unusual name, he would say, "How is it spelled?"

During the conversation, he took the trouble to repeat the name several times, and tried to associate it in his mind with the man's features, expression, and general appearance. If the man were someone of importance, Napoleon went to even further pains. As soon as he was alone, he wrote the man's name down on a piece of paper, looked at it, concentrated on it, fixed it securely in his mind, and then tore up the paper. In this way, he gained an eye impression of the name as well as an ear impression.

All this takes time, but "good manners," said Emerson, "are made up of petty sacrifices."

Remember that a man's name is to him the sweetest and most important sound in the English language.